17/6

A 725

Graham Book

PROPERTIES OF MATTER

BLACKIE & SON LIMITED
66 Chandos Place, LONDON
17 Stanhope Street, GLASGOW

BLACKIE & SON (INDIA) LIMITED
103/5 Fort Street, BOMBAY

BLACKIE & SON (CANADA) LIMITED
TORONTO

PROPERTIES OF MATTER

BY

F. C. CHAMPION, M.A., PhD.(Cantab.)

Reader in Physics, University of London (King's College)

AND

N. DAVY, D.Sc.(London)

Senior Lecturer in Physics, University College, Nottingham

BLACKIE & SON LIMITED

LONDON AND GLASGOW

First published 1936
Reprinted, with corrections, 1937, 1941
Reprinted 1942, 1943
Reprinted, with corrections, 1944
Reprinted 1946
Reprinted 1947
Reprinted 1948

Printed in Great Britain by Blackie & Son, Ltd., Glasgow

PREFACE

The subjects comprising the Properties of Matter form an ill-defined group and the authors have attempted to treat selected topics adequately rather than to cover a very wide field. It is felt that the advanced student, for whom this book is primarily intended, will already be familiar with the simple physical principles underlying Kinematics, Dynamics, Central Orbits and Gyroscopic Motion. These subjects have therefore been omitted, for their advanced study can be profitably pursued only from the mathematical standpoint. The aim throughout the present work has been to treat the matters considered from a physical point of view, and particularly to avoid regarding the material as exercises in applied mathematics. For example, the propagation of longitudinal and transverse waves is immediately associated here with the geophysical problems of Seismic Waves.

The introduction of newer and more accurate methods for measuring various quantities such as the Newtonian Constant of Gravitation has necessitated only brief reference to older methods, but classical work such as that of Boys has been fully described.

It is now impossible to draw a dividing line between General Physics and Physical Chemistry in some topics. A concise account of Debye and Hückel's theory of strong electrolytes has therefore been given, and a whole chapter has been devoted to the new and important subject of Surface Films.

The authors have tried as far as possible to indicate the original sources of their material by references in the text and at the end of the chapters. They take this opportunity of apologizing to any writer whose work may inadvertently have been used without acknowledgment.

F. C. CHAMPION.
N. DAVY.

ACKNOWLEDGMENTS

We gratefully acknowledge our indebtedness to various authors, societies, and publishers for permission to copy plates and diagrams which have appeared in the following books and periodicals:

Adam, *The Physics and Chemistry of Surfaces* (Clarendon Press).

Bouasse, *Cours de Physique* (Masson).

Bridgman, *Compressibility* (Bell).

Ewald, Pöschl and Prandtl, *Physics of Solids* (Blackie & Son).

Jeans, *Dynamical Theory of Gases* (Camb. Univ. Press).

Loeb, *Kinetic Theory of Gases* (McGraw-Hill).

Newman, *Recent Advances in Physics* (Churchill).

Newman and Searle, *Properties of Matter* (Benn).

Prescott, *Applied Elasticity* (Longmans, Green & Co.).

J. K. Roberts, *Heat and Thermodynamics* (Blackie & Son).

G. F. C. Searle, *Experimental Elasticity* (Camb. Univ. Press).

G. F. C. Searle, *Experimental Physics: Miscellaneous Experiments* (Camb. Univ. Press).

Watson, *Text-book of Physics* (Longmans, Green & Co.).

Philosophical Magazine.

Proceedings of the Physical Society.

Proceedings of the Royal Society.

American Journal of Physical Chemistry.

Bulletin of the American Bureau of Standards.

Annalen der Physik.

Ergebnisse der exakten Naturwissenschaften.

Handbuch der Experimentalphysik.

Handbuch der Physik.

Physikalische Zeitschrift.

CONTENTS

CHAPTER I

UNITS AND DIMENSIONS

CHAPTER II

THE ACCELERATION DUE TO GRAVITY

CHAPTER III

THE NEWTONIAN CONSTANT OF GRAVITATION

X   CONTENTS

CHAPTER VI

SEISMIC WAVES

CHAPTER VII

CAPILLARITY

CONTENTS

CHAPTER VIII

SURFACE FILMS

CHAPTER IX

KINETIC THEORY OF MATTER

CHAPTER X

OSMOTIC PRESSURE

CHAPTER XI

DIFFUSION

CHAPTER XII

VISCOSITY

CHAPTER XIII

ERRORS OF MEASUREMENT; METHODS OF DETERMINING PLANCK'S CONSTANT

CONTENTS

PROPERTIES OF MATTER

CHAPTER I

Units and Dimensions

1. Introduction.

The statement that a given body weighs 10 pounds implies that a given unit of weight, the pound, has been chosen, and that the ratio of the weight of the body to that of the unit is 10. In general, a *conventional* choice of certain units is made, and any physical entity may then be expressed by a number which states how many of these units the entity in question contains. The units chosen should be (1) well defined, (2) not subject to secular change, (3) easily compared with similar units, (4) easily reproduced.

Physical laws consist in the relations which have been found to exist between the numbers which represent physical quantities. Hence although each type of physical quantity requires its own unit, these units are not necessarily independent; actually, many of the units may be expressed in terms of a certain few, called *fundamental units*. The choice of the latter is initially quite *arbitrary*, but when once settled it is fundamental for subsequent work. Gauss called such a system of units an *absolute system*, but the term is unfortunate, since the system chosen is quite conventional. There are, in fact, several "absolute" systems of units in use, depending on the fundamental units chosen and the physical laws used in expressing the remaining *derived units*. Thus there is the *British system* with the *foot, pound*, and *second* as the fundamental units, while that used for purely scientific work is almost invariably the C.G.S. or centimetre, gramme, and second system.

2. Fundamental Units.

Three of the fundamental units which have been chosen are those of *mass, length*, and *time*, and many physical units may be expressed in terms of these three. If, however, physical entities other than those

1

which have an immediate " explanation " in " mechanical " terms are under consideration, additional fundamental units are required. For example, in the science of heat the *calorie* is the fundamental unit of quantity of heat in the C.G.S. system; again, the *unit degree Kelvin* is adopted as the fundamental unit of temperature in the same system.

The British unit of mass is the *pound avoirdupois*, which is simply the mass of a piece of platinum preserved in the office of the Exchequer and marked " P.S. 1844, 1 lb.". It bears no simple relation to the unit of volume in the same system and thus differs from the unit of mass in the French or metric system. This, the *kilogramme*, was initially made as close as possible to the weight of 1000 c.c. of water at its temperature of maximum density. Although subsequent work has shown that this relation is not quite accurate, the original kilogramme has been retained and is now simply taken as the weight of a piece of platinum preserved at the Bureau of Metric Standards.

The unit of length, like the unit of mass, is quite arbitrary in the British system, the *yard* being defined as the straight distance between the transverse lines in two gold plugs on the bronze bar at 62° F.(!) preserved in the Exchequer office. In the metric system, the standard of length is that of a bar, originally made to be as nearly as possible equal to one ten-millionth part of a quadrant of the earth passing through Paris. This relation was subsequently found to be inaccurate, and the *metre* is now simply taken as the distance between two marks on the platinum bar at 0° C. preserved at the International Bureau of Standards at St. Cloud, near Paris.

Both systems have the same unit of time, the *mean solar second*, which is simply the mean solar day divided by 86,400.

3. Derived Units.

Consider now the expression for the area of a surface. The unit in which the area is expressed is the area of a square whose side is the unit of length. Similarly, the unit in which a volume is expressed is that of a cube whose side is the unit of length. Further, the unit in which a velocity is expressed is obtained by dividing the unit of length by the unit of time. Such units, which depend on powers of one or more of the fundamental units, are termed derived units. The unit of area is often represented symbolically by L^2, that of volume by L^3, and that of velocity by $V = L/T$ or LT^{-1}, and these expressions are called the *dimensional formulæ* of the quantities considered. Again, the *dimensions* of a physical quantity may be defined as the powers of the fundamental units in terms of which it may be expressed. Area and volume, therefore, have dimensions two and three in length respectively.

The dimensional formula for mechanical energy is $E = MV^2 = ML^2T^{-2}$. Since (in Newtonian mechanics, at least) the numerical measure of energy is *one-half* the product of the number representing the mass and the square of the number representing the velocity, dimensional formulæ are neither complete numerical laws nor even definitions. The dimensional formula merely states (1) the nature of the experiments (i.e. of length, mass, &c.) on the fundamental quantities which must be made in order to determine the given quantity, (2) the powers to which the primary quantities have to be raised. It is clear that (2) will be important in deciding on the accuracy of measurement required in any part of an experiment.

4. Dimensional Analysis.*

The study of dimensional analysis will be introduced by the consideration of a simple example. The elementary formula for the time of oscillation of a simple pendulum in the earth's gravitational field is

$$t = 2\pi \left(\frac{l}{g}\right)^{\frac{1}{2}}, \quad \ldots \ldots \quad (1)$$

where l is the length of the pendulum and g is the acceleration due to gravity. As this is purely a mechanical problem, the variables t, l and g may all be expressed in terms of the three primary quantities M, L and T. Writing down the dimensional formulæ, we have $t = T$, $l = L$ and $g = LT^{-2}$. The 2π is a so-called pure number; since it does not depend on a fundamental physical unit, it cannot be represented in dimensional analysis. It is interesting to note that π may be obtained experimentally as the *ratio* of the circumference of a circle to its diameter, and since both are measured in the same units, the units are eliminated. Now the L.H.S. of equation (1) clearly has the dimensions T, while the R.H.S. has dimensions $(L/LT^{-2})^{\frac{1}{2}} = T$. Hence the dimensions of both sides of the equation are the same. This property is true of all equations representing possible physical phenomena, and may be stated as follows:

Law I.—*Physical equations must be dimensionally homogeneous.*

Consider now the inverse problem. Suppose that the equation for the time of oscillation of a simple pendulum is not known. From the physical nature of the problem the time of oscillation might reasonably be expected to depend upon the following quantities: l, the length of the pendulum, m, the mass of the bob, and g, the acceleration due to gravity. Then

$$t = f(m, l, g), \quad \ldots \ldots \quad (2)$$

* The best method of presenting dimensional analysis and its relation to the principle of dynamical similarity is still a subject of acute discussion, but the writer (F. C. C.) has attempted to present a set of rules which are consistent and which do not lead to error in any applications so far considered.

where the nature of the function f has to be found. Assume that the R.H.S. of (2) may be expressed as a *power formula*. Then

$$t = km^a l^\beta g^\gamma, \qquad \ldots \ldots \ldots \quad (3)$$

where k is a possible dimensionless constant which will not be represented in the dimensional analysis. Writing (3) in its dimensional form, we have

$$T = M^a L^\beta L^\gamma T^{-2\gamma}. \qquad \ldots \ldots \quad (4)$$

The indices of the primary quantities on the two sides of (4) must be equal if Law I is true. Hence

(1) length: $0 = \beta + \gamma,$
(2) mass: $0 = a,$
(3) time: $1 = -2\gamma.$

Substituting in (3), we have

$$t = k\left(\frac{l}{g}\right)^{\frac{1}{2}}. \qquad \ldots \ldots \ldots \quad (5)$$

5. Dynamical Similarity.

Consideration of equation (5) shows that the problem may be regarded in another way, namely, as involving not three variables t, l and g, but a single variable $t(g/l)^{\frac{1}{2}}$, which groups together a whole system of experiments of essentially the same type. In the foregoing analysis the time t might have been taken to represent the time required for the pendulum to swing out to a given angle a; then $t = k\sqrt{l/g}$, where k is now constant only when a is constant. If at different places where the accelerations due to gravity are g_1 and g_2, pendulums of lengths l_1 and l_2 are allowed to oscillate, then both pendulums will pass through the same angular displacement at times t_1 and t_2 given by $t_1(g_1/l_1)^{\frac{1}{2}} = t_2(g_2/l_2)^{\frac{1}{2}}$. Systems which can be grouped together quite generally as passing through identical phases for equal values of a dimensionless grouping of corresponding quantities are said to possess dynamical similarity. Simple *geometrical* similarity, however, is not necessarily a sufficient condition for dynamical similarity. For example, two compound pendulums would not be dynamically similar if the density of the material of which they were composed were not distributed in both in identically the same way.

6. Uses and Limitations of Dimensional Analysis.

Dimensional analysis affords a simple and rapid solution of physical problems, but this advantage is offset by the lack of information on the presence of pure numbers. It is true that the latter can be determined by experiment, subsequent to the analysis, but matters are further complicated by the presence of *dimensional constants* like G, the gravitational constant. As an example of this difficulty, suppose it is required to find the time of revolution of one body revolving round another under mutual gravitational forces. Then

$$t = f(m_1, m_2, r), \quad \ldots \ldots \ldots \quad (6)$$

where r is the distance between the two bodies and m_1, m_2 are their masses. Now since the L.H.S. of (6) has the dimensions of T and the R.H.S. dimensions only of M and L, there appears to be no solution. Physical judgment suggests that a relevant variable may have been omitted from the R.H.S. of (6), and the gravitational constant G is introduced. If force is already considered to be defined by Newton's second law of motion, G is a dimensional constant given by Newton's

law of gravitational attraction, $F = G\dfrac{m_1 m_2}{r^2}$ or $G = M^{-1}L^3T^{-2}$. Hence (6) becomes

$$t = f(m_1, m_2, r, G) = k m_1{}^\alpha m_2{}^\beta r^\gamma G^\delta. \quad \ldots \ldots \quad (7)$$

Writing down the dimensional formulæ and equating the indices of the same primary quantities, we have

$$\left.\begin{array}{lll}
(1)\ T & \quad 1 = -2\delta, \\
(2)\ M & \quad 0 = \alpha + \beta - \delta, \\
(3)\ L & \quad 0 = \gamma + 3\delta.
\end{array}\right\}$$

Since there are four unknowns and only three equations, the final solution of (7) may be written in terms of one of the unknowns:

$$t = k m_1{}^{(-\frac{1}{2}-\beta)} m_2{}^\beta G^{-\frac{1}{2}} r^{3/2} = k\,\frac{r^{3/2}}{G^{\frac{1}{2}} m_1{}^{\frac{1}{2}}}\left(\frac{m_2}{m_1}\right)^\beta. \quad \ldots \quad (8)$$

Now $(m_2/m_1)^\beta$ is dimensionless and therefore its value cannot affect the dimensional homogeneity of (8). It may therefore be present as a function of any type and (8) may be written in the general form

$$t = k_1\,\frac{r^{3/2}}{G^{\frac{1}{2}} m_1{}^{\frac{1}{2}}}\,f\left(\frac{m_2}{m_1}\right). \quad \ldots \ldots \quad (9)$$

The preceding problem involved one unknown function, and, in general, the number of unknowns that ultimately remain is equal to the difference between the number of variables and the number of primary quantities considered. In dimensional analysis, therefore, three main questions arise.

(1) What dimensional constants are to be introduced?
(2) How many variables are to be used, and which?
(3) How many primary quantities are to be considered?

It may be stated at once that the answering of these questions is a matter for physical intuition; that is, physical intuition, acting over long experience, decides from known solutions of problems analogous to the one requiring solution that certain variables are likely to be relevant and others irrelevant.

The main uses of dimensional analysis are as follows:

(1) *To test the correctness of equations.*

After a long analysis it is useful to check the final equation for dimensional homogeneity by substitution of the dimensional formulæ on both sides of the equation.

(2) *To derive equations without complete analysis.*

If the differential equation appropriate to any physical problem can be formulated and solved, a complete solution of the problem is possible. The solution contains, in general, the same number of physical variables and dimensional constants as the original differential equation. When the problem is complicated, the formulation of the differential equation is often impossible. Recourse is then made to dimensional methods, and if the relevant variables and dimensional constants can be guessed correctly, at least a partial analysis is possible. Frequently the intermediate case occurs: the differential equation can be formulated but not solved; the variables to be used in the dimensional analysis are then known.

(3) *To recapitulate important formulæ.*

With a complicated formula, such as Poiseuille's equation for the flow of a viscous liquid through a right circular cylinder, it may be easier to recover the equation from a knowledge of the dimensions of viscosity than to memorize it or deduce it from first principles.

(4) *To suggest relations between fundamental constants.*

This is a dubious use of dimensional analysis and will only be briefly considered. The existence of dimensionless grouping is often found to indicate a relation between the components of the group. If we consider the fundamental constants

$$\begin{cases} G, \text{ the gravitational constant,} \\ e, \text{ the charge on the electron,} \\ m, \text{ the mass of the electron,} \\ c, \text{ the velocity of light,} \\ h, \text{ Planck's constant of action,} \end{cases}$$

we find that (hc/e^2) is dimensionless, and $(hc/2\pi e^2)$ is actually a factor which is constantly involved in the wave mechanical and quantum treatment of the interaction of atomic particles. Again, G has the same dimensions as $(e/m)^2$, and this may indicate an electromagnetic theory of gravity. The relation is not, however, likely to be simple, since the ratio $G(m/e)^2$ is about 10^{-43}. In the preceding example $(hc/2\pi e^2)$ is equal to 137.

7. Extension of Dimensional Analysis.

Consider now the dimensional formula for $\varkappa$, the coefficient of thermal conduction. The constant $\varkappa$ is defined by the differential equation

$$\frac{dQ}{dt} = \varkappa A \frac{d\theta}{dx},$$

where A is the area of each of two planes situated a distance dx apart and maintained at a difference of temperature $d\theta$; dQ is the amount of heat flowing across in time dt. If Q, θ, M, L and T are taken as primary quantities, the dimensional formula for $\varkappa$ is $Q\theta^{-1}L^{-1}T^{-1}$. Inspection of this formula shows that for geometrically similar bodies of uniform conductivity and similar temperature distributions, the quantity of heat transferred across corresponding cross-sections is proportional to the time, the conductivity, the linear dimensions, and the maximum temperature difference.

This conclusion, however, does not follow if the number of primary quantities is reduced. For example, Q is often assigned the dimensions of mechanical energy ML^2T^{-2}, from Joule's law $Q = E/J$, where Q is the quantity of heat which appears when a certain amount of mechanical energy E disappears. Similarly θ is often given the same dimensions, ML^2T^{-2}, from the equation of a perfect gas, $pV = R\theta$. The crucial point is whether J and R are dimensional or dimensionless constants. Now the problem of heat conduction is concerned neither with the "equivalence" of heat and mechanical energy, nor with the properties of perfect gases. It is therefore illegitimate to assign the dimensions of energy to either Q or θ *in the case of heat conduction*.

Consider, however, the dimensional formula for *entropy*. The concept of entropy was initially deduced from considerations of (1) the properties of gases, (2) the relation between heat and mechanical energy. In this case, therefore, both Q and θ may be given the dimensions of mechanical energy. Since the change of entropy is given by dQ/θ, entropy is seen to be dimensionless. If, on the other hand, quantity of heat were defined by the expression $Ms\theta$, where s is the specific heat (itself a ratio, since it may be defined as the ratio of the amount of heat required to raise a given mass of the material through a given temperature range, to that required to raise the same mass of a standard material (water) through the same temperature range), the dimensions of entropy would clearly be those of mass. Now the entropy of the universe is continually increasing; it is much more probable that some purely dimensionless quantity rather than the total mass is undergoing this change. Further, the dimensionless formula is in agreement with statistical theory.* The above results may be summed up in Law II:

Laws that are not directly relevant to the problem under consideration must not be used to assign dimensions.

The implications of Law II must be strictly followed out in assigning dimensions to κ, the dielectric constant, and μ, the magnetic permeability. If the problem is directly associated with Coulomb's law $F = q_1 q_2 / \kappa r^2$, where F is the force between two point changes q_1 and q_2 separated by a distance r in an enveloping medium of dielectric constant κ, electrostatic dimensions are appropriate. If the problem is directly connected with Ampère's law, electromagnetic dimensions must be assigned. In the special case where κ is the same for all the components involved in the problem, κ may be regarded as being dimensionless, since it may be defined as the ratio of the capacities of two identical condensers, one of which is filled with the dielectric and the other empty. Similarly, if the problem is entirely electromagnetic and μ is constant, the latter may be regarded as dimensionless.

8. Examples of Dimensional Analysis.

The preceding principles will now be illustrated by examples from different branches of physics; further examples for the reader will be found at the end of the book.

(1) Mechanics. *Motion of a body through a resisting medium.*

Suppose it is required to find how the resistance to bodies of similar shape but different size depends on the variables of the problem. Guessing the variables and writing down their dimensional formulæ, we have

(a) Resisting force	R	MLT^{-2},
(b) Velocity	v	LT^{-1},
(c) Linear dimensions	d	L,
(d) Density of resisting medium	ρ	ML^{-3},
(e) Viscosity of resisting medium	η	$ML^{-1}T^{-1}$.

Let
$$R = kv^\alpha \rho^\beta d^\gamma \eta^\delta;$$
then we have
$$MLT^{-2} = L^\alpha T^{-\alpha} M^\beta L^{-3\beta} L^\gamma M^\delta L^{-\delta} T^{-\delta}:$$
hence

(1) M		$1 = \beta + \delta$,
(2) L		$1 = \alpha - 3\beta + \gamma - \delta$,
(3) T		$-2 = -\alpha - \delta$.

* In *The Nature of the Physical World* (Cambridge University Press, 1929), Eddington defines increase of entropy as " the increase of the random element in the universe . . . a measure of the continuous loss of organization of the universe ". This agrees with the dimensionless formula.

Let α remain uneliminated; then

$$R = k \left(\frac{v \rho d}{\eta} \right)^{\alpha} \frac{\eta^2}{\rho}$$

$$R = k \frac{\eta^2}{\rho} f\left(\frac{v \rho d}{\eta} \right). \quad \cdots \cdots \cdot (10)$$

Now systems for which the dimensionless expression $(v \rho d/\eta)$ is constant possess dynamical similarity. For bodies of similar shape with η and ρ constant, the resisting force R is therefore the same if vd is constant. Hence the *law of similar speeds*, that for the same resistance to motion the velocity is inversely proportional to the linear dimensions, has been deduced. It is therefore advantageous to construct large airships rather than small ones, since the lifting power is approximately proportional to the volume, that is, depends on L^3. With very fast aeroplanes, the velocity of sound must be included as a further variable.

(2) Heat. *Convection.*

Attention will here be confined to natural convection, the problem of forced convection being left as an example for the reader. It is required to find how h, the heat lost per unit area in unit time from geometrically similar bodies placed in a fluid, depends on the variables concerned. If we take Q, θ, L and T as the primary quantities, the variables

(a) Temperature of the body θ θ,
(b) Linear dimensions of the body l L,
(c) Thermal conductivity of the fluid $\varkappa$ $Q \theta^{-1} L^{-1} T^{-1}$,

will certainly be required. To avoid having to consider the density of the fluid, we use the remaining variables in the following form:

(d) Thermal capacity of the fluid *per unit volume* c $Q \theta^{-1} L^{-3}$,
(e) Acceleration of gravity g LT^{-2},
(f) Temperature coefficient of density change of the fluid a θ^{-1},
(g) Kinematic viscosity ν $L^2 T^{-1}$.

The quantities (e) and (f) are grouped together in the form of the product ga. This is justified by the fact that the upward thrust on unit volume of the fluid of density $\rho - \Delta \rho$, if the surrounding fluid has density ρ, is $g \Delta \rho$, and since the mass of the fluid is ρ, the acceleration produced on the fluid will be proportional to $g \Delta \rho / \rho$, which in turn is proportional to $g \frac{1}{\rho} \frac{d\rho}{d\theta}$ or ga, where a is the temperature coefficient of density change of the fluid. The effect of change of density on the viscosity of the fluid is thereby neglected; in practice, the viscosity is taken to be that of the fluid at a temperature which is the mean of that of the body and the main bulk of the fluid. Finally, the viscosity is used in the form of the kinematic viscosity $\nu = \eta/\rho$, where η is the ordinary coefficient of viscosity defined in Chapter XII (p. 243).

Writing the required relation as a power formula in the usual way, we have

$$h = \theta^{\alpha} \varkappa^{\beta} c^{\gamma} (ga)^{\delta} l^{\varepsilon} \nu^{\mu}$$

or

$$QL^{-2}T^{-1} = \theta^{\alpha} Q^{\beta} L^{-\beta} \theta^{-\beta} T^{-\beta} Q^{\gamma} \theta^{-\gamma} L^{-3\gamma} L^{\delta} T^{-2\delta} \theta^{-\delta} L^{\varepsilon} L^{2\mu} T^{-\mu}$$

(1) Q $1 = \beta + \gamma$,
(2) L $-2 = -\beta + \delta + \varepsilon + 2\mu - 3\gamma$,
(3) T $-1 = -\beta - \mu - 2\delta$,
(4) θ $0 = \alpha - \beta - \gamma - \delta$.

Expressing the other unknowns in terms of δ and μ, we have

$$\alpha = 1 + \delta,$$
$$\beta = 1 - 2\delta - \mu,$$
$$\gamma = 2\delta + \mu,$$
$$\varepsilon = 3\delta - 1.$$

Substituting these values in the expression for h, we obtain three interrelated dimensionless groups:

$$\frac{hl}{\theta \varkappa} = \left(\frac{\theta gac^2 l^3}{\varkappa^2}\right)^{\delta} \left(\frac{cv}{\varkappa}\right)^{\mu},$$

or in general,

$$\frac{hl}{\theta \varkappa} = F\left(\frac{\theta gac^2 l^3}{\varkappa^2}\right) f\left(\frac{cv}{\varkappa}\right). \quad \ldots \ldots \quad (11)$$

Consider the application of these formulæ to cylinders whose length is great compared with the diameter. Then h depends only on the diameter d, and d may be substituted for l. Further, if H is the heat lost per unit length per second per degree temperature excess, we have

$$H = \frac{\pi hd}{\theta};$$

hence

$$\frac{H}{\varkappa} = F\left(\frac{\theta gac^2 d^3}{\varkappa^2}\right) f\left(\frac{cv}{\varkappa}\right). \quad \ldots \ldots \quad (12)$$

For cylinders surrounded by diatomic gases, (1) $cv/\varkappa$ is nearly constant; (2) $1/v^2$ may be written for $c^2/\varkappa^2$ in the first function, since the two expressions have the same dimensions; (3) g is constant, and for a constant temperature of the surrounding gas, a is the same for all gases; hence we have

$$\frac{H}{\varkappa} = F_1\left(\frac{\theta d^3}{v^2}\right). \quad \ldots \ldots \ldots \quad (13)$$

Plotting the values of $H/\varkappa$ as ordinates and the corresponding values of $\theta d^3/v^2$ as abscissæ, we find that for the natural convective cooling of long cylinders all the points lie on a single curve.* The agreement between the results for steam-pipes and those for fine wires is very remarkable.

(3) Light. *The blue of the sky.*

The law governing the scattering of light by small obstacles was first deduced dimensionally by the late Lord Rayleigh. The variables which present themselves are:

(a) Amplitude of the incident wave	a	L,
(b) Volume of obstacles	v	L^3,
(c) Distance of point considered from obstacle	r	L,
(d) Wave-length of incident light	λ	L.

Then the amplitude of the scattered wave at r is

$$s = k\frac{av\lambda^{\alpha}}{r}, \quad \ldots \ldots \ldots \quad (14)$$

since s is known to be proportional to a and v and inversely proportional to r. To make the equation dimensionally homogeneous, we must have $\alpha = -2$. Since the scattered intensity is proportional to the *square* of the scattered amplitude, the amount of light scattered is inversely proportional to the fourth power

* Cf. Roberts, *Heat and Thermodynamics*, p. 242 (Blackie & Son, Ltd., 1933).

of the wave-length. This is almost sixteen times as great for the violet as for the red end of the spectrum. Consequently the blue present in white light is scattered to a much greater extent than the red.

(4) Sound. *Tuning-forks of similar shape.*

For tuning-forks of similar shape and of isotropic material, the restoring force is due to the elasticity of the prongs, and the time of oscillation t will depend on the following quantities:

(a) Linear dimensions of the fork l L,
(b) Young's modulus of the material q $ML^{-1}T^{-2}$,
(c) Density of the material ρ ML^{-3}.

Hence
$$t = kl^{\alpha}q^{\beta}\rho^{\gamma},$$
or, dimensionally,
$$T = L^{\alpha}M^{\beta}T^{-2\beta}L^{-\beta}M^{\gamma}L^{-3\gamma}.$$

We have

(1) M $0 = \beta + \gamma$,
(2) T $1 = -2\beta$,
(3) L $0 = \alpha - \beta - 3\gamma$.

Hence
$$t = klq^{-\frac{1}{2}}\rho^{\frac{1}{2}}. \qquad \ldots \ldots \ldots (15)$$

(5) Electricity and magnetism. *Electromagnetic mass of a charged sphere.*

The most likely variables would seem to be these:

(a) Charge q $M^{1/2}L^{3/2}T^{-1}$,
(b) Radius of sphere a L.

Hence
$$m = kq^{\alpha}a^{\beta}.$$

This equation is dimensionally inhomogeneous in T; as a further variable we try the constant c, which is the ratio of the units of charge in the electromagnetic and electrostatic systems respectively. Its dimensions are those of a velocity: hence
$$m = kq^{\alpha}a^{\beta}c^{\gamma},$$
or, dimensionally,
$$M = M^{\alpha/2}L^{3\alpha/2}T^{-\alpha}L^{\beta}L^{\gamma}T^{-\gamma}.$$

We have

(1) M $\alpha/2 = 1$,
(2) L $0 = 3\alpha/2 + \beta + \gamma$,
(3) T $0 = -\alpha - \gamma$,

or
$$m = \frac{kq^2}{ac^2}. \qquad \ldots \ldots \ldots (16)$$

Complete analysis gives $k = 2/3$.

REFERENCES

Lord Rayleigh, *Collected Papers.*
A. W. Porter, *The Method of Dimensions* (Methuen, 1933).
N. Campbell, *Measurement and Calculation* (Longmans, 1928).

CHAPTER II

The Acceleration Due to Gravity

1. Introduction.

The force on a body situated at a point in the gravitational field of the earth can be written in the form mg, where m is the mass of the body and g is a quantity known as the acceleration of gravity, or the acceleration of a body falling freely in vacuo, at that point. It is also the strength of the gravitational field at the point, for it is the force on unit mass. Owing to the spin of the earth, the direction and magnitude of the vector g will depend on the latitude (see Ex. 1, Ch. II, p. 275). The quantity g is independent of the mass of the body concerned. The most accurate methods of measuring g now in use are based upon pendulum observations. It is convenient to summarize the development of the theory and practice of this work.

2. Simple Pendulum with Friction.

We take it for granted that the student knows how to obtain the expression $T_0 = 2\pi(l/g)^{\frac{1}{2}}$ for the period of a simple pendulum. The

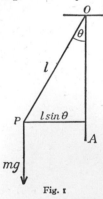

Fig. 1

assumptions involved are that the pendulum consists of a particle suspended from a rigid support by an inelastic string of negligible mass, and that it oscillates in vacuo with oscillations of infinitely small amplitude. When the viscous drag of the medium on the bob is not neglected, the equation of motion is altered. Let θ be the angular displacement (fig. 1). Experiment proves that the viscous retarding force is proportional to the linear velocity of the bob $l\dot{\theta}$ and to the viscosity of the medium. The moment of this force about an axis through the point O, perpendicular to the plane of the figure, may be written in the form $lk\dot{\theta}$, where k is a constant and l is the length of the string. The weight gives rise to a restoring moment $mgl \sin\theta$, which when θ is small may be taken as $mgl\theta$. Hence the equation of rotational motion about the axis through O is

$$ml^2\ddot{\theta} + kl\dot{\theta} + mgl\theta = 0, \quad \ldots \ldots \quad (1)$$

for $ml^2\ddot{\theta}$ is the product of the moment of inertia and the angular acceleration.

If we divide throughout by ml^2 and write $k/ml = 2b$ and $g/l = c^2$, the equation becomes

$$\ddot{\theta} + 2b\dot{\theta} + c^2\theta = 0. \quad \ldots \ldots \quad (2)$$

The general solution of this equation may be written in the form

$$\theta = Ae^{-bt}\cos\{(c^2 - b^2)^{\frac{1}{2}}t + \phi\}. \quad \ldots \ldots \quad (3)$$

It represents what are called *damped* (that is, decaying) *oscillations*, whose period is given by

$$T = 2\pi/(c^2 - b^2)^{\frac{1}{2}} = 2\pi/(g/l - b^2)^{\frac{1}{2}}. \quad \ldots \quad (4)$$

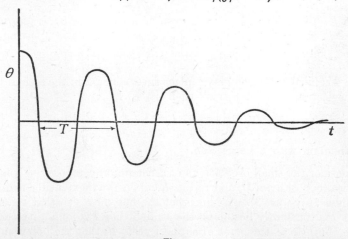

Fig. 2

A graph connecting θ and t reveals the decay of the oscillations. In fig. 2, ϕ is assumed to be equal to zero. On comparing $T = 2\pi/(g/l - b^2)^{\frac{1}{2}}$ with the simple formula $T_0 = 2\pi/(g/l)^{\frac{1}{2}}$, we see that $T/T_0 = \{g/l/(g/l - b^2)\}^{\frac{1}{2}} = (1 - b^2l/g)^{-\frac{1}{2}}$. In the practical case of a pendulum vibrating in air b is small, and the expression on the right may be expanded to two terms by the binomial theorem, giving $T/T_0 = 1 + b^2l/2g$ approximately. Writing $T_0 = 2\pi(l/g)^{\frac{1}{2}}$ and $l/g = T_0^2/4\pi^2$, we have

$$T/T_0 = 1 + b^2T_0^2/8\pi^2. \quad \ldots \ldots \quad (5)$$

For a pendulum in air, this slightly exceeds unity, the second term representing the correction for viscous drag of the air on the bob.

3. Pendulum with Finite Amplitude of Swing.

If θ is so large that it is not permissible to write $\sin \theta = \theta$, equation (1) must be replaced by

$$ml^2\ddot{\theta} + kl\dot{\theta} + mgl \sin \theta = 0. \quad \cdots \quad (6)$$

For the present purpose, which is simply to find the effect of a finite amplitude of swing, the viscous term $kl\dot{\theta}$ may be neglected, giving

$$ml^2\ddot{\theta} + mgl \sin \theta = 0. \quad \cdots \quad (7)$$

The solution of this equation is beyond the scope of the present book. The period of oscillation is found to be

$$T = 2\pi K(\theta)(l/g)^{\frac{1}{2}}, \quad \cdots \quad (8)$$

where $K(\theta)$ is a function of θ, known as a *complete elliptic integral of the first kind*. It can be expanded in a series of sines of $\theta/2$, giving

$$T = 2\pi(l/g)^{\frac{1}{2}}\{1 + (1/2)^2 \sin^2 \theta/2 + (1 \cdot 3/2 \cdot 4)^2 \sin^4 \theta/2 + \ldots\}.$$

When θ is fairly small, we may replace $\sin \theta/2$ by $\theta/2$ in the second term and neglect subsequent terms; then

$$T = 2\pi(l/g)^{\frac{1}{2}}\{1 + \theta^2/16\} = T_0\{1 + \theta^2/16\}. \quad \cdots \quad (9)$$

4. Pendulum with a Large Bob.

Consider the small oscillations of a pendulum composed of a heavy spherical bob of mass M and radius R cm., on an inextensible string of negligible mass (fig. 3). Assume that the bob moves so that the same radius PQ constantly lies along the straight line PO joining the centre of the bob P to O, the point of support; that is, that the bob is simply oscillating about an axis through O, perpendicular to the plane of the figure. The moment of inertia of a sphere about an axis parallel to a diameter, and l cm. from it, is $2MR^2/5 + Ml^2$, by the theorem of parallel axes. The equation of rotational motion for small oscillations (viscous forces being neglected) is

$$(2MR^2/5 + Ml^2)\ddot{\theta} + Mgl\theta = 0. \quad \cdots \quad (10)$$

Hence the period of oscillation is

$$T_1 = 2\pi\{(2R^2/5 + l^2)/lg\}^{\frac{1}{2}}. \quad \cdots \quad (11)$$

A real pendulum would scarcely swing in the assumed manner; its bob would oscillate about Q after the string had reached its extreme position on either side. The supporting fibre would have a definite mass and moment of inertia. These and other defects cause the rejection of this apparatus as a means of measuring g accurately.

5. Compound Pendulum.

Accurate methods of measuring g are chiefly based on the measurement of the period of small oscillations of a compound pendulum, that is, of a rigid body, about a fixed horizontal axis, which is usually a metal knife-edge. Fig. 4 represents a rigid body, suspended so as to oscillate about a horizontal axis through O, perpendicular to the plane of the figure. C represents its centre of gravity when in a displaced position. If the moment of inertia of the body about an axis through C is Mk^2, that about a parallel axis through O is $Mk^2 + Ml^2$, by the

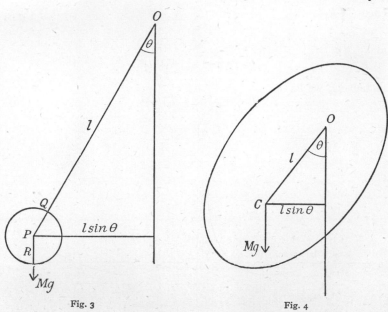

Fig. 3   Fig. 4

theorem of parallel axes. The equation of rotational motion about the axis through O, if we neglect viscous forces and write θ for $\sin\theta$, is

$$(Mk^2 + Ml^2)\ddot{\theta} + Mgl\theta = 0, \quad \dots \quad (12)$$

giving a period

$$T = 2\pi\{(k^2 + l^2)/lg\}^{\frac{1}{2}}. \quad \dots \quad (13)$$

A graph connecting T and l has the form shown in fig. 5. To obtain such a graph experimentally, a metal bar with numerous holes drilled in it is swung from a fixed peg through any one of the holes. The centre of gravity of the bar can be determined fairly accurately by balancing it on a horizontal knife-edge; l is the distance from the centre of gravity to the top of the peg. The period T is obtained by timing a few hundreds of swings with a stop-watch, or by some special

labour-saving method. Experiment and graph both show that there
are two values of l, when the point of support is on the same side of
the centre of gravity, for which the period of oscillation is the same.
AB and AC are two such lengths. Call them l_1 and l_2 respectively.
Corresponding to the point B we have

$$T = 2\pi\{(k^2 + l_1{}^2)/l_1 g\}^{\frac{1}{2}}, \quad \ldots \ldots \quad (14)$$

and corresponding to C,

$$T = 2\pi\{(k^2 + l_2{}^2)/l_2 g\}^{\frac{1}{2}}. \quad \ldots \ldots \quad (15)$$

Hence

$$g l_1 T^2/4\pi^2 = k^2 + l_1{}^2$$

and

$$g l_2 T^2/4\pi^2 = k^2 + l_2{}^2.$$

Subtracting, we have

$$T = 2\pi\{(l_1 + l_2)/g\}^{\frac{1}{2}}. \quad \ldots \ldots \quad (16)$$

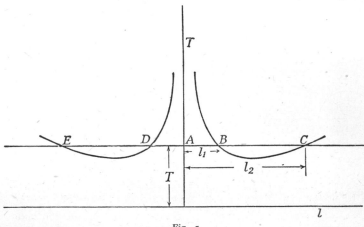

Fig. 5

On the other side of the centre of gravity there are two other points
D and E, for which the period is the same (T). $AD = AB = l_1$, and
$AE = AC = l_2$. Also $CD = BE = l_1 + l_2$. Thus C and D are two
points, unsymmetrically placed with respect to the centre of gravity,
whose distance apart is equal to the length of the simple pendulum
whose period of oscillation is the same as that of the body, when the
latter is oscillating about axes through C or D respectively. When the
axis passes through C, C is called the *centre of suspension* and D the
centre of oscillation or *centre of percussion*. When the axis passes
through D, the names are interchanged.

6. Accurate Measurement of g. Kater's Pendulums.

The best method of measuring g involves the application of equation (16). This was suggested by Prony (1800), by Bohnenberger (1811), and by Kater (1817). Kater was probably the first to make pendulums of a form to which equation (16) could be applied with precision. One type of pendulum constructed by Kater consists of a metal bar carrying two fixed knife-edges. These are set facing one another, one on each side of the centre of gravity. They serve as axes about which the body can oscillate under the action of gravity. On the bar are also mounted two sliding masses, one of which is much larger than the other. By adjusting the position of the larger mass it is easy to make the times of oscillation about the two knife-edges approximately equal. The small mass can then be adjusted until the difference of the two periods is less than any required limit, e.g. 0·001 sec. Such an adjustment is possible, though tedious. The distance between the two knife-edges is the $l_1 + l_2$ of equation (16), and it can be measured very accurately. Hence, apart from various corrections,

$$T = 2\pi\{(l_1 + l_2)/g\}^{\frac{1}{2}},$$

and

$$g = 4\pi^2(l_1 + l_2)/T^2.$$

The best way of measuring the actual period T' must be sought in a textbook of practical physics. A second type of Kater pendulum has one knife-edge fixed and one movable, and the theory differs somewhat from that of the first type. In each case, experiment results in the determination of a period T'. The corrections to be applied to T' in order to obtain T and g may be summarized as follows:

(1) The amplitudes of the actual oscillations are not infinitely small, as is assumed in calculating T. Suppose that during the timing of the oscillations the amplitude falls from θ_1 to θ_2 radians. Then by calculations similar to those on p. 14, $T = T'(1 - \theta_1\theta_2/16) = T'(1 - \alpha)$, say, where $\alpha \ll 1$.

(2) The upthrust of the air displaced by the pendulum reduces the weight Mg in the last term of equation (12), p. 15. This causes the measured period T' to exceed T. A rather long calculation gives the value of the correction β to be applied for this, which is done by writing $T = T'(1 - \beta)$.

(3) Du Buat's correction. The pendulum drags air with it in its motion, and the increased effective mass thus produced increases the moment of inertia and makes T' greater than T. The correction γ for this is applied by writing $T = T'(1 - \gamma)$.

(4) The viscous resistance of the air causes T' to exceed T slightly, as on p. 13. The correction δ for this is applied by writing $T = T'(1-\delta)$.

(5) Any increase in temperature makes T' greater than T. For this we write $T = T'(1 - \epsilon)$, where ϵ is the correcting term.

(6) The supports of the pendulum always yield a little in practice. They exert a horizontal force on the pendulum, which makes T' greater than T. For this reason we put $T = T'(1 - \sigma)$, where $\sigma \ll 1$.

(7) A correction on account of the fact that real knife-edges are cylindrical in shape may be avoided by making the radii of curvature of the two knife-edges equal. This was proved by Bessel.

The combined effect of the six actual corrections may be represented by

$$T = T'\{1 - (\alpha + \beta + \gamma + \delta + \epsilon + \sigma)\}, \quad . \quad . \quad (17)$$

where α, β, γ, δ, ϵ and σ are all very much less than unity.

Bessel's Improvements.

(1) The adjustment of the type of Kater pendulum described on p. 17, in order to make the two periods of oscillation exactly equal or their difference very small, is a tedious business. Bessel showed that it was also unnecessary. If we call the two periods T_1 and T_2 respectively, it is sufficient to adjust until $(T_1 - T_2) < 1 \cdot 5 \times 10^{-4} T_1$, which is comparatively easy. This is proved as follows. By the theory of p. 16, the two periods are given by the equations

$$g l_1 T_1{}^2 / 4 \pi^2 = k^2 + l_1{}^2$$

and

$$g l_2 T_2{}^2 / 4 \pi^2 = k^2 + l_2{}^2.$$

By subtraction,

$$g(l_1 T_1{}^2 - l_2 T_2{}^2)/4\pi^2 = l_1{}^2 - l_2{}^2. \quad . \quad . \quad . \quad . \quad (18)$$

Inverting, we have

$$4\pi^2/g = (l_1 T_1{}^2 - l_2 T_2{}^2)/(l_1{}^2 - l_2{}^2).$$

Using partial fractions, we obtain

$$4\pi^2/g = (T_1{}^2 + T_2{}^2)/2(l_1 + l_2) + (T_1{}^2 - T_2{}^2)/2(l_1 - l_2). \quad . \quad . \quad (19)$$

In the expression on the right-hand side, the first term is very much greater than the second, when T_1 and T_2 are nearly equal. It also contains $l_1 + l_2$, the distance between the knife-edges, which is accurately measurable. The second term has the small quantity $T_1{}^2 - T_2{}^2$ in its numerator and the large quantity $l_1 - l_2$ in its denominator, for T_1 and T_2 are nearly equal, but l_1 and l_2 are quite different from one another. To evaluate $l_1 - l_2$ in the small second term it is sufficient to balance the pendulum horizontally on another knife-edge not forming part of the bar, and thus to find the centre of gravity. The distances of this knife-edge from each of the others give l_1 and l_2 respectively, and $l_1 - l_2$, with sufficient accuracy, for the small term.

(2) Bessel also proved that Du Buat's correction factor γ (see p. 17) is zero if the external form of the pendulum is symmetrical about its middle point. In this case the knife-edges of the pendulum are equidistant from the centre of its geometrical figure, though not from its centre of gravity.

7. Measurement of g at Sea.

It was formerly thought that the vibrations of ships prohibited the use of pendulums on board. The earlier methods of measuring g at sea, such as those of Hecker and Duffield,* depend upon the simultaneous measurement of the atmospheric pressure P in two ways. The height of the column of mercury in a barometer tube gives H in the equation $P = g\rho H$, where g is the gravitational acceleration and ρ the density of mercury. A simultaneous measurement of the temperature at which water boils enables P to be obtained from tables of the temperatures and saturation pressures of water vapour. The point is that the second method of measuring P must not involve g. Alternatively, P can be measured by an aneroid barometer, or by causing a gas to exert a pressure equal and opposite to that of the atmosphere. Then $g = P/\rho H$. This method gives values of g with a probable error (see p. 262) of about $\pm 0\cdot 01$ cm./sec.^{2}, which is relatively large compared with that obtained in pendulum experiments on land. The chief cause of this relatively large error is the so-called " bumping ", that is, oscillations of the mercury in the barometer tube due to movements of the ship.

Vening-Meinesz † has devised a method which is far more accurate than that just described. He has shown that pendulum methods can be used on board ship, especially if the ship is a submerged submarine. Pendulums are subject to four disturbances due to the motion of the vessel and caused by

(1) Horizontal acceleration of the point of suspension.
(2) Vertical acceleration.
(3) " Rocking ", that is, the angular movement of the support.
(4) Slipping of the knife-edges on the agate planes on which they rest.

By conducting experiments while the submarine is submerged, the total angular deviation due to the first three causes is kept below 1°, and the knife-edges do not slide on the agate planes. The horizontal acceleration has the greatest disturbing effect of the three. Its effect is completely eliminated by swinging two similarly made half-second pendulums (that is, pendulums whose full period is one second) together in the same vertical plane from the same support, but with different phases. If the pendulums are assumed to be isochronous (that is, having equal periods), the difference of the two angular displacements θ_1 and θ_n gives an angle $\theta_1 - \theta_2$ which may be regarded as the angular displacement of a pendulum undisturbed by the horizontal acceleration of its support. For the equations of motion of the two pendulums may be written

$$M(k^2 + l^2)\ddot{\theta}_1 + Mgl\theta_1 + A = 0$$

and

$$M(k^2 + l^2)\ddot{\theta}_2 + Mgl\theta_2 + A = 0,$$

where A is a term representing the effect of the horizontal acceleration of the support, and is the same in the two cases. By subtraction,

$$M(k^2 + l^2)(\ddot{\theta}_1 - \ddot{\theta}_2) + Mgl(\theta_1 - \theta_2) = 0,$$

an equation from which any disturbing term is absent. The effect of the vertical accelerations of the point of support cannot be eliminated without eliminating

* Duffield, *Proc. Roy. Soc.*, Vol. 92, p. 505 (1916).
† Vening-Meinesz, *Geographical Journal*, Vol. 71, p. 144 (1928).

g itself. It appears, however, that the measured value of g is affected by the mean value of the vertical acceleration during the whole time of observation, and as the vertical movement is alternately up and down, fluctuating about the value zero, the mean value of the vertical acceleration is small. The corresponding error in g is made very small by making the duration of the observations very great. The third source of disturbance, rocking of the plane of oscillation, involves a small correction, which is easily computed from the recorded value of the rocking angle.

In practice, continuous photographic records are made, using three pendulums all swinging together from the same support. By an optical arrangement the differences $\theta_1 - \theta_2$, $\theta_2 - \theta_3$ are recorded on a strip of sensitized paper, along with time-marks from two very accurate chronometers. Thus two sets of values of g are obtained. The pendulums are of brass, as invar pendulums are liable to magnetic disturbances arising from the ferromagnetic structure and machinery of the submarine. Corrections for temperature effects are applied, although the apparatus is thermally insulated. The whole system is suspended in gimbals, and is thus screened from external shocks and effects due to small angular movements of the vessel. It is claimed that the probable error reached in a series of measurements conducted in a Dutch naval submarine proceeding in 1926–7 from Holland to Java via Panama is $\pm 0 \cdot 0018$ cm. per sec. per sec.

8. Relative Measurement of g.

When the values of g at various points in a country are to be compared with the value of g at some standard position, it is not usual

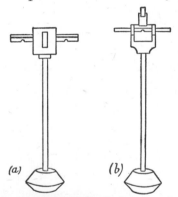

(a)   (b)

Fig. 6.—(From *Handbuch der Experimentalphysik* (Akademische Verlagsgesellschaft, Leipzig).)

to employ the same technique as when an absolute measurement is contemplated. Suppose that the period of oscillation of one particular pendulum is measured, first at the standard position (T_0), and then at any other place (T_1). At the standard position $T_0 = 2\pi(l/g_0)^{\frac{1}{2}}$, where l is the length of the simple equivalent pendulum and g_0 is the value of g at the standard position. At the other place $T_1 = 2\pi(l/g_1)^{\frac{1}{2}}$, where g_1 is the new value of g. On dividing, squaring, and rearranging, we have $g_1 = g_0 T_0^2/T_1^2$, which gives the value of g_1 in terms of g_0. In this manner a gravity survey is extended throughout a country. Similar methods are in use in most countries; a brief account of the German method of experimenting is given here.

Half-second pendulums of a type invented by von Sterneck are used, that is, pendulums whose equivalent length is about 25 cm. and whose complete period is about one second. These are now made of the nickel-steel alloy *invar*, whose coefficient of linear expansion with temperature is extremely small. Figs. 6(*a*) and 6(*b*) show the general shape of two types of pendulum in common use; they differ only in the arrangement of the knife-edges. Four similar pendulums hang from the same massive support in four separate compartments of the apparatus.

The casing is made of mu-metal or some similar alloy, to screen the pendulums from magnetic fields. Oscillation experiments are conducted with three of these. The fourth is a " dummy " carrying a thermometer whose readings are assumed to give the temperature of the three experimental pendulums. In the latest form of apparatus the vessel housing the pendulums is evacuated, in order to eliminate du Buat's correction and other corrections.

Each pendulum carries an agate knife-edge, which rests on an agate plane on the support. The knife-edge forms the axis of oscillation when the pendulum swings. All the pendulums, except the dummy, carry a small plane mirror on their knife-edges, the normal to the centre of the mirror being in the plane of oscillation of the central line of the pendulum. The time of oscillation of each pendulum is determined by comparison with the time of oscillation of a standard clock or with signals from an accurate chronometer. For this purpose a method of coincidences is used. A small plane mirror is mounted on a fixed support so as to face the mirror on one of the experimental pendulums. It is parallel to that mirror when the pendulum is at rest. The standard clock or chronometer operates an electric relay, so that a horizontal electric spark is produced by breaking a certain circuit, once for every complete oscillation of the pendulum of the standard clock. An optical image of this spark, formed by rays of light reflected from each plane mirror in turn, is seen in the focal plane of the eyepiece of a telescope. The standard and experimental pendulums are so arranged that this image is seen in coincidence with the horizontal crosswire when the pendulums are " in phase " and each is passing through its rest-position. The mean interval between two coincidences is measured, over a period of about two hours. Let T_0, τ_0 sec. be the periods of one complete oscillation of the experimental and standard pendulums respectively. T_0 is about $1\cdot0$ sec. and τ_0 is about $2\cdot0$ sec. Let the mean interval between coincidences be I sec. In I sec. let the standard pendulum make n complete oscillations. Then $n\tau_0 = I$. Let the experimental pendulum make N complete oscillations in the same time. Then $NT_0 = I$. It is known that T_0 is approximately equal to $\tau_0/2$, and we may write $T_0 = \tau_0/2 \pm \alpha$; then $I = N(\tau_0/2 \pm \alpha) = n\tau_0$, where α is a small period of time. Hence $2n\tau_0 = N(\tau_0 \pm 2\alpha)$ and $(2n - N)\tau_0 = \pm 2N\alpha$. Dividing both sides by τ_0, we obtain $2n - N = \pm 2N\alpha/\tau_0$. Now $2n - N$ must be an integer, since n and N are both integers. Hence the least value of $2n - N$, other than zero, must be ± 1, and the shortest interval I between two successive coincidences is that which makes $2n - N = \pm 1$. Hence $2N\alpha/\tau_0 = 1$. The equations $n\tau_0 = I = NT_0$ can be written in the form $n\tau_0 = I = (2n \pm 1)T_0$, whence $T_0 = I/(2n \pm 1) = I/(2I/\tau_0 \pm 1) = I\tau_0/(2I \pm \tau_0)$, which gives T_0 if τ_0 and I are known.

Various precautions are necessary in carrying out the experiment. (1) An automatic setting device is required, to place the knife-edge of the pendulum on the same part of the agate planes every time. (2) The agate planes need frequent repolishing. (3) They must be set horizontally before every experiment. (4) The support must be stable and free from tremors. (5) The deposition of dust and water vapour on the pendulum must be prevented. In a certain case water vapour altered T_0 by 3×10^{-6} sec.

The chief corrections to the measured value of T_0 are: (1) Correction for temperature variation; results are reduced to some standard temperature. (2) Corrections for air resistance and increased moment of inertia due to carried air; in the older technique results are reduced to the standard pressure 76 cm. of mercury; in the new vacuum apparatus these effects and corrections are eliminated. (3) Correction of T_0 to sidereal seconds. (4) Correction to zero amplitude; the initial amplitude does not exceed 1°. In recent work the standard clock is kept at a base station, and wireless signals are sent to the place of observation.

9. Variation of g with Time. Method of Tomaschek and Schaffernicht.

The " Bifilar Gravimeter " of Tomaschek and Schaffernicht * affords an accurate method of measuring minute temporal changes in the absolute value of g at a given place (figs. 7 and 8).

To a torsion head T is attached a long vertical spiral spring, made of wire of a special alloy (Krupp's Alloy W.T. 10) which is distinguished by the absence of " creep " in its elastic properties. A flat circular disc C is attached to the lower end of the spring. Below the disc another disc P is suspended by means of a short wire. To opposite ends of a diameter of C are attached supporting fibres, forming a kind of bifilar suspension, which carries part of the weight of the system. When the torsion head is twisted through an angle θ, the disc C rotates in the same direction through an angle φ and finally comes to rest. Then the moment of the displacing couple due to the twisted spring is equal and opposite to the moment of the restoring couple due to the tension in the fibres of the bifilar suspension. The angles θ and φ increase together. If the disc C remained at the same level during the twisting, the moment of the restoring couple would increase to a maximum when φ was 90°, and would then diminish again as φ increased. The 90° position would be one of instability and the system would suddenly swing round through a large angle. In practice, on account of the raising of the disc and consequent alteration in the tension of the fibres, the position of instability is only reached when φ = 145° approx. The spring is deliberately set so that this position is reached. Then when the value of g alters, the weights of the two discs alter and the system rotates through a small angle. This angle is measured by means of the usual device of a mirror, lamp, and scale, the mirror being mounted on the wire between the two discs.

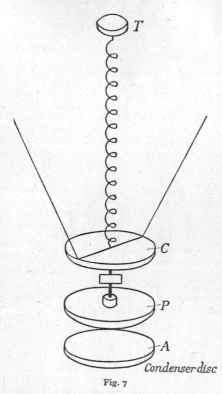

Fig. 7

Figs. 8 (a) and (b) represent the disc C in equilibrium after a displacement φ. The moment of the restoring couple due to the tension T in the strings is twice the horizontal component of the tension in each, multiplied by the perpendicular distance z from the axis on to the line of action XY of the horizontal component. Hence

$$\text{Moment of restoring couple} = 2Txz/l. \qquad \ldots \quad (20)$$

* Tomaschek and Schaffernicht, *Ann. d. Physik*, Vol. 15, p. 787 (1932).

Since the disc is not moving vertically, we also have

$$2T \cos B = Mg, \quad \ldots \ldots \ldots \ldots \quad (21)$$

where Mg is the weight of the discs, &c., less the weight supported by the spring. Now $\cos B = h/l$; and

$$\text{Twice area of triangle } OXY = zx = ab \sin \varphi. \quad \ldots \quad (22)$$

Hence the moment of the restoring couple is $Mgab \sin \varphi / h$. The moment of the displacing couple is that due to torsion of the spring; it is equal to $f(\theta - \varphi)$, where f is the torsional constant of the spring. Equating the moments of the couples and rearranging, we get

$$g = hf(\theta - \varphi)/Mab \sin \varphi. \quad \ldots \ldots \quad (23)$$

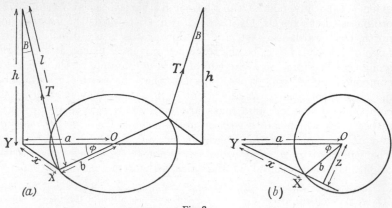

(a)   (b)

Fig. 8

When g varies, the change in h is extremely small. Hence, in differentiating equation (23), h is treated as a constant, and we have

$$dg = -hf\{\sin \varphi + (\theta - \varphi) \cos \varphi\} d\varphi / Mab \sin^2 \varphi. \quad \ldots \quad (24)$$

This gives the change in g corresponding to a change in φ. The movements of the spot of light corresponding to $d\varphi$ and dg are registered photographically. A displacement of 2 mm. on the sensitized film corresponds to a variation $dg = 10^{-8}g$. The extreme sensitiveness thus attained enables the changes in g due to movements of the sun and moon to be separated and measured. To obtain such results it is necessary to insulate the apparatus thermally and to prevent temperature changes of more than $0 \cdot 001°$ C. The spring is specially treated beforehand so that its elastic constants do not change during an experiment. It is also necessary to work in a deep cellar (25 m.) to avoid disturbances due to traffic and machinery. Equation (24) can be written

$$dg = K d\varphi / M, \quad \ldots \ldots \ldots \ldots \quad (25)$$

where K is, in effect, a constant. Its percentage change due to the small change in φ is extremely small. K is found, that is, the instrument is calibrated, by bringing a parallel horizontal disc A under the lower disc P of the gravimeter, applying a known electric potential difference V e.s.u. to the discs A and P, and measuring the deflection $d\varphi_0$. As in an attracted disc electrometer, the downward force on P is $V^2S/8\pi x^2$ dynes, where S sq. cm. is the effective area of each disc and x cm. is the distance between A and P. Writing $V^2S/8\pi x^2 = M.dg_0$, we see that the force $V^2S/8\pi x^2$ dynes corresponds to a change in g of $dg_0 = V^2S/8\pi x^2 M$. Substituting in equation (25), we have $V^2S/8\pi x^2 M = Kd\varphi_0/M$ and $K = V^2S/8\pi x^2 d\varphi_0$.

10. Changes of g with Direction. The Eötvös Torsion Balance.

It is possible to measure accurately, not only the absolute value of g at any point, but also the rate of change of g with distance in any horizontal direction, and some other important quantities connected with the earth's gravitational field. These measurements are carried out with the Eötvös torsion balance, of which the theory will now be given. Take any point O on the earth's surface as an origin of co-ordinates. Let axes Ox, Oy, Oz be drawn, Ox towards the geographical north, Oy towards the east, and Oz downwards in the direction of the force of gravity. Let g_0 be the force per unit mass placed at the origin, along Oz. The force on a particle of mass m grammes at the origin has components 0, 0, mg_0 dynes. Assume that the earth's gravitational field has a potential U at any point (x, y, z) and that at (x, y, z) the component forces on unit mass are $+\partial U/\partial x$, $+\partial U/\partial y$, and $+\partial U/\partial z$ respectively, which can be written in the form $\partial U/\partial x = g_x$, $\partial U/\partial y = g_y$, and $\partial U/\partial z = g_z$. At the origin $\partial U/\partial x = 0$, $\partial U/\partial y = 0$, $\partial U/\partial z = g_0$. The values of g_x, g_y, and g_z at any point (x, y, z) very close to the origin may be calculated by Maclaurin's theorem. Any function

$$f(x, y, z) = f(0, 0, 0) + x\frac{\partial f}{\partial x_0} + y\frac{\partial f}{\partial y_0} + z\frac{\partial f}{\partial z_0} + \text{smaller negligible terms,}$$

provided x, y, and z are small. The suffix 0 indicates that the values of the differential coefficients to be used are those at the origin. Hence

$$g_x = g_{x_0} + x\frac{\partial g_x}{\partial x_0} + y\frac{\partial g_x}{\partial y_0} + z\frac{\partial g_x}{\partial z_0} \text{ approx.}$$

$$= 0 + x\frac{\partial^2 U}{\partial x_0{}^2} + y\frac{\partial^2 U}{\partial x\partial y_0} + z\frac{\partial^2 U}{\partial x\partial z_0}, \quad \cdots \quad (26)$$

since $g_x = \partial U/\partial x$, &c.

Similarly,

$$g_y = 0 + x\frac{\partial^2 U}{\partial y\partial x_0} + y\frac{\partial^2 U}{\partial y_0{}^2} + z\frac{\partial^2 U}{\partial y\partial z_0} \quad \cdots \quad (27)$$

and

$$g_z = g_0 + x\frac{\partial^2 U}{\partial z\partial x_0} + y\frac{\partial^2 U}{\partial z\partial y_0} + z\frac{\partial^2 U}{\partial z_0{}^2}. \quad \cdots \quad (28)$$

These are the forces per unit mass along Ox, Oy, Oz respectively, at the point x, y, z. Taking moments about the axis Oz, we see that the clockwise moment of forces acting on unit mass at (x, y, z) is $g_y x - g_x y$ (fig. 9). On a large body distributed over a certain space the clockwise moment is $\int(g_y x - g_x y)\,dm$, where dm is the mass concentrated at any point (x, y, z) and the integral sign simply indicates the summation over all the elements of mass in the body.

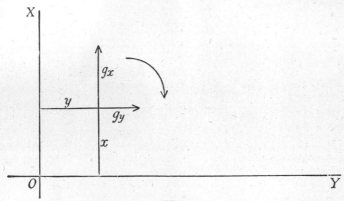

Fig. 9

One of the common forms of the Eötvös balance (fig. 10) involves the above theory. The principal part is a torsion head from which hangs a thin torsion wire, usually of a platinum-iridium alloy, about 30×10^{-3} to 40×10^{-3} mm. in diameter and 25 to 60 cm. in length. This carries a horizontal rectangular beam of aluminium about 40 cm. long. One end of this beam carries a cylindrical weight of platinum, gold, or silver of mass about 30 gm., with its axis horizontal. From the other end of the beam hangs a cylindrical weight of mass about 25 gm., supported by a platinum-iridium wire about 40 cm. long. This suspension system carries a small plane mirror just above the level of the beam. The system, regarded as a whole, forms a body acted on by a torque whose moment is given by the above expression. Let the origin O of co-ordinates be the mid-point of the beam. The moment of the torque is $\int(g_y x - g_x y)\,dm$, and the integral is to be taken over the whole of the suspension system. If we substitute for g_x and g_y from equations (26) and (27), the moment becomes

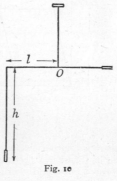

Fig. 10

$$\left(\frac{\partial^2 U}{\partial y_0{}^2} - \frac{\partial^2 U}{\partial x_0{}^2}\right)\int xy\,dm + \frac{\partial^2 U}{\partial x\,\partial y_0}\int (x^2 - y^2)\,dm$$

$$+ \frac{\partial^2 U}{\partial y\,\partial z_0}\int zx\,dm - \frac{\partial^2 U}{\partial x\,\partial z_0}\int yz\,dm. \quad \cdot \quad \cdot \quad \cdot \quad \cdot \quad (29)$$

In experiments with the Eötvös torsion balance the suspension system is released and takes up some position of equilibrium in which the axis of the beam, though horizontal, makes an angle α, called the azimuth angle, with Ox, and $90 - \alpha$ with Oy. In order to use the above expression for the moment of gravitational forces, the various integrals must be evaluated. For this purpose new axes of co-ordinates are selected, namely, $O\xi$ along the geometrical axis of the beam, $O\eta$ horizontal and perpendicular to $O\xi$, and so directed that when $O\xi$ points to the north, $O\eta$ points to the east, and Oz vertically downwards as before. From fig. 11,

$$x = \xi \cos\alpha - \eta \sin\alpha,$$
$$y = \xi \sin\alpha + \eta \cos\alpha.$$

Then

$$\int xy\,dm = \tfrac{1}{2}\sin 2\alpha \int (\xi^2 - \eta^2)\,dm + \cos 2\alpha \int \xi\eta\,dm,$$

$$\int (x^2 - y^2)\,dm = \cos 2\alpha \int (\xi^2 - \eta^2)\,dm - 2\sin 2\alpha \int \xi\eta\,dm,$$

$$\int zx\,dm = \cos\alpha \int z\xi\,dm - \sin\alpha \int z\eta\,dm,$$

and

$$\int yz\,dm = \sin\alpha \int z\xi\,dm + \cos\alpha \int z\eta\,dm.$$

The suspension system is so constructed that its mass is symmetrically distributed with respect to the axis $O\xi$ and also the vertical plane ξOz (fig. 12).

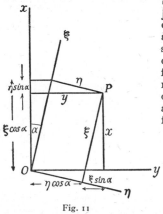

Symmetry with respect to the axis $O\xi$ makes $\int \xi\eta\,dm = 0$, for it means that for every element with co-ordinates (ξ, η, z) there is another element with co-ordinates $(\xi, -\eta, z)$, so that the expression under the integral sign can be divided into pairs of terms of the form $+\xi\eta\,dm$ and $-\xi\eta\,dm$, which together make zero. Again, the beam and the weight on it are symmetrical with respect to the axis $O\xi$; hence, as far as they are concerned, for every element with co-ordinates (ξ, η, z)

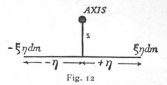

Fig. 11   Fig. 12

there is another element with co-ordinates $(\xi, \eta, -z)$. For the beam and weight on it, $\int \xi z\,dm = 0$, because the integral can be split up into pairs of terms of the form $+\xi z\,dm$ and $-\xi z\,dm$, which add up to zero. The lower weight and wire contribute an amount mhl to the integral $\int \xi z\,dm$, where m is their mass, h is the z-co-ordinate of their centre of gravity, and l is its ξ-co-ordinate. Symmetry about the plane ξOz implies that for every element with co-ordinates (ξ, η, z) there is another with co-ordinates $(\xi, -\eta, z)$. Hence $\int \eta z\,dm = 0$, for it can be divided into pairs of terms of the form $+\eta z\,dm$ and $-\eta z\,dm$, which add up to zero. In the remaining integral $\int (\xi^2 - \eta^2)\,dm$, $\eta^2 \ll \xi^2$ for most elements of mass. Hence $\xi^2 - \eta^2 = \xi^2 + \eta^2$, very nearly, and as $\int (\xi^2 + \eta^2)\,dm = K$, the moment of inertia of the suspension system about Oz, $\int (\xi^2 - \eta^2)\,dm = K$, to a close approximation. On substituting the results just obtained in the expression (29) for the moment of the gravitational forces, the moment becomes

$$\tfrac{1}{2} K \sin 2\alpha \left(\frac{\partial^2 U}{\partial y_0^2} - \frac{\partial^2 U}{\partial x_0^2}\right) + K \cos 2\alpha \frac{\partial^2 U}{\partial x \partial y_0} + mhl\left\{\cos\alpha \frac{\partial^2 U}{\partial y \partial z_0} - \sin\alpha \frac{\partial^2 U}{\partial x \partial z_0}\right\}. \quad (30)$$

This moment tends to displace the torsion system. A restoring torque, whose moment is $c\theta_a$, is called into play in the suspending wire; c is the torsional constant and θ_a is the angular displacement from the position when there are no torques acting. When the system is at rest, the displacing and restoring moments are equal. The usual mirror, lamp, and scale are used to measure deflections. Let n_a be the scale reading corresponding to the displacement 0_a, n that corresponding to zero displacement, and D the distance between mirror and scale. Then $n_a - n = 2D\theta_a$ and $c\theta_a = c(n_a - n)/2D$. The equality of displacing and restoring moments is represented by the equation

$$ n_a - n = \left\{ DK\,\frac{U_{yy} - U_{xx}}{c} \right\} \sin 2\alpha + \left\{ 2KD\,\frac{U_{xy}}{c} \right\} \cos 2\alpha $$
$$ + \left\{ 2D\,\frac{mhl}{c} \right\}(U_{yz} \cos\alpha - U_{xz} \sin\alpha), \quad \ldots \ldots \quad (31) $$

where

$$ U_{yy} = \partial^2 U/\partial y_0^2, \quad U_{xx} = \partial^2 U/\partial x_0^2, \quad U_{xy} = \partial^2 U/\partial x\,\partial y_0, $$
$$ U_{yz} = \partial^2 U/\partial y\,\partial z_0, \ \text{and} \ U_{xz} = \partial^2 U/\partial x\,\partial z_0. $$

This can be written in the form

$$ n_a - n = P \sin 2\alpha + Q \cos 2\alpha + A \sin\alpha + B \cos\alpha, \quad \ldots \quad (32) $$

where n, P, Q, A and B are five unknowns and n_a and α are two experimentally measurable quantities. In general, to determine five unknowns, five equations are required. This involves five separate readings of n_a for five separate values of the azimuth angle α. In practice, the procedure is simplified by taking readings in six azimuths, in which $\alpha = 0°$, $60°$, $120°$, $180°$, $240°$ and $300°$ respectively. Calculation gives n, P, Q, A and B. Then, at the origin,

$$ U_{yy} - U_{xx} = Pc/DK, \quad \ldots \ldots \quad (33) $$
$$ U_{xy} = Qc/2DK, \quad \ldots \ldots \quad (34) $$
$$ U_{xz} = -Ac/2Dmhl, \quad \ldots \ldots \quad (35) $$
$$ U_{yz} = Bc/2Dmhl. \quad \ldots \ldots \quad (36) $$

These are the four quantities usually measured at any point. U_{xz} and U_{yz} are, of course, the same as $\partial g/\partial x_0$ and $\partial g/\partial y_0$, the rates of change of g in horizontal directions near the origin. The other two quantities represent quantitative properties of the gravitational field near the origin. $U_{zz} = \partial g/\partial z_0$ is not measured by this apparatus.

The quantity c is determined by applying a known displacing couple C to the system and measuring the angle φ produced. Then $c = C/\varphi$. K is determined by an oscillation experiment; m, D, h and l are found by ordinary weighing and length-measuring methods.

11. The Gravity Gradient and Horizontal Directive Tendency.

In connexion with gravitational surveys and the construction of maps indicating the results, it has been found convenient to introduce two other quantities connected with the earth's gravitational field and with the expressions in equations (33), (34), (35) and (36). These are called the *gravity gradient* and the *horizontal directive tendency* respectively.

The term gravity gradient is an abbreviation for " maximum gradient of g in a horizontal direction near a point", where g is $\partial U/\partial z$, the vertical gravitational intensity at the point. The gravity gradient is therefore equal to $\partial g/\partial s$, the rate of variation of g per unit of length measured in the direction of maximum rate of change of g; it is a vector quantity. Let $\partial g/\partial s$ make an angle ϕ with Ox, and let its components along Ox and Oy be $\partial g/\partial x$ and $\partial g/\partial y$. Then $\partial g/\partial x = \cos\phi\,(\partial g/\partial s)$ and $\partial g/\partial y = \sin\phi\,(\partial g/\partial s)$. Writing $g = \partial U/\partial z$, we have $\partial g/\partial x = \partial^2 U/\partial x \partial z = U_{xz}$ and $\partial g/\partial y = \partial^2 U/\partial y \partial z = U_{yz}$. Denoting the gravity gradient $\partial g/\partial s$ by G, we have

$$\left.\begin{array}{l} U_{xz} = G\cos\phi \\ U_{yz} = G\sin\phi \end{array}\right\}, \quad \ldots \ldots \quad (37)$$

and

or

$$G = (U_{xz}{}^2 + U_{yz}{}^2)^{\frac{1}{2}}. \quad \ldots \ldots \quad (38)$$

Hence G can be calculated if we know U_{xz} and U_{yz}, which may be derived by experiments with the Eötvös torsion balance as on p. 27.

The horizontal directive tendency (H.D.T.) * at any point is a directed quantity but not a true vector. It is given by $R = g(1/a_1 - 1/a_2)$, where g has its usual meaning and a_1, a_2 are the maximum and minimum radii of curvature of the gravitational equipotential or level surface at the point. Its direction is conventionally assumed to be that horizontal direction in which the vertical downward curvature of the level surface is least and the radius of curvature greatest. Let its direction make an angle θ with Ox. It can be shown that R is related to the differential coefficients in equations (33), (34), (35) and (36), as follows:

$$R\sin 2\theta = 2U_{xy}, \quad \ldots \ldots \ldots \quad (39)$$
$$R\cos 2\theta = U_{xx}{}^2 - U_{yy}{}^2. \quad \ldots \ldots \quad (40)$$

Rankine has shown that equation (31) may be transformed by the aid of substitutions from equations (39) and (40) into the form

$$n_a - n = (DKR/c)\sin 2(\theta - a) + (2DmhlG/c)\sin(\phi - a). \quad (41)$$

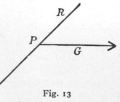

Fig. 13

This form brings out the separate importance of G and R, and indicates what features must be possessed by torsion balances suitable for the measurement of G or R separately. In survey maps, G is represented in magnitude and direction by an arrow drawn from the point P which possesses this value of G. R is represented in direction and magnitude by a straight line without any pointed or feathered end, drawn through P (fig. 13). Curves joining those points on a level surface, where g

* Ger. *Krümmungsgrösse.*

has equal values, are called *isogams*. G is always directed along a normal to an isogam. The dimensions of both G and R are those of (time)$^{-2}$, and they are usually expressed in the so-called Eötvös units. One Eötvös $= 10^{-9}$ sec.$^{-2}$. With a well-made Eötvös balance, a deflection of one scale division corresponds to a change of about one Eötvös unit. Measurements of $G, R,$ and other quantities are now employed commercially in the detection of heavy ores. The Kursk region of Russia, in longitude 36° 52′ E., offers an example of an extensive region in which both the gravitational and the magnetic fields of the earth show very marked anomalies.

12. Alteration in Direction of the Force of Gravity with Time. The Horizontal Pendulum.

A problem which has recently received much attention is that of finding the change in direction, as time goes on, of the force of gravity at a point on the earth's surface. This is equivalent to finding the change in direction of a plumb-line. The point of support of a plumb-line is attached firmly to the earth and moves with the earth's surface, and a plumb-line sets itself normal to a gravitational equipotential surface. Hence deformations of the earth's surface and of the equipotential surface cause changes in the direction of a plumb-line.

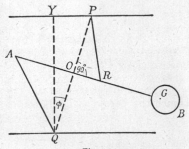

Fig. 14

As these changes amount at most to 0·1 second of angle, their direct determination with a plumb-line is out of the question.

Perhaps the commonest instrument used to measure temporal changes in the direction of the force of gravity is the horizontal pendulum, said to have been devised in 1832 by Hengler. In principle this instrument (fig. 14) consists of a rod AB, supported in an inclined position by two light strings AQ and PR, attached to rigid supports at P and Q. The straight line PQ makes an angle ϕ with the direction of the force of gravity. The rod AB takes up a position of equilibrium in a certain plane, which is parallel to the force of gravity, as shown in fig. 14. When AB is slightly displaced laterally, for example, if B is drawn towards the observer and released, the pendulum describes slow small oscillations, whose period may be calculated as follows.

The centre of gravity G of the pendulum describes a circular arc GG' (fig. 15) as the pendulum oscillates. The centre of this circle is O, the point where AB crosses PQ. The circle lies in a plane making an angle ϕ with a plane normal to the force of gravity. Consider the restoring force on the pendulum when it has rotated through a small angle θ in the inclined plane. At G there is a force mg acting in the direction of gravity. This may be resolved into two components:

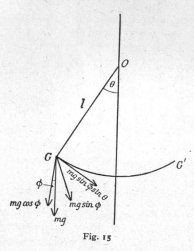

Fig. 15

(1) $mg \cos\phi$ in a direction perpendicular to the inclined plane in which the pendulum rotates, and (2) $mg \sin\phi$ in the inclined plane of rotation of the pendulum. The force $mg \sin\phi$ may be further resolved into two components, along and perpendicular to OG. The component $mg \sin\phi \sin\theta$, perpendicular to OG, is important here, as it is the force which restores the pendulum to its initial position. Its moment about the inclined axis is $mgl \sin\phi \sin\theta$, where $OG = l$. When θ is small this becomes $mgl \sin\phi . \theta$. The equation of motion of the pendulum about the inclined axis PQ is therefore $mk^2\ddot\theta + mgl \sin\phi . \theta = 0$, where mk^2 is the moment of inertia and frictional or viscous forces are neglected. Hence the period of oscillation is

$$T = 2\pi(k^2/gl \sin\phi)^{\frac{1}{2}}. \quad \ldots \ldots \quad (42)$$

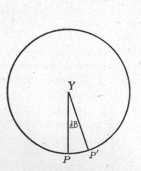

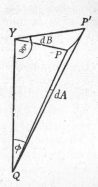

Fig. 16

In practice φ is made very small, so that T is very great. When $\varphi = 90°$, $T = T_{90°} = 2\pi(k^2/gl)^{\frac{1}{2}}$. Hence

$$T/T_{90°} = (1/\sin\varphi)^{\frac{1}{2}}$$

and

$$\sin\varphi = T_{90°}^2/T^2. \quad \ldots \ldots \ldots \quad (43)$$

Oscillation experiments give $T_{90°}$ and T, whence $\sin \varphi$ and φ are calculated. Changes in φ represent changes in the direction of gravity, taking place in the plane of equilibrium $AYPBQ$ of the pendulum (fig. 14). Changes of the direction of gravity in a perpendicular plane may be considered as follows. Imagine the line PQ in figs. 14 and 16 to rotate through a small angle about YQ, a fixed line, while Q remains fixed (fig. 16). $Y\overline{P}$ rotates through an angle dB, say, so that P goes to P'. Then the arc $PP' = YP \cdot dB = PQ \sin \varphi \cdot dB$. Also the arc $PP' = PQ \cdot dA$, where dA is the change in direction of gravity required. Hence $dA = \sin \varphi \cdot dB = T_{90°}{}^2 dB/T^2$, by equation (43). In practice it is the angle dB which is measured. This is done by means of the usual mirror, lamp, and scale. T and $T_{90°}$ are measured as before by oscillation experiments, so that dA can be calculated.

Another method of finding the change of direction of gravity in a perpendicular plane is to mount two horizontal pendulums inside one case, so set that by the first method one gives $\varphi = \varphi_1$ and the other $\varphi = \varphi_2$, in two perpendicular azimuths. In very accurate measurements by Schweydar $T_{90°} = 0.435$ sec., $T =$ about 15 sec., and on the scale measuring dA, a deflection of 1 mm. corresponds to a value of dA of 0.022 sec. of angle.

CHAPTER III

The Newtonian Constant of Gravitation

1. Newton's Law of Gravitation.

According to Newton's law of gravitation, every particle of matter in the universe attracts every other particle with a force which is proportional to the mass of each particle concerned and inversely proportional to the square of their distance apart. In symbols, the law may be written

$$F = G\frac{m_1 m_2}{d^2}, \quad \cdots \cdots \quad (1)$$

where F is the force of attraction between the particles, m_1 and m_2 are their masses, and d is their distance apart. G is a constant known as the Newtonian constant of gravitation, whose dimensions are $+3$ in length, -1 in mass, and -2 in time.

Astronomical measurements prove that, except where relativistic corrections are appreciable, the law holds even when d is very great. Since two different atoms cannot be absolutely superposed on one another, it would seem that a repulsive force must come into play between two atoms, when d is of the order 10^{-7} cm., and that Newton's law then ceases to hold. (Actually, conditions are complicated by electrical forces which result from the ultimate electrical nature of matter.) For all greater values of d it appears to be true. Further, if the index of d is written in the form $2 + k$, $k \leqq 1\cdot5 \times 10^{-7}$, that is, $k = 0$ within the limits of experimental error.

It is proved in Ex. 2, p. 276, that a sphere or spherical shell of homogeneous attracting matter made up of particles obeying Newton's law exerts, as a whole, an attraction upon an external particle as if the whole mass of the sphere or shell were concentrated at the centre. Thus the attraction of a sphere of mass M gm. on a particle of mass m gm. situated R cm. from the centre of the sphere and outside it is GMm/R^2 dynes. This applies if the sphere is (a) uniform throughout or (b) composed of homogeneous spherical shells. To a first approximation we may regard the earth as a sphere of type (b), though there are actually many local variations of density, even in that part of the earth, the crust, which is accessible to direct investigation. Moreover, the shape of the earth's surface is not exactly spherical, but is that of a spheroid with its minor axis in the direction of the earth's geographical axis. Neglecting these points, we see that owing to the earth's attraction a particle placed at a point on the surface will move, if free, towards the centre of the earth. If we denote the acceleration by g and the mass by m, the attractive force is mg, by Newton's second law of motion. It is also GMm/R^2, by the law of gravitation. Hence $GMm/R^2 = mg$ and

$$\frac{GM}{R^2} = g. \quad \cdots \cdots \cdots \quad (2)$$

If ρ is the mean density of the earth and R its radius, $M = 4\pi R^3 \rho/3$, and, eliminating M from (2), we obtain

$$g = \tfrac{4}{3}\pi G R \rho. \quad \cdots \cdots \cdots \quad (3)$$

This relation contains four quantities, G, g, R, and ρ, and may be used to calculate any one of them, provided the other three are known. The present chapter will be mainly concerned with experimental determinations of G. The value of ρ can be calculated if g, G, and R are known. Equation (2) may also be used to determine G if a value of M, derived by astronomical methods, is assumed.

The gravitational constant has been measured experimentally by (a) large-scale experiments and (b) laboratory experiments. Of the former, which are now of historical interest only and in which the earth is one of the attracting masses, may be mentioned (a) Bouguer's measurements in Peru of the relative masses of a mountain (whose mass was estimated from its volume and density) and the earth from the deflection of a plumb-line placed near the mountain, (b) experiments of Airy and others on the relative masses of a spherical shell of the earth (whose mass was estimated from its volume and density) and the entire earth, from observations of the times of oscillation of a pendulum at the bottom of a mine shaft and at ground level respectively.

2. Measurement of *G*.   Boys' Method.

Perhaps the most important methods of measuring G are those in which a torsion balance is used. The original type of apparatus, designed by Michell, has been improved by Cavendish, Cornu, and others, particularly by Boys (1889). The delicate torsion balance used by Boys consists, first, of a central vertical fibre of quartz, suspended from a metal disc called the torsion head. The fibre carries a horizontal glass beam; from grooves in both ends other quartz fibres of unequal length hang vertically, each supporting a small gold sphere. This suspension system is hung inside a glass tube, of internal diameter about 3·8 cm., and is thus protected from draughts. Further, the air pressure inside can be adjusted to any required value. Outside the tube two equal spheres of lead about 10·8 cm. in diameter are suspended at equal distances from the axis. The centres of these spheres are respectively situated in the same horizontal planes as the centres of the gold balls, that is, they are at different levels. Each lead sphere exerts an attraction on each gold sphere, but by having the two different levels, the attraction of a lead sphere on that gold sphere whose centre is on a level with its own is made far greater than that on the other. The effect of the attractions is to produce a torque about the axis, and the central fibre is twisted through an angle θ. The suspension system comes to rest when the resultant moment of the displacing forces due to gravitational attraction is equal and opposite to the moment of the restoring forces called into play in the twisted fibre. The position of the centres of the lead spheres is chosen so as

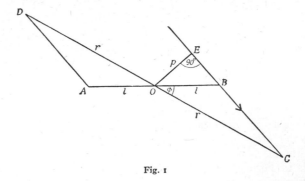

Fig. 1

to make the moment of the displacing forces as large as possible. The angular deflection θ is obtained by use of a mirror, lamp, scale and telescope, the mirror being the horizontal glass beam itself. The large spheres are then moved to new and similar positions on the opposite sides of the gold spheres, so as to produce a maximum displacing moment in the opposite direction, and the change in scale reading is that which is actually read.

The value of G is calculated as follows. Let M, m represent the masses of the two kinds of spheres respectively. In fig. 1, which represents a plan of the system after equilibrium has been reached, A, B represent the centres of the gold spheres, and C, D those of the lead spheres respectively. The attractions between spheres at different levels are neglected. The attraction along BC is GMm/BC^2. The moment of this attraction about O is $GMmp/BC^2$, where p is the perpendicular from O on the line of action of the attraction. Allowing for an equal moment due to the attraction along AD, the total moment of the displacing forces becomes $2GMmp/BC^2$. Now $p \cdot BC = 2$. area of $\Delta OBC = lr \sin \varphi$, where $OB = l$, $OC = r$, and angle $BOC = \varphi$. Hence the total displacing moment is

$$2GMmlr \sin \varphi/BC^3 = 2GMmlr \sin \varphi/\{l^2 + r^2 - 2lr \cos \varphi\}^{\frac{3}{2}}.$$

The moment of the restoring forces is $c\theta$, where c is the torsional constant of the central quartz fibre and θ is the angular deflection of the suspension system from its equilibrium position. Hence

$$G = c\theta\{l^2 + r^2 - 2lr \cos\varphi\}^{\frac{3}{2}}/2Mmlr \sin\varphi. \quad \ldots \quad (4)$$

As θ corresponds to one-half of the change in the scale reading when the large spheres are moved from the first position to the second, it is calculated by dividing the change in the scale reading by four times the distance from the scale to the mirror. The torsional constant c is obtained by measuring T, the period of the natural oscillations of the suspension system in the absence of the large masses. $T = 2\pi(I/c)^{\frac{1}{2}}$, where I is the moment of inertia of the suspension system about its axis, a quantity which can be obtained by measurements of its mass and linear dimensions.

The value of G obtained by Boys is $6 \cdot 658 \times 10^{-8}$ c.g.s. units, which corresponds to a mean density of the earth of $5 \cdot 527$ gm. per c.c. The probable error is not calculated by Boys. A few dimensional details are appended. In one experiment the length of the central quartz fibre is $43 \cdot 2$ cm., and its diameter is about $0 \cdot 0125$ mm.; the beam is 23 mm. long, the scale is 700 cm. from it and is divided into half-millimetres. The large spheres have masses of about 7407 gm., and the small ones of $2 \cdot 65$ gm. The difference in level is about 15 cm. The scale deflection corresponding to a rotation of $\theta_1 + \theta_2$ is $18 \cdot 48$ cm. The angle BOC is $64° 38'$. The distance CD is 15 cm. The period of oscillation T is about 96 sec.

The principal advantage introduced by Boys is the use of thin quartz fibres, which are extremely sensitive and which retain their elastic properties. The great reduction in the dimensions of the apparatus which is thus rendered possible (1) eliminates the difficulty of convection currents arising from unequal temperatures of different parts of the bulky apparatus, (2) enables the size of the cumbersome lead attracting spheres to be reduced.

3. Measurement of G. Heyl's Method.

Probably the most accurate value of G hitherto obtained is that of Heyl * (1930). He uses the " time of swing method " formerly used by Braun. The suspension system of a torsion balance, consisting of two small equal spheres hanging with their centres at the same level, is allowed to describe small oscillations in the gravitational field of two large masses, whose centres of gravity are also at the same level. The large masses are placed in two separate positions, represented in plan in fig. 2. The two small masses are placed with their centres at the same level, because of the greater precision possible in the important measurement of the distance between the centres. The accuracy is improved, as compared with Braun's work, by using very heavy large masses of about $66 \cdot 3$ Kgm. each.

The theory of the experiment, when the large masses are in the " near " position, may be discussed with reference to fig. 3. Consider the total energy of the suspension system when the centres of the small masses are in the displaced positions C, D. The equilibrium

---

* Heyl, *Bureau of Standards Journal of Research*, Vol. 5, p. 1243 (1930).

positions are at A and B. The centres of the large masses are fixed at X and Y. The total energy is made up of (1) kinetic energy equal to $I\dot{\theta}^2/2$, where I is the moment of inertia of the suspension system about its vertical axis of symmetry, and θ is the angular displacement; (2) potential energy due to torsion of the fibre, equal to $k\theta^2/2$, where

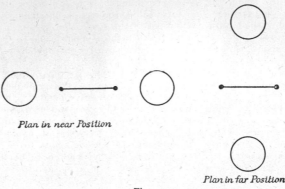

Plan in near Position

Plan in far Position

Fig. 2

k is the torsional constant of the fibre; (3) potential energy due to the proximity of the large and small masses, that is, due to the fact that D is near X and Y, and that C is also near X and Y. The large masses are vertical steel cylinders, and the evaluation of the gravitational potential at D and C respectively, due to a cylinder whose centre of gravity is at X or Y, involves zonal harmonics and is beyond the scope of this book. The final expression for the gravitational potential

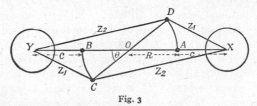

Fig. 3

energy of the whole displaced suspension system may, however, be written in the form $GA_1\theta^2/2$. A_1 is the product of one large mass and one small mass and a purely geometrical function of R and c, where $R = OA$, $c = AX$, and G is the Newtonian constant sought. If friction is neglected, the total energy is a constant. Hence

$$I\dot{\theta}^2/2 + k\theta^2/2 + GA_1\theta^2/2 = \text{a constant.}$$

On differentiating with respect to time and dropping the factor $\dot{\theta}$, we have

$$I\ddot{\theta} + (k + GA_1)\theta = 0,$$

representing an oscillation whose period, uncorrected for small errors, is

$$T_1 = 2\pi\{I/(k + GA_1)\}^{\frac{1}{2}}. \quad \ldots \ldots \quad (5)$$

Here k as well as G is regarded as unknown; A_1 is calculated from the geometry of the system. In a similar way, when the large masses are moved to the " far " position, and the torsion pendulum again describes small oscillations, its equation of motion is $I\ddot{\phi} + (k + GA_2)\phi = 0$, where A_2 is the new geometrical constant which replaces A_1. The uncorrected period of oscillation is

$$T_2 = 2\pi\{I/(k + GA_2)\}^{\frac{1}{2}}. \quad \ldots \ldots \quad (6)$$

On eliminating k from equations (5) and (6), and solving for G, we have

$$G = 4\pi^2 I(T_2{}^2 - T_1{}^2)/(A_1 - A_2)T_1{}^2 T_2{}^2. \quad \ldots \ldots \quad (7)$$

As regards experimental details, the large masses are cylinders of forged and machined steel, of mass about 66·3 Kgm. each, suspended from a supporting system capable of rotation about a vertical axis, midway between them. In three sets of experiments the small masses are pairs of gold, platinum, and optical glass spheres respectively, in each case of mass about 50 gm. They are suspended from a very light torsion system, consisting of (1) a torsion wire of tungsten about 1 m. long and 0·025 mm. in diameter, (2) a separating rod of aluminium 20·6 cm. long and of mass 2·44 gm., (3) various supporting wires as shown in fig. 4. Over 99 per cent of the moment of inertia is in the small spheres themselves. This system is enclosed in a large brass container resting on a plate-glass base. The air pressure within is reduced to about 2 mm. of mercury. The usual arrangement of mirror, lamp, scale and telescope is used to observe the oscillations, which are started by bringing

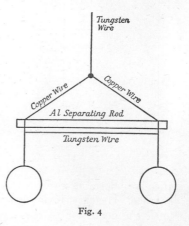

Fig. 4

bottles of mercury near the small spheres and then removing them. Transits of lines on the image of a scale on glass, across the vertical crosswire of the telescope, are noted by an observer and recorded on one pen of a two-pen chronograph. The other pen records seconds signals from a standard clock.

The gold balls are found to absorb mercury vapour from the air of the laboratory. Hence their mass increases by about 0·138 gm. in 49 gm. in seven months. Results obtained with them were discarded. With varnished platinum balls the value obtained, as the mean of five results, is $G = 6\cdot664 \times 10^{-8}$ c.g.s. units, and with glass balls, as the mean of five results, $G = 6\cdot674 \times 10^{-8}$ c.g.s. units. The mean of the means is $6\cdot669 \times 10^{-8}$ c.g.s. units, as compared with $6\cdot658 \times 10^{-8}$ in Boys' and Braun's experiments. The cause of the differing results with platinum and glass balls is not accounted for, though it has been proved that this is not directly due to the differing natures of the materials.

4. Measurement of G. Zahradnicek's Resonance Method.

The apparatus * used consists of two coaxial torsion balances, the axes being vertical. For the sake of brevity they are called primary and secondary. The primary balance is relatively robust and consists of a central steel wire with a beam in the form of ⊓, made of brass tubing. Heavy equal lead spheres are mounted at the same level, near the ends of the vertical arms (fig. 5). The secondary balance is smaller, and its axis is vertically below that of the primary. Its beam is

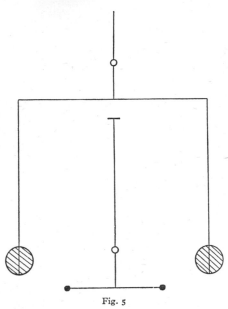

Fig. 5

simply a horizontal piece of aluminium wire with small equal lead spheres at the ends. Each suspension wire carries a mirror and has its own lamp, and the oscillations of each balance are registered photographically on a drum covered with sensitized paper. The rest-positions of the two balances are adjusted to be in the same vertical plane, and each balance when displaced and released describes damped harmonic oscillations about its rest-position, since the two systems exert gravitational forces and couples on each other. The damping of the primary balance is exceedingly small. To exclude draughts, the secondary balance is enclosed in a wooden case inside the case protecting the primary balance. The experiment consists in the adjustment of the two systems until the condition of resonance is established, that is, until the two periods of oscillation are equal. An equal number of turning points of both systems are noted. Then the masses and linear dimensions of each balance being known, G can be calculated.

The theory is as follows. Take the central point of the secondary beam as origin (fig. 6). Let Ox be horizontal and in the rest-position of the axis of the beam, Oy horizontal and perpendicular to Ox, Oz vertical and upwards. When the secondary beam is displaced through an angle ϕ, let the co-ordinates of the centres of the small spheres (mass m_1) be $x_1 = R_1 \cos\phi$, $y_1 = R_1 \sin\phi$, $z_1 = 0$, and $-x_1$, $-y_1$, 0 respectively. When the primary beam is displaced through an angle ψ,

---

* Zahradnicek, *Phys. Zeits.*, Vol. 34, p. 126 (1933).

let the co-ordinates of the centres of the large spheres (mass m_2) be $x_2 = R_2 \cos \psi$, $y_2 = R_2 \sin \psi$, $z_2 = c$, and $-x_2$, $-y_2$, $+z_2$ respectively. The attractions between unlike spheres are $F_1 = G m_1 m_2 / r_1^2$ and $F_2 = G m_1 m_2 / r_2^2$ respectively, where

$$r_1^2 = (R_1 \cos \phi - R_2 \cos \psi)^2 + (R_1 \sin \phi - R_2 \sin \psi)^2 + c^2$$
$$= R_1^2 + R_2^2 - 2R_1 R_2 \cos(\psi - \phi) + c^2 \quad \cdots \cdots \quad (8)$$

and

$$r_2^2 = R_1^2 + R_2^2 + 2R_1 R_2 \cos(\psi - \phi) + c^2. \quad \cdots \quad (9)$$

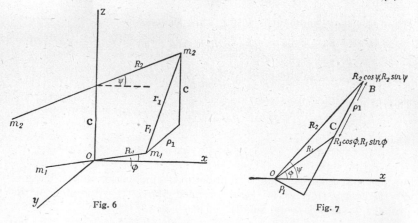

Fig. 6   Fig. 7

The horizontal components of these forces are $f_1 = F_1 \rho_1 / r_1$ and $f_2 = F_2 \rho_2 / r_2$ respectively, where

$$\rho_1^2 = (x_1 - x_2)^2 + (y_1 - y_2)^2$$
$$= (R_1 \cos \phi - R_2 \cos \psi)^2 + (R_1 \sin \phi - R_2 \sin \psi)^2$$

and

$$\rho_2^2 = (x_1 + x_2)^2 + (y_1 + y_2)^2$$
$$= (R_1 \cos \phi + R_2 \cos \psi)^2 + (R_1 \sin \phi + R_2 \sin \psi)^2.$$

The turning moment of f_1 at one end of the secondary beam is $f_1 p_1$, where p_1 is the perpendicular from O to the line of action of f_1 (fig. 7). Also $p_1 \rho_1 = R_1 R_2 \sin(\psi - \theta)$, for each is twice the area of the triangle OBC. Hence the turning moment of both forces f_1 on the secondary beam is

$$2 F_1 \rho_1 p_1 / r_1 = 2 F_1 R_1 R_2 \sin(\psi - \phi) / r_1.$$

Similarly, the moment of both forces f_2 is in the opposite direction and is $2 F_2 R_1 R_2 \sin(\psi - \phi) / r_2$. The net moment in the first direction is

$$2 R_1 R_2 \sin(\psi - \phi)\{F_1 / r_1 - F_2 / r_2\}$$
$$= 2 G m_1 m_2 R_1 R_2 \sin(\psi - \phi)\{1 / r_1^3 - 1 / r_2^3\},$$

and when ϕ and ψ are sufficiently small, this becomes

$$2Gm_1m_2R_1R_2\Delta(\psi - \phi),$$

where

$$\Delta = 1/\{(R_1 - R_2)^2 + c^2\}^{\frac{3}{2}} - 1/\{(R_1 + R_2)^2 + c^2\}^{\frac{3}{2}}.$$

Let the differential equation of motion of the secondary system, in the absence of the primary, be

$$K\ddot{\phi} + P\dot{\phi} + D\phi = 0.$$

When the above moment is acting, this becomes

$$K\ddot{\phi} + P\dot{\phi} + D\phi = 2Gm_1m_2R_1R_2\Delta(\psi - \phi) = E(\psi - \phi), \quad (10)$$

say, where

$$E = 2Gm_1m_2R_1R_2\Delta. \quad \ldots \quad \ldots \quad (11)$$

Then

$$K\ddot{\phi} + P\dot{\phi} + \overline{D}\phi = E\psi,$$

where

$$\overline{D} = D + E.$$

Assume that ψ corresponds to an undamped simple harmonic oscillation, $\psi = \psi_0 \cos\omega_2 t$ (for, as we have assumed above, the damping of the primary system is very small). Then

$$K\ddot{\phi} + P\dot{\phi} + \overline{D}\phi = E\psi_0 \cos\omega_2 t.$$

The particular integral of this is the important part of the solution, and is obtained by the use of operators or otherwise. It is

$$\phi = \phi_0 \cos(\omega_2 t - \epsilon),$$

where

$$\phi_0 = E\psi_0/K\{(2\delta\omega_2)^2 + (\omega_0{}^2 - \omega_2{}^2)^2\}^{\frac{1}{2}}, \quad \ldots \quad (12)$$

$$\tan\epsilon = 2\delta\omega_2/(\omega_0{}^2 - \omega_2{}^2), \quad \ldots \quad \ldots \quad (13)$$

and

$$\delta = P/2K, \quad \omega_0{}^2 = \overline{D}/K. \quad \ldots \quad \ldots \quad (14)$$

Resonance occurs when ϕ_0 is a maximum as ω_2 varies. By differentiation, this occurs when $2\delta^2 = \omega_0{}^2 - \omega_2{}^2$, that is, when

$$\phi_0 = E\psi_0/2K\delta\{\omega_2{}^2 + \delta^2\}^{\frac{1}{2}}. \quad \ldots \quad \ldots \quad (15)$$

Here ϕ_0 and ψ_0 are the amplitudes corresponding to the case of resonance. We now replace E by $2Gm_1m_2R_1R_2\Delta$ and rearrange. We then obtain

$$G = \phi_0K\delta\{\omega_2{}^2 + \delta^2\}^{\frac{1}{2}}/\psi_0 m_1m_2R_1R_2\Delta. \quad \ldots \quad (16)$$

The value of ϕ_0/ψ_0 is obtained from a number of observed turning points of both systems; K is the moment of inertia of the secondary balance; $\omega_2 = 2\pi/T_2$, where T_2 is the period of oscillation; $\delta = 2\lambda/T_1$, where λ is the logarithmic decrement, and T_1 the natural period of the secondary in the absence of the primary. R_1, R_2 and Δ are obtained from the linear dimensions of the apparatus. An important correction is applied for the attraction on parts of the secondary balance other than the masses m_1, e.g. the beam, due to the masses m_2. A small correction is required for the slight damping of the primary balance. Zahradnicek gives $G = 6{\cdot}659 \pm 0{\cdot}02$ as the value derived from seven experiments. The method seems to be very accurate. It has the advantage that a large number of values can be obtained in a relatively short time.

5. Measurement of G. Poynting's Method.

G has been measured by the aid of the " common balance " by (a) von Jolly, (b) Richarz and Krigar-Menzel, and (c) Poynting. Poynting's method will be described here. The balance used (fig. 8) is of the large

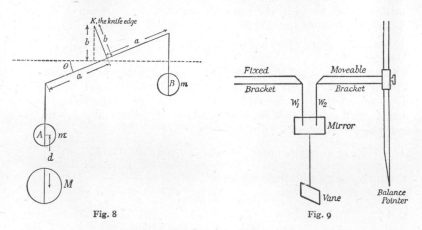

Fig. 8   Fig. 9

" bullion balance " type, that is, it is strongly made, with a gun-metal beam and steel knife-edges and planes. From the ends of the beam are suspended equal spherical masses A and B, made of an alloy of lead and antimony. Each has a mass of about 21·6 Kgm. A spherical attracting body M, of mass about 153 Kgm., made of the same alloy, is mounted on a special turntable, so that it can be brought to a point vertically under A, and then under B. In each case the downward attraction is given by $F = GMm/d^2$, and this force tilts the balance beam downwards on the side where the attraction is applied. The tilt is measured in each case by an optical device (see fig. 9) involving the so-called double suspension mirror of Lord Kelvin. In this arrangement the pointer of the balance is attached to a movable bracket supporting one of two wires, which in turn support a small mirror. The other wire is attached to a fixed bracket. When the balance beam moves, the pointer and one wire W_2 move. Thus the mirror rotates about the stationary wire W_1. The angular tilt of the balance beam is magnified 150 times by this device. Facing the mirror, and about five metres from it, is a scale graduated in half-millimetres, and an image of this is formed in the mirror. This image is viewed by a vertical telescope, pointing through a hole in the ceiling, from the room above. In this way it is found that the change in the angle of tilt, due to moving M from under A to under B, is a little more than one second. This same angle is produced by the addition of a weight of 0·0004 gm. to one end of the balance beam, a fact which is proved by displacing a rider of mass 0·01 gm. a definite distance along the beam and thus increasing its turning moment by a known amount.

The calculation is as follows. Assume that the beam is horizontal when M is removed altogether. Let the length of the beam be $2a$ and let its mid-point be b cm. from the central knife-edge. For equilibrium of the beam in the position shown in fig. 8, when M is under A, the moments of the downward forces on A and B are equal, and

$$(mg + GMm/d^2)(a \cos \theta - b \sin \theta) = mg(a \cos \theta + b \sin \theta),$$

where θ is the angle which the beam makes with the horizontal. A similar equation holds when M is placed under B, and the beam is depressed on the right through θ. Again, when M is removed altogether and a small extra mass m' is attached to A, let the angular tilt once more be θ. Then

$$(mg + m'g)(a \cos \theta - b \sin \theta) = mg(a \cos \theta + b \sin \theta).$$

From these two equations we have

$$GMm/d^2 = m'g \qquad \cdots \cdots \quad (17)$$

and

$$G = m'g d^2/Mm. \qquad \cdots \cdots \quad (18)$$

Corrections have to be applied for (a) the cross attraction of M on the mass which is not above it, (b) the metal removed in making boreholes through A and B to admit the supporting rods, (c) the attraction of M on the balance beam itself. This last correction is made by raising the masses A and B about 25 cm. higher, in another experiment, and finding the attraction of M once more, M being in its former position. Thus the attraction of M on the beam is the same as in the previous case, but the attraction on A and B is altered. Equation (17) now becomes, in the two cases,

$$GMm/d_1^2 + Z = m'g$$

and

$$GMm/d_2^2 + Z = m''g,$$

where Z is the force exerted by M on the beam. By subtraction Z is eliminated, and

$$G = (m'' - m')g/Mm(1/d_2{}^2 - 1/d_1{}^2). \quad \ldots \ldots \quad (19)$$

The change of position of M is found to tilt the floor through an angle of about one-third of a second. This is eliminated by mounting a mass $M/2$ on the turntable at twice the distance of M from the axis and diametrically opposite M. Allowance is made for the attraction of this mass on A and B. The balance is enclosed in a case to reduce air currents and the deposition of dust. The beam is kept free, supported on its knife-edge and therefore under strain, throughout a set of readings, because it cannot be lowered and raised so that the knife-edge again comes into precisely the same line. All moving parts, such as supports for weights and riders, are supported independently of the balance case. Poynting's final results are

$$G = 6.6984 \times 10^{-8} \text{ c.g.s. units,}$$
$$\text{Mean density of the earth} = 5.4934 \text{ gm. per c.c.}$$

The probable errors are not given.

6. Possible Variations in G.

Experiments have been made to test whether the force of gravitational attraction is affected by various changes in conditions. Work by Eötvös and others with the torsion balance revealed no change in G exceeding the limit of experimental error, that is, greater than $10^{-9} G$, when the nature of the attracting masses was varied over a wide range of substances; in other words, G is independent of the nature of the masses. The same researches proved that G is independent of the state of chemical combination of the elements in the masses. The fact that an element is radioactive has also been shown to have no effect on G. Shaw, using a torsion balance in the same manner as Boys, varied the temperature of the large lead masses from $0°$ to $250°$ C., but no change in G exceeding the limit of experimental error could be detected. That is, any variation in G with temperature is less than $2 \times 10^{-6} G$ per degree centigrade. Poynting and Phillips obtained the same negative result, using the balance method. Various experimenters have investigated the gravitational attractions of crystals, that is, of anisotropic bodies. The value of G obtained remains independent of the direction of the crystallographic axes to within $10^{-9} G$, the limit of experimental error. For example, the weight of a crystal does not depend on the orientation of its axes with respect to the vertical. Eötvös and his collaborators, and also Majorana and Austin and Thwing, have investigated the effect of interposing layers of different media between attracting and attracted bodies. Very dense media, such as lead and mercury, were used. No effect could be detected. For example, in one case 5 cm. of lead produced no detectable change; that is, any change produced did not exceed $2 \times 10^{-11} G$.

7. Relativity and the Law of Gravitation.

The discovery of the laws of relativity has profoundly changed the views of physicists on the subjects of mass and gravitation. A detailed exposition must be sought in works on relativity,* but a few special points may be noted here. In discussing these it is advisable to consider the mass of a body from two points of view. The mass is often defined as the quantity of matter in a body. If a body is known to be moving with a certain acceleration, Newton's second law states that it experiences a force equal to the product of the mass and the acceleration. The mass in this sense is often called the " inert " mass. On the other hand, a body placed in a gravitational field of force experiences a force equal to the mass multiplied by the strength of the field at that point. The mass in this sense is called the " heavy " mass. As was mentioned on p. 43, the experiments of Eötvös and others have proved that the accelerations of bodies of different materials placed in the same gravitational field of force are the same to within one part in 10^9. Further, bodies of any " inert " mass, light, medium or heavy, have exactly the same acceleration in the same field of force. If we write " Force on a body = inert mass × acceleration ", and " Force on a body = heavy mass × field strength ", and apply these statements to one and the same body, we see that the forces are equal, and after dividing and rearranging, we have

Acceleration = heavy mass × field strength/inert mass.

Since the acceleration is constant and independent of the nature of the body, in the same field of force, we have

Heavy mass/inert mass = a constant. . . . (20)

With suitable units the constant is equal to unity. Einstein interpreted this well-known result as meaning that the same quality of a body exhibits itself in one set of circumstances as inertia and in another as weight. He deduced that it is impossible to distinguish between the two following states of a system of bodies: (1) a state of accelerated motion in the absence of a gravitational field of force, (2) a state of rest in a field of gravitational force.

One of the consequences of the restricted theory of relativity, which has been confirmed by experiment, is that of the " inertia of energy "; that is, whenever the energy of a body is changed in any way the mass of the body also undergoes a change. The two changes are connected by the relation

Change of mass in grammes = change of energy in ergs/c^2,

* For a brief account, see Wilson, *Modern Physics*, Chaps. XVIII, XIX (Blackie & Son Ltd., 1930).

where c is the velocity of light in vacuo, in cm. per sec. This applies to all forms of energy, including electromagnetic radiation, heat, &c. Thus gravitation is linked up with light and other electromagnetic phenomena. Further, the theory shows that the mass m of a body in motion with velocity v cm. per sec. is not the same as its mass m_0 when it is at rest, but

$$m = m_0/\{1 - v^2/c^2\}^{\frac{1}{2}}. \quad \ldots \quad \ldots \quad (21)$$

This expression has been confirmed by experiments with β-particles.

The point of view of the generalized theory of relativity can only be hinted at here. All matter or energy modifies the properties of space-time in its neighbourhood, producing what is called a field of gravitation. The property of acting upon a body or an electromagnetic wave belongs to space-time modified in this way by the presence of matter or energy. It is not a direct, instantaneous action at a distance produced by an attracting body. The cause of the deformation of space-time in the neighbourhood of matter or energy, that is, the cause of gravitation, is still unknown. The generalized theory enables the law of gravitation to be stated in its most general form, in tensor notation, a form in which it contains the laws of conservation of energy, momentum and mass of classical physics as special cases. As is well known, the generalized theory had three important successes. (1) It accounted for the displacement of the perihelion position of the planet Mercury. (2) It predicted a lateral displacement of rays of light passing through a gravitational field. (3) It predicted a spectral shift of solar rays of light.

CHAPTER IV

Elasticity

I. Introduction.

The behaviour of bodies subjected to deforming forces constitutes the study of elasticity. If the body entirely regains its original size and shape, it is said to be *perfectly elastic*; if it entirely retains its altered shape and size, it is said to be *perfectly plastic*. Actual bodies are intermediate in their behaviour, and the same material will behave differently according as it is in the form of a single crystal or a heterogeneous mass of crystals such as constitute e.g. an ordinary metal bar or wire. The behaviour of single crystals will not be considered in this book,* as their study involves a fair knowledge of crystal structure; besides, it is not representative of the behaviour of ordinary matter in bulk. Further, attention will be confined to isotropic substances, that is, substances which exhibit under test the same properties in all directions; anisotropic substances require laborious and complicated mathematical treatment.

The change of shape or size (or both) is termed a *strain*; the forces in equilibrium which produce the strain are often loosely termed the stresses. More correctly, the *stress* is defined as follows. Let F be the force acting across a small plane area A at any angle to its surface. Then the normal component of F divided by the area A is termed the *normal stress*; the tangential component of F divided by the area A is termed the *mean tangential stress*. The criteria of a perfectly elastic body are these:

(*a*) A given stress always produces the same strain.
(*b*) Maintenance of a given stress results in a constant strain.
(*c*) Removal of stress results in complete disappearance of strain.

2. Deviations from Hooke's Law.

It was found experimentally by Hooke in 1679 that, over a considerable range, the strain produced is proportional to the stress applied. This relation, which is termed Hooke's law, forms the basis of the theory of elasticity. If the strain is a simple stretching of the material,

---

* See e.g. *The Physics of Solids and Fluids*, p. 118 *et seq.* (Blackie & Son Ltd., 1936).

the graphical relation between the stress p and the strain (extension) e is called the stress-strain curve, the load-extension curve, or, briefly, the p-e curve. Typical p-e curves are shown in fig. 1. For steel the graph runs somewhat as in fig. 1(a). Each property, proportionality and elasticity, holds only up to certain limits, termed the *limit of proportionality* and the *elastic limit*. These two points do not in general coincide. In fig. 1(b), the former is represented by the point P. Its definition is comparatively simple and certain, whereas the direct

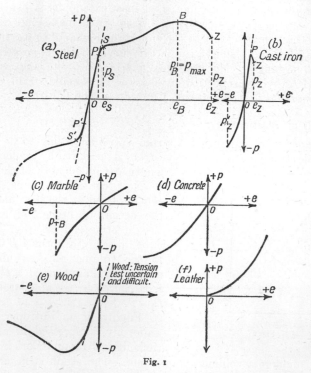

Fig. 1

determination of the elastic limit is a difficult process. Immediately after passing the limit of proportionality the curve shows a marked kink, which after a short interval, about the point S, is followed by a rapid increase of the extension for slowly increasing (and sometimes even for diminishing!) stress. The point S at which the material may be said to flow is called the *yield point*. On further increase of the load, the stress reaches at the point B its greatest value $p_B = p_{max}$, and up to that point the strains extend fairly uniformly over the whole rod. In all materials, however, localized weaknesses due to slight differences in structure are present, and beyond B a local constriction (" necking ") occurs in ductile materials. The constriction increases rapidly, and at some point Z, for values p_z and e_z, the rod is ruptured. The maximum stress and strain p_B and e_B are termed the *breaking stress* and *breaking strain* respectively.

The behaviour of materials under compression is shown by the continuation of the curve below the x-axis. Referring to the p-e curve for steel, we see that a region of proportionality is again initially observed; the point S', which is the yield-point under compression, is also known as the *crushing limit*; finally a region of flow is obtained, which for ductile materials like steel may extend for a considerable distance without fracture occurring. With brittle metals like cast iron, fracture occurs immediately at the end of the region of proportionality, or after a kink and a short drop in the curve. There is no yield-point and no "necking". Materials like marble, concrete and wood are characterized by no proportionality between stress and strain, even for small stresses, as is shown in figs. 1 (c), (d), (e) and (f).

3. Moduli of Elasticity.

The method of measuring a strain varies according to its nature. For simple stretching of a wire, the strain is measured by the increase in length per unit length of the wire.

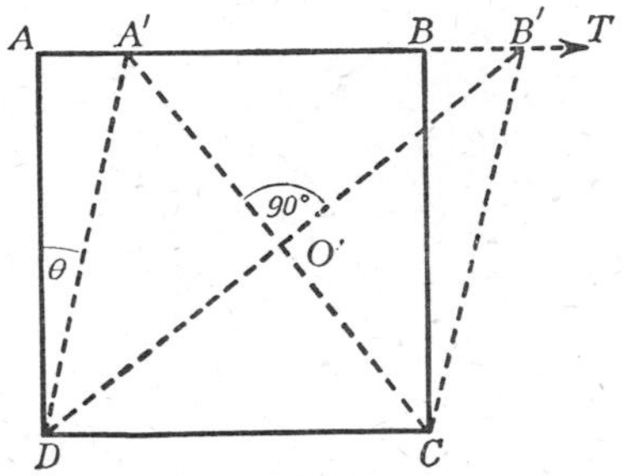

Fig. 2

Now consider a cube of side $ABCD$, fixed at the base and under the action of tangential forces in the direction $AA'BB'$ (fig. 2). The cube takes up the form $A'B'CD$, that is, the volume remains unaltered; such a strain is termed a *shear* and is measured by the angular deformation θ.

Finally, if an isotropic body is uniformly compressed in all directions, it will retain its original shape but will undergo a volume compression. The strain is measured by the change in volume divided by the original volume.

The ratio of the stress to the strain produced in a body is termed the *elastic modulus*. There are three elastic moduli, according to the nature of the strain, namely:

$$\text{Young's modulus } q = \frac{\text{Applied load per unit area of cross-section}}{\text{Increase in length per unit length}}.$$

$$\text{Rigidity modulus } n = \frac{\text{Tangential stress per unit area}}{\text{Angular deformation } \theta}.$$

$$\text{Bulk modulus } K = \frac{\text{Compressive (or tensile) force per unit area}}{\text{Change in volume per unit volume}}.$$

It is found experimentally that when a body undergoes a linear tensile strain it experiences a lateral contraction as well. Since this contraction is directly proportional to the extension, a fourth elastic constant termed *Poisson's ratio* and denoted by σ is introduced; this is defined as the decrease in width per unit width divided by the longitudinal strain. The four elastic constants are interdependent, since any change in size and shape of a body may be obtained by first changing the size but not the shape (volume strain) and then changing the shape but not the size by means of a shear.

4. Components of Stress and Strain.

Consider a parallelepiped *ABCDEFGH* of the material with its sides parallel to the axes of co-ordinates Ox, Oy and Oz as in fig. 3. Then simple considerations of equilibrium show that if no translational or rotational motion is to occur, the most general distribution of forces reduces to three different normal stresses X_x, Y_y, Z_z and three different pairs of tangential stresses $X_y = Y_x$, $Z_x = X_z$, $Y_z = Z_y$. The notation is such that the subscript indicates the axis perpendicular to the face across which the normal or tangential force is acting. The strain may likewise be resolved into six components e_{xx}, e_{yy}, e_{zz} and $e_{yz} = e_{zy}$, $e_{zx} = e_{xz}$, $e_{yx} = e_{xy}$, where the former constitute the strains produced by the normal stresses and the latter the shearing strains. Thus e_{yz} is the relative displacement of planes perpendicular to Oy and Oz respectively and initially at unit distance apart.

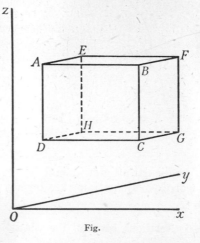

Fig.

5. Strain Ellipsoid.

Consider a sphere with radius r and centre O, and let (x, y, z) be the co-ordinates of a point on its surface (fig. 4). Suppose that it is strained into a symmetrical figure with centre O', that $O'A'$, $O'B'$, $O'C'$ have magnitudes a', b', c' and correspond to OA, OB, OC, and that (x', y', z') corresponds to (x, y, z).

Since the ratio of parallel lines is unaltered by strain, we see by fig. 4 that

$$\frac{x}{r} = \frac{x'}{a'}, \quad \frac{y}{r} = \frac{y'}{b'}, \quad \frac{z}{r} = \frac{z'}{c'}.$$

(F 103)

3

Now

$$x^2 + y^2 + z^2 = r^2.$$

Hence

$$\frac{x'^2}{a'^2} + \frac{y'^2}{b'^2} + \frac{z'^2}{c'^2} = 1,$$

or (x', y', z') is a point on an ellipsoid with a', b', c' as conjugate diameters. Since there are only three diameters of an ellipsoid which are mutually perpendicular, there are, in general, only three mutually perpendicular diameters of the sphere which remain mutually per-

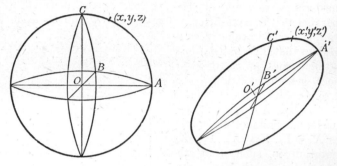

Fig 4

pendicular after straining. These are termed the *axes of strain* and the corresponding strains are termed the *principal strains*.

6. Relations between the Elastic Constants.

Since for isotropic substances the directions of the axes of strain will be those of the normal stresses, the most general stress at a point will be P_1, P_2, P_3 along Ox, Oy, Oz respectively. Hence $X_x = P_1$, $Y_y = P_2$ and $Z_z = P_3$, while $X_y = Y_z = Z_x = 0$. The corresponding strains will be

$$e_{xx} = \frac{1}{q}\{P_1 - \sigma(P_2 + P_3)\},$$

$$e_{yy} = \frac{1}{q}\{P_2 - \sigma(P_3 + P_1)\},$$

$$e_{zz} = \frac{1}{q}\{P_3 - \sigma(P_1 + P_2)\},$$

while $e_{xy} = e_{yz} = e_{zx} = 0$.

Solving for P_1, P_2 and P_3, we have

$$P_1 = \lambda\delta + 2n'e_{xx},$$
$$P_2 = \lambda\delta + 2n'e_{yy},$$
$$P_3 = \lambda\delta + 2n'e_{zz}, \tag{1}$$

where

$$\delta = e_{xx} + e_{yy} + e_{zz}, \lambda = \sigma q/(1+\sigma)(1-2\sigma) \text{ and } 2n' = q/(1+\sigma).$$

The *dilatation* δ measures, to a first order, the fractional change in volume, since it is the sum of the principal extensions.

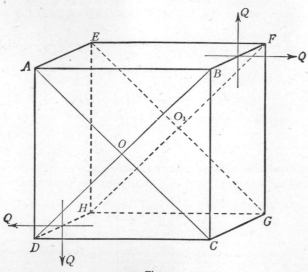

Fig. 5

For a uniform compression or dilatation $P_1 = P_2 = P_3 = P$. Hence, adding equations (1), we have

$$\delta = \frac{3P}{3\lambda + 2n'}. \quad \cdots \cdots \quad (2)$$

Now the bulk modulus K is defined by

$$K = P/\delta.$$

Hence

$$K = \frac{q}{3(1-2\sigma)}. \quad \cdots \cdots \quad (3)$$

It remains to identify n' with n, the rigidity modulus. We see from fig. 5 that if a simple stress Q acts on four sides of a cube $ABCDEFGH$, the stresses across the diagonal planes $ACGE$, $BDHF$

will be compressive and extensive respectively and each of magnitude Q. Taking the axes Ox, Oy, Oz as parallel to OB, OA, OO_1, we have $X_x = Q$, $Y_y = -Q$, $Z_z = 0$, with corresponding strains

$$e_{xx} = -e_{yy} = \left(\frac{1+\sigma}{q}\right)Q, \; e_{zz} = 0.$$

Then

$$\tan DA'O' = \frac{DO'}{A'O'} = \frac{1+e_{xx}}{1+e_{yy}}\frac{DO}{AO} = \frac{1+e_{xx}}{1+e_{yy}},$$

where the dashed letters correspond to the strained cube (see fig. 2). Since the shear strain $\theta = \angle DA'B' - \angle DAB = 2\angle DA'O' - \pi/2$,

$$\tan\frac{\theta}{2} = \frac{\tan DA'O' - 1}{1 + \tan DA'O'} = \frac{e_{xx} - e_{yy}}{2 + e_{xx} + e_{yy}} = \tfrac{1}{2}(e_{xx} - e_{yy}).$$

For small angles, therefore,

$$\theta = e_{xx} - e_{yy} = 2(1 + \sigma)Q/q.$$

Now the modulus of rigidity is defined by

$$n = Q/\theta = q/2(1 + \sigma), \quad \ldots \ldots \quad (4)$$

and, by comparison with equations (1), $n' = n$.

Eliminating σ from (3) and (4), we obtain the important relations

$$\left.\begin{array}{l} q = \dfrac{9nK}{3K + n} \\[2em] \sigma = \dfrac{3K - 2n}{6K + 2n} \end{array}\right\} \quad \ldots \ldots \ldots \quad (5)$$

or

The expression for Poisson's ratio may be written $3K(1 - 2\sigma) = 2n(1 + \sigma)$. Since K and n are both positive, σ cannot be greater than $\frac{1}{2}$ nor less than -1.

7. Principle of Superposition.

The preceding theory is based on the assumption that the effects produced by the different stresses are quite independent of one another. The applicability of this principle of superposition is confirmed by experiment. In particular, Guest * made a careful study of the behaviour of thin tubes under combined stresses. He showed that various stresses, such as internal compression, tension, and torsion, could be applied simultaneously and combined in different proportions, but that initial yielding occurred only when a specific *total* shearing stress was attained.

* *Phil. Mag.* (5), Vol. 50, p. 69 (1900).

8. Bending of Beams.

When a beam is bent by an applied couple, the filaments of the beam are compressed in the region nearest the inside of the curve and extended in the region nearest the outside. The filament which experiences no change in length when the curvature is applied is termed the *neutral filament* or *neutral axis*.

Suppose a rod $ABCD$ (fig. 6) is bent into a circle and that the radius of the neutral axis PQ is ρ. Then if we consider a filament $P'Q'$ of the rod, a distance z from PQ, we have

$$P'Q' = (\rho + z)\phi.$$

Hence the extension of the filament is

$$e = P'Q' - PQ = (\rho + z)\phi - \rho\phi = z\phi \quad \cdot \quad \cdot \quad (6)$$

and the strain, since the original length was $\rho\phi$, is z/ρ. If the area of cross-section is a, the force across the area is $\dfrac{qz}{\rho} a$.

The couple due to these forces is thus $\dfrac{qz}{\rho} az$, and the total couple, or *bending moment*, due to all the filaments in the rod, which must equal the external applied couple G when the rod is in equilibrium, will be

$$G = \frac{q}{\rho} \Sigma az^2. \quad \cdot \quad (7)$$

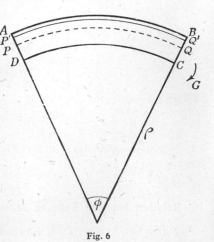

Fig. 6

The quantity Σaz^2 is analogous to the moment of inertia about the axis $z = 0$ and is termed the *geometrical moment of inertia* of the cross-section about that axis, which is perpendicular to the plane of the paper. If the actual area is A and the radius of gyration is denoted by k,

$$G = \frac{qAk^2}{\rho}. \quad \cdot \quad \cdot \quad \cdot \quad \cdot \quad \cdot \quad \cdot \quad (8)$$

The quantity qAk^2 is sometimes termed the *flexural rigidity*.

9. Beams under Distributed Loads.

Consider an element of the rod, of length dx, at a distance x from some origin on the neutral axis, and let the load per unit length be w (fig. 7). Then $w\,dx$ is the load on dx; let the shearing forces and the bending moments be F, G, $F + dF$, $G + dG$ at x and $x + dx$ respectively. Then

$$\frac{dF}{dx} = -w \qquad \cdots \cdots \cdots (9)$$

and

$$\frac{dG}{dx} = -F, \qquad \cdots \cdots \cdots (10)$$

or

$$\frac{d^2G}{dx^2} = w. \qquad \cdots \cdots \cdots (11)$$

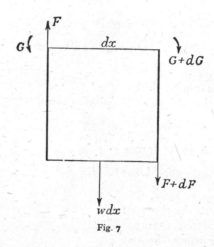

Fig. 7

10. Relation between Bending Moment and Deflection.

If ρ is the radius of curvature of the beam at a point where the depression is y (fig. 8), we have

$$\pm \frac{1}{\rho} = \frac{d^2y/dx^2}{\left\{1 + \left(\dfrac{dy}{dx}\right)^2\right\}^{\frac{3}{2}}}.$$

Fig. 8

Since $\left(\dfrac{dy}{dx}\right)^2 \ll 1$, it is approximately true that

$$\frac{1}{\rho} = \pm \frac{d^2y}{dx^2}.$$

Hence, from (8),

$$G = qAk^2 \frac{d^2y}{dx^2}. \quad \cdots \cdots \quad (12)$$

Combining equations (10), (11) and (12), we have

$$qAk^2 \frac{d^4y}{dx^4} = w \quad \cdots \cdots \quad (13)$$

and

$$qAk^2 \frac{d^3y}{dx^3} = -F. \quad \cdots \cdots \quad (14)$$

11. Solutions of Beam Problems.

The four constants of integration required for the solution of (13) are determined by the end conditions of the beam. Three cases usually occur:

(1) *Free end with no load.*

$$F = 0, \text{ hence } \frac{d^3y}{dx^3} = 0,$$

and

$$G = 0, \frac{d^2y}{dx^2} = 0.$$

If a load W is attached to the free end, $F = W$.

(2) *End supported but not gripped.*

$$G = 0, \text{ hence } \frac{d^2y}{dx^2} = 0, \text{ and } y \text{ is known.}$$

(3) *End clamped.*

$\frac{dy}{dx}$ is known and usually equal to zero, and y is known.

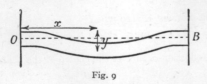

Fig. 9

EXAMPLE.—*Uniform beam clamped horizontally at both ends under a uniformly distributed load* (fig. 9).

This example of the application of equations (12), (13) and (14) will now be worked out; other examples for the reader will be found on p. 277.

Writing D for d/dx, D^2 for d^2/dx^2, &c., and using (13), we have

$$qAk^2D^4y = w.$$

Integrating four times, we have

$$qAk^2D^3y = wx + A, \quad \dots \dots \dots \quad (15)$$

$$qAk^2D^2y = \frac{wx^2}{2} + Ax + B, \quad \dots \dots \quad (16)$$

$$qAk^2Dy = \frac{wx^3}{6} + \frac{Ax^2}{2} + Bx + C, \quad \dots \dots \quad (17)$$

$$qAk^2y = \frac{wx^4}{24} + \frac{Ax^3}{6} + \frac{Bx^2}{2} + Cx + H. \quad \dots \quad (18)$$

From case (3) above, the end conditions are

$$Dy = y = 0 \text{ for } x = 0, \quad Dy = y = 0 \text{ for } x = l,$$

where l is the length of the beam.

Hence, from (17) and (18), $C = H = 0$,

$$\tfrac{1}{2}Bl^2 + \tfrac{1}{6}Al^3 + \tfrac{1}{24}wl^4 = 0,$$
$$Bl + \tfrac{1}{2}Al^2 + \tfrac{1}{6}wl^3 = 0.$$

Solving for A and B, we obtain

$$A = -\tfrac{1}{2}wl,$$
$$B = \tfrac{1}{12}wl^2.$$

The complete solution is therefore

$$\begin{aligned} qAk^2y &= \tfrac{1}{24}wx^4 - \tfrac{1}{12}wlx^3 + \tfrac{1}{24}wl^2x^2 \\ &= \tfrac{1}{24}wx^2(x^2 - 2lx + l^2) = \tfrac{1}{24}wx^2(x - l)^2. \quad \dots \quad (19) \end{aligned}$$

Further,

$$\begin{aligned} G &= qAk^2D^2y \\ &= \frac{w}{12}(6x^2 - 6lx + l^2), \quad \dots \dots \quad (20) \end{aligned}$$

and

$$\begin{aligned} F &= -qAk^2D^3y \\ &= w(\tfrac{1}{2}l - x). \quad \dots \dots \dots \quad (21) \end{aligned}$$

By (20), the bending moment is zero when

$$6x^2 - 6lx + l^2 = 0,$$

and the maximum deflection occurs at the centre of the beam and is given by

$$y = \frac{wl^4}{384\,qAk^2}.$$

12. Thin Rods under Tension or Thrust: Euler's Theory of Struts.

It can be shown that the bending moment is always equal to qAk^2/ρ, even if a tension or thrust is present in addition to the bending couple.

Let a thrust P act at the ends of a thin rod of length l (fig. 10).

As P is increased there occurs a critical value at which the rod will buckle, unless it is constrained, when it will ultimately fail by crushing.

To find the critical value of P, let the rod be initially slightly bent and consider any point S on the rod with co-ordinates (x, y). If G is the bending moment, and we take moments about S, we have

$$G = -Py. \quad \ldots \ldots \quad (22)$$

But

$$G = qAk^2D^2y.$$

Hence

$$qAk^2D^2y = -Py.$$

If we write this in the form $D^2y = -m^2y$, where $m^2 = P/qAk^2$, the solution is

$$y = A \cos mx + B \sin mx.$$

Substituting for the boundary conditions

$$y = 0 \text{ when } x = 0, \quad y = 0 \text{ when } x = l,$$

we have

$$A = 0, \quad \text{and} \quad B \sin ml = 0.$$

Fig. 10

The latter condition is satisfied if $B = 0$, when the rod is straight, or for $\sin ml = 0$, when $ml = \pi, 2\pi, 3\pi$, &c.

The first stable bending position therefore occurs when $m = \pi/l$: the force is then

$$P = qAk^2\pi^2/l^2 \quad \ldots \ldots \quad (23)$$

and

$$y = B \sin \pi x/l. \quad \ldots \ldots \quad (24)$$

Since at the centre of the rod $x = l/2$, from (24), $B = y_{\text{max}}$. The rod may therefore bend to any extent within certain limits, provided P reaches the critical value given by (23). In the calculation the curvature has been put equal to D^2y, and this approximation gives the value of the limits of bending.

When $m = 2\pi/l$, equilibrium is again obtained: the various positions clearly correspond to multiples of half a sine-wave.

Euler's theory is only in approximate agreement with experiment; Southwell has given a more satisfactory but much more complicated treatment.

13. Uniform Vertical Rod Clamped at Lower End. Distributed Load.

The problem of a uniform vertical rod under a distributed load and clamped at its lower end has many important applications. Thus e.g. there is a limit to the height to which a tree can grow before it bends under its own weight. In fig. 11 consider two points Q and Q', with co-ordinates (x, y) and (x', y'), on the bending rod OB. The weight per unit length w is generally a function of x; let the weight of an element of length at Q' be $w\,dx'$.

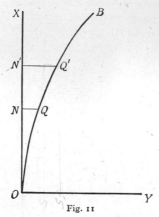

Fig. 11

The moment of this element about Q will be $w\,dx'(y' - y)$, and the total bending moment about that point is

$$G = \int_l^x w(y - y')\,dx',$$

where l is the length of the rod.

Differentiating both sides with respect to the upper limit x, we have

$$\frac{dG}{dx} = \int_l^x w\,\frac{dy}{dx}\,dx' + [w(y - y')]_{x'=x}$$

$$= \frac{dy}{dx}\int_l^x w\,dx'.$$

Now the total load above Q is $-\int_l^x w\,dx' = W$, say. Hence

$$\frac{dG}{dx} = -W\,\frac{dy}{dx}$$

or

$$qAk^2\frac{d^3y}{dx^3} = -W\,\frac{dy}{dx}. \qquad \ldots \ldots (25)$$

The solution of (25) depends on the nature of W and may be very complicated. For the special case of a uniform distribution of load, $W = w(l - x)$. Then

$$qAk^2\frac{d^2p}{dx^2} = -w(l - x)p \qquad \ldots \ldots (26)$$

or

$$\frac{d^2p}{dx^2} = -\beta(l - x)p,$$

where

$$p = \frac{dy}{dx} \quad \text{and} \quad \beta = w/qAk^2.$$

Finally, putting $l - x = z$, we have, since $\dfrac{d^2p}{dx^2} = \dfrac{d^2p}{dz^2}$,

$$\frac{d^2p}{dz^2} = -\beta zp. \qquad \ldots \ldots (27)$$

To solve equation (27) we express p in terms of a power series

$$p = \alpha_0 + \alpha_1 z + \alpha_2 z^2 + \alpha_3 z^3 + \ldots \quad \ldots \quad (28)$$

Then

$$\frac{d^2p}{dz^2} = 2\alpha_2 + 2.3\alpha_3 z + 3.4\alpha_4 z^2 + \ldots \quad \ldots \quad (29)$$

Hence, combining equations (27), (28) and (29), and equating coefficients of powers of z, we obtain

$$2\alpha_2 = 0, \quad 2.3.\alpha_3 = -\beta\alpha_0, \quad \&c.$$

Hence

$$p = \alpha_0\left(1 - \frac{\beta z^3}{2.3} + \frac{\beta^2 z^6}{2.3.5.6} - \ldots\right)$$
$$+ \alpha_1\left(z - \frac{\beta z^4}{3.4} + \frac{\beta^2 z^7}{3.4.6.7} - \ldots\right).$$

The constants α_0, α_1 are determined from the boundary conditions,

$$p = 0 \text{ when } z = l, \quad \frac{dp}{dz} = 0 \text{ when } z = 0.$$

Hence $\alpha_1 = 0$ and

$$0 = 1 - \frac{\beta l^3}{6} + \frac{\beta^2 l^6}{180} - \ldots \quad \ldots \ldots \quad (30)$$

The smallest value of βl^3 which will satisfy equation (30) is found by trial and error and successive approximation to be 7·84. Instability therefore occurs when $wl^3/qAk^2 = 7.84$.

If ρ is the density, then $w = g\rho A$, and the maximum length is given by

$$l = 1.99\left(\frac{qk^2}{g\rho}\right)^{\frac{1}{3}}. \quad \ldots \ldots \ldots \quad (31)$$

If $\rho = 0.6$ and $q = 10^{11}$ dynes/sq. cm. for deal, the maximum height of a pine tree 15 cm. across is about 27 metres.

14. Torsion of Rods.

Consider an element of a circular rod, of area α and at a distance r from the axis of symmetry OO' of the rod (fig. 12). Let the rod be fixed at its lower end at a distance l from α and let α be twisted through an angle ϕ by an external couple. Then if the tangential stress across α is F, the element of couple about the axis which this contributes is

$$dQ = F\alpha r.$$

Now if the angle of shear is θ,

$$r\phi = l\theta.$$

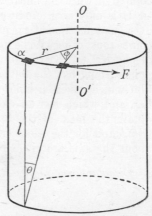

Fig. 12

Also, since $n = F/\theta$, where n is the rigidity modulus,

$$dQ = \frac{n\phi}{l}\, ar^2.$$

Hence the total couple about the axis is

$$Q = \frac{n\phi}{l} \Sigma ar^2.$$

Since the rod has a circular cross-section, Σar^2 is the geometrical moment of inertia of the section of the rod about the axis. Since

$$\Sigma ar^2 = \int_0^R 2\pi r\, dr \cdot r^2 = \tfrac{1}{2}\pi R^4 = Ak^2,$$

$$Q = \frac{1}{2}\frac{\pi n\phi R^4}{l}, \qquad \cdots \cdots \quad (32)$$

where R is the radius of the rod. The quantity Ql/ϕ is sometimes termed the *torsional rigidity*.

For rods of any other cross-section $Ql/n\phi$ is less than Ak^2. The solutions for elliptic, equilaterally triangular and square sections were given by St. Venant, who showed that the torsion involves a longitudinal displacement in the cross-section. The treatment of St. Venant is based on a general principle enunciated by him, that the strains which are produced in a body by the application, to a small part of its surface, of a system of forces statically equivalent to zero force and zero couple are of negligible magnitude at distances which are large compared with the linear dimensions of the part.

It is only with cross-sections of a high degree of symmetry, however, that mathematical expressions can be obtained for $Ql/n\phi$. Recourse must otherwise be made to analogous equations in other branches of physics, which are more susceptible to investigation. Thus Prandtl pointed out that the deviation from a plane of the surface of a soap film which covers a hole of the same size as the cross-section of the bar, and which has an excess pressure on one side, may be used to obtain the form of the function determining $Ql/n\phi$. The values for $Ql/n\phi$ and for the geometrical moments of inertia of different sections about the axis are given below.

Circular area, radius R.

$$Ql/n\phi = \tfrac{1}{2}\pi R^4; \quad Ak^2 = \tfrac{1}{2}\pi R^4.$$

Elliptical area, semi-axes a and b.

$$Ql/n\phi = \frac{\pi a^3 b^3}{a^2 + b^2}; \quad Ak^2 = \tfrac{1}{4}\pi ab(a^2 + b^2).$$

Rectangular area, sides 2a and 2b.

$$Ql/n\phi = \frac{16ab^3}{3} - b^4\left(\frac{4}{\pi}\right)^5 \left\{ \sum_{m=0}^{m=\infty} \frac{1}{(2m+1)^5} \tanh \frac{(2m+1)\pi a}{2b} \right\},$$

where m has the values $0, 1, 2, 3, \ldots$:

$$Ak^2 = \tfrac{4}{3}ab(a^2 + b^2).$$

For a *square*, this gives

$$Ql/n\phi = 2 \cdot 2492a^4, \quad Ak^2 = 8a^4/3 = 2 \cdot 667a^4.$$

If $a = 3b$, the sum of the infinite series of hyperbolic tangents differs by less than 1 part in 5000 from $1 \cdot 0045$.

For a *flat strip*, therefore,

$$Ql/n\phi = ab^3(\tfrac{16}{3} - 3 \cdot 361b/a).$$

Hence for circular, elliptic, and rectangular strips of the same cross-sectional area and length, the relative torsional rigidities are in the ratio $1 : 2b/a : 2\pi b/3a$.

Rectangular suspensions have the double advantage of small torsional rigidity combined with large surface area for radiation of heat and are therefore often used in the construction of galvanometers.

15. Energy in a Strained Body.

(a) *A bent beam.*

Consider a short length dl of a filament of a bent beam (fig. 13). Let the cross-section of the filament be α and let it be situated at a distance z from the neutral axis. Then if we use the results of section 8, p. 53, the work done in stretching this filament by an amount e will be

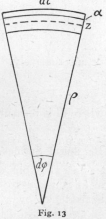

Fig. 13

$$\text{Force} \times \text{Distance} = \text{Stress} \times \text{Area} \times \text{Distance}$$

$$= \text{Elastic Modulus} \times \text{Strain} \times \text{Area} \times \text{Distance}$$

$$= \int_0^e q\alpha \frac{e}{dl} de = \tfrac{1}{2}q\alpha z^2 \frac{dl}{\rho^2}.$$

Hence the total energy of the whole cross-section A of the rod of length dl is

$$dV = \frac{1}{2}\frac{q}{\rho^2}\,dl\,\Sigma az^2$$

$$= \frac{dl}{2\rho^2}\,qAk^2.$$

But

$$G = \frac{qAk^2}{\rho}.$$

Hence the energy of the whole rod is

$$V = \int_0^l \frac{G^2}{2qAk^2}\,dl. \quad \ldots \ldots \quad (33)$$

(b) *A rod of circular cross-section under torsion.*

If the couple applied to a rod under torsion is Q, the work done in twisting the rod through an angle $d\phi$ is

$$dV = Q\,d\phi.$$

Now from equation (32)

$$Q = \frac{\pi n\phi R^4}{2l}.$$

Hence

$$V = \frac{n\pi R^4}{2l}\int_0^{\phi_0}\phi\,d\phi = \tfrac{1}{2}Q_0\phi_0 = \frac{Q_0^2 l}{n\pi R^4},$$

or, alternatively,

$$V = \int \frac{Q_0^2}{n\pi R^4}\,dl, \quad \ldots \ldots \quad (34)$$

where dl is measured along the rod.

16. Spiral Springs.

Let the coils of a spiral spring (fig. 14) be inclined at an angle a to the horizontal plane when the spring is stretched by a force W. We consider any point A on the coils; if a is the radius of the cylinder on which the coils are wound, the external couple at A is Wa. This couple results in a torsional shear $F = W\cos a$ in the tangent plane to the coils at A and a tension $T = W\sin a$ along the tangent to the coils.

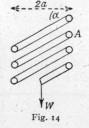

Fig. 14

The couple across the section at A can be resolved into a *torque* $Q = Wa\cos a$ acting in the plane of the section and a *bending moment* $G = Wa\sin a$ with its axis perpendicular to the section at A.

Then if x is the extension of the spring, the work done in stretching is

$$V = \int_0^x W dx,$$

which must be equal to the sum of equations (33) and (34). Hence

$$V = \frac{1}{2} \int \frac{G^2}{qAk^2} dl + \int \frac{Q^2}{\pi n R^4} dl,$$

or

$$\int_0^x W dx = \frac{1}{2} \frac{G^2 l}{qAk^2} + \frac{Q^2 l}{\pi n R^4}.$$

Substituting for G and Q, we have

$$\int_0^x W dx = \frac{1}{2} \frac{W^2 a^2 l \sin^2 \alpha}{qAk^2} + \frac{W^2 a^2 l \cos^2 \alpha}{\pi n R^4}.$$

Differentiating both sides with respect to x, we have

$$\frac{dx}{dW} = a^2 l \left(\frac{\sin^2 \alpha}{qAk^2} + \frac{2 \cos^2 \alpha}{\pi n R^4} \right).$$

Since $W = 0$ when $x = 0$,

$$x = W a^2 l \left(\frac{\sin^2 \alpha}{qAk^2} + \frac{2 \cos^2 \alpha}{\pi n R^4} \right). \qquad \cdots \quad (35)$$

If α is small, this becomes approximately

$$x = \frac{2 W a^2 l}{\pi n R^4}. \qquad \cdots \cdots \cdots \quad (36)$$

Substituting the value $Ak^2 = \frac{1}{4} \pi R^4$ for a wire of circular section in (35), we obtain

$$x = \frac{2 W a^2 l}{\pi R^4} \left(\frac{2 \sin^2 \alpha}{q} + \frac{\cos^2 \alpha}{n} \right). \qquad \cdots \quad (37)$$

In addition to the vertical motion of the free end, there is an angular displacement in the horizontal plane. If the end of the wire is twisted through ϕ, the torsion gives rise to a horizontal angular displacement $\beta = \phi \sin \alpha$. Since

$$Q = W a \cos \alpha = \frac{\pi n R^4 \phi}{2l},$$

$$\beta = \frac{2 W a l \sin \alpha \cos \alpha}{\pi n R^4}; \qquad \cdots \cdots \quad (38)$$

this will cause the spring to coil up, since it acts inwards.

On the other hand, the bending moment produces a horizontal angular rotation of the free end amounting to

$$\int_0^l \frac{dl\,\cos\alpha}{\rho} = \frac{Wa\sin\alpha\cos\alpha}{qAk^2}\int_0^l dl = \frac{4Wal\sin\alpha\cos\alpha}{q\pi R^4},$$

and this causes the spring to uncoil, since it acts outwards.

The total angular displacement as the spring coils up is therefore

$$\frac{2Wal\sin\alpha\cos\alpha}{\pi R^4}\left(\frac{1}{n} - \frac{2}{q}\right), \quad \cdot\ \cdot\ \cdot\ \cdot\ (39)$$

and is greatest when $\alpha = 45°$.

The spring will coil or uncoil according as $\dfrac{1}{n} \gtrless \dfrac{2}{q}$. Since for most metals $q > 2n$, spiral springs of circular section generally coil up when stretched.

17. Vibrations of Stretched Bodies.

The general treatment of the vibrations of stretched bodies is beyond the scope of this book. A few simple cases, however, are of considerable importance.

(a) *Transverse vibrations of a loaded bar.*

Consider a light rod projecting horizontally from a clamped end, with the free end carrying a weight W.

If the restoring force is F when the deflection is y_1,

$$F = -W\,d^2y_1/dt^2.$$

Further, from Ex. 3, p. 277,

$$qAk^2y_1 = \frac{Fl^3}{3}.$$

Hence

$$\frac{d^2y_1}{dt^2} = -m^2y_1, \quad \cdot\ \cdot\ \cdot\ \cdot\ \cdot\ \cdot\ (40)$$

where

$$m^2 = \frac{3qAk^2}{Wl^3}.$$

The solution of (40) gives

$$t = \frac{2\pi}{m} = 2\pi\sqrt{\frac{Wl^3}{3qAk^2}}. \quad \cdot\ \cdot\ \cdot\ \cdot\ \cdot\ (41)$$

(b) *Vertical oscillations of a loaded spring.*

In the case of a flat spring, only the torsional energy comes into account. The potential energy when the spring is subjected to a couple Wa has been shown to be

$$V = \frac{W^2a^2l}{\pi nR^4}.$$

But from (36), if the vertical extension is x,

$$x = \frac{2Wa^2l}{\pi nR^4}.$$

Hence

$$V = \frac{\pi nR^4}{4la^2}\,x^2. \quad \cdots \cdots \quad (42)$$

Let the velocity of the moving mass be dx/dt at the instant when the extension is x. Then the kinetic energy of the mass is $\frac{1}{2}W(dx/dt)^2$. The kinetic energy of the spring itself must also be taken into consideration. If the extremity of the wire moves with a velocity dx/dt, the kinetic energy of an element ds of the wire a distance s from the fixed end will be $\frac{1}{2}m\left(\dfrac{s}{l}\dfrac{dx}{dt}\right)^2 ds$, where m is the mass per unit length of the spring and l is its total length. The total kinetic energy associated with the spring is therefore

$$\int_0^l \tfrac{1}{2}m\left(\frac{dx}{dt}\right)^2 \frac{s^2}{l^2}\,ds = \tfrac{1}{6}w\left(\frac{dx}{dt}\right)^2,$$

where w is the weight of the whole spring. The total kinetic energy of the system is therefore

$$\tfrac{1}{2}(W + w/3)\left(\frac{dx}{dt}\right)^2.$$

Since the sum of the potential and kinetic energies of the whole system is constant,

$$\tfrac{1}{2}(W + w/3)\left(\frac{dx}{dt}\right)^2 + \frac{\pi nR^4}{4la^2}\,x^2 = \text{const.}$$

Differentiating with respect to t, we have

$$(W + w/3)\frac{d^2x}{dt^2} + \frac{\pi nR^4}{2la^2}\,x = 0.$$

This is of the form $\dfrac{d^2x}{dt^2} = -m^2x$, where

$$m^2 = \frac{\pi nR^4/2la^2}{(W + w/3)}.$$

The period is $\quad t = 2\pi/m = 2\pi\sqrt{\dfrac{W + w/3}{\pi nR^4/2la^2}}. \quad \cdots \cdots \quad (43)$

18. Experimental Determination of the Elastic Constants.

Methods for measuring q and n will now be described; the measurement of K is described in the chapter on compressibility (p. 81).

Extension may be measured in the following ways: (1) by a micrometer screw, (2) by an indicating dial, (3) by a microscope, (4) by a

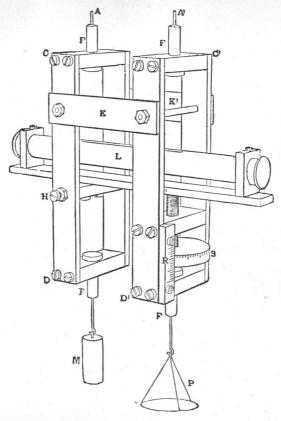

Fig. 15

(From Searle, *Experimental Elasticity* (Camb. Univ. Press))

multiplying lever (mechanical magnification), (5) by optical magnification, (6) by optical interference, (7) by change in electrical resistance (e.g. Bridgman's work, Chapter V, p. 82), (8) by Whiddington's method[*] of observing the alteration of pitch of a heterodyne beat note, produced by the change in capacity of a condenser when the distance between the plates is varied.

[*] Whiddington, *Phil. Mag.*, Vol. 40, p. 634 (1920).

19. Young's Modulus.

(a) Searle's statical method.

The apparatus consists of a framework $CC'D'D$ (fig. 15), which is supported by two vertical wires A, A' fastened to clamps at F. Inside the framework rests a spirit-level L supported by the horizontal bar H and the end of a thick screw S. A large graduated drum-head is attached to S and moves over a vertical scale R, as shown. From one side of the framework is suspended a heavy constant weight M and from the other a heavy scale-pan P. In using the apparatus the spirit-level is first adjusted to the horizontal position by turning the drum-head on S. A known load is then placed in P and the distance through which S has to be turned in order to bring the level back to a horizontal position is noted. Further loads are then added and the process is repeated until a given maximum is reached. Readings are then taken with decreasing load.

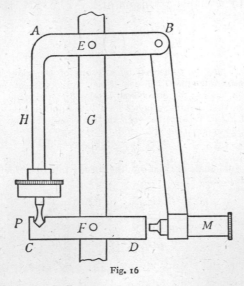

Fig. 16

Since Young's modulus is defined by stress/strain and in this case stress equals load per unit area of cross-section of the wire and strain equals increase in length per unit length, the diameter and length of the wire have still to be determined. The diameter is measured in several places with a micrometer screw gauge, while the length of the wire is obtained by means of a calibrated steel tape. Young's modulus is given by $q = WgL/\pi r^2 l$, where r is the radius of the wire, L its original length, and l its extension under the load W; the value of l/W is determined from the slope of the load-extension diagram.

(b) Ewing's extensometer.

The preceding method is suitable only for wires; an extensometer such as Ewing's may be used for thicker specimens (fig. 16).

Two horizontal arms AB and CD are pivoted at E and F by screws which pass through the specimen G. The arm BA is bent round to form the vertical rod H, which carries at its lower end a point P; the point rests in a V-shaped slot cut in the arm CD. Between H and P there is a fine screw-head which may be used to adjust the position of P and to calibrate the instrument. From B is suspended the microscope M, which carries a micrometer scale in the eye-piece and which is focussed on a fine horizontal scratch on the end of CD. When a load is applied to G, P acts as a fulcrum and the extension of the rod is given by FP/DP times the displacement observed in the microscope. Extensions as small as $1/50{,}000$ of an inch may be measured.

(c) Bending of a beam.

The most convenient experimental arrangement is with the load in the middle of the beam and the ends free but supported by knife-edges. Then by a simple extension of Ex. 3, p. 277, the depression is given by

$$y_2 = \frac{W}{2}\frac{1}{3}\left(\frac{l}{2}\right)^3\frac{1}{qAk^2}.$$

The depression may be measured by any one of the eight methods already enumerated. König introduced the use of two mirrors fixed vertically at either of the free ends of the bar, together with a telescope and scale. Then if d is the total change in the scale reading when a load W is applied, s the distance between the mirrors, and S the distance between the scale and the first mirror, it can be shown by simple geometry that

$$d = (2s + 4S)\varphi,$$

where φ is the actual angle of twist of either of the mirrors.

But by Ex. 3, p. 277,

$$\varphi = Dy = \frac{W}{2}\frac{1}{qAk^2}\left(\frac{l}{2}x - \frac{x^2}{2}\right)_0^{l/2}.$$

Hence

$$\varphi = \frac{W}{2}\frac{1}{qAk^2}\frac{l^2}{8}$$

so that

$$q = \frac{W}{2}\frac{l^2}{8Ak^2}\frac{(2s + 4S)}{d}.$$

(d) By angular oscillations of a loaded spring.

This method is a direct application of the solution of Ex. 8, p. 277.

(e) By transverse vibrations of a rod.

It may be shown,[*] by using an analysis somewhat more complicated than that of section 17, p. 64, that for a rod of circular cross-section fixed, for example, in a lathe-chuck and allowed to execute transverse vibrations, the frequency of oscillation is given by

$$n = \frac{m^2 r}{4\pi l^2}\sqrt{\frac{q}{\rho}},$$

[*] G. F. C. Searle, *Experimental Physics*, pp. 54–8 (Camb. Univ. Press, 1934).

where q is Young's modulus, l length of rod, ρ density of material of rod, r radius of rod, and m is given by $\cosh m \cos m = -1$. The frequency may be determined by resonance with a tuning-fork, and since the remaining quantities are easily found, a value for q is obtained.

20. Measurement of the Rigidity Modulus.

(a) Barton's statical method.

This method is a direct application of formula (32),

$$Q = \frac{1}{2}\frac{\pi n \phi R^4}{l}.$$

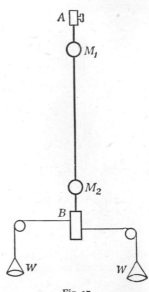

The specimen AB hangs vertically (fig. 17), being clamped at A and having a brass cylinder attached firmly to it at B by means of a set-screw. The torque is supplied by weights W carried in small scale-pans, and is made effective by cords acting tangentially to the brass cylinder. The twist between two points a distance l apart on the specimen is obtained by fixing two mirrors M_1 and M_2 to the points by means of set-screws and using the usual lamp and scale method. If a is the radius of the brass cylinder,

$$2Wag = \frac{1}{2}\frac{\pi n \varphi R^4}{l},$$

so that when $2R$ has been determined for several positions on the specimen n may be found.

Fig. 17

(b) Vertical oscillations of a loaded spring.

This method is a direct application of equation (43), p. 65.

21. Searle's Method for n and q.

Two equal brass bars A and C of square section are joined by the wire W as shown in fig. 18. The system is suspended by two parallel torsionless threads. If the ends P and P' are made to approach one another symmetrically and are then liberated, the bars will vibrate in a horizontal plane. The centres of the bars O and O' remain approximately at rest, so the action of the wire on the bar and vice versa is simply a couple. If each bar is twisted through θ and l is the length of the wire, the radius of curvature of the circle into which W is bent is given by $2\theta = l/\rho$. Hence if I is the moment of inertia of either bar about a vertical axis through its centre, we have

$$I\frac{d^2\theta}{dt^2} = -\frac{qAk^2}{\rho} = -\frac{2qAk^2\theta}{l}.$$

This is of the form $\dfrac{d^2\theta}{dt^2} = -m^2\theta$, where

$$m^2 = \frac{2qAk^2}{Il}.$$

and hence the time of oscillation is

$$t_1 = 2\pi \sqrt{\frac{Il}{2qAk^2}},$$

where

$$Ak^2 = \frac{\pi R^4}{4}. \qquad \cdots \cdots \cdots \quad (44)$$

To determine n for the same wire, the suspensions are removed, and one of the bars is fixed horizontally while the other is suspended from the now vertical

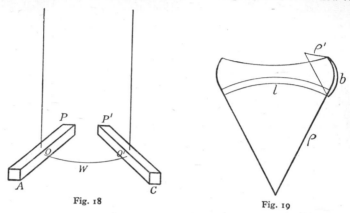

Fig. 18   Fig. 19

wire. If the suspended bar is twisted through an angle φ and allowed to oscillate, the equation of motion is

$$I \frac{d^2\varphi}{dt^2} = - \frac{\pi n R^4}{2l}\, \varphi,$$

which is of the form

$$\frac{d^2\varphi}{dt^2} = -m^2\varphi,$$

where $m^2 = \dfrac{\pi n R^4}{2Il}$, and hence the time of oscillation is

$$t_2 = 2\pi \sqrt{\frac{I}{\frac{1}{2}\pi n R^4/l}}. \qquad \cdots \cdots \cdots \quad (45)$$

The ratio q/n is therefore given by $t_2{}^2/t_1{}^2$, and for the determination of this the values of R, l and I are not required.

22. Determination of Poisson's Ratio.

(a) *Direct method.*

The lateral strain is measured directly with a micrometer screw gauge, while the longitudinal extension is determined by Searle's method or with an extensometer.

(b) *Bar method.*

When a flat bar of rectangular cross-section is bent by an applied couple, besides the curvature in the plane of the paper (see fig. 19), there is an anticlastic curvature of radius ρ' in the plane perpendicular to this. It has been shown that the longitudinal strain e at any distance z from the neutral axis is z/ρ, where ρ is the radius of curvature of the axis. The lateral contraction f is similarly given by z/ρ'. Hence Poisson's ratio $\sigma = f/e = \rho/\rho'$. The radii may be determined directly by clamping pointers to the rod and observing the distances and angles traversed when a given couple is applied.

(c) *Use of thin tubes as in bulk modulus determination.* See Chapter V, § 3, p. 79.

23. Optical Interference Methods for Elastic Constants.

Since the determination of strain involves a measurement of change of length, the change produced in an optical interference pattern affords a sensitive method for the determination of elastic constants. A few

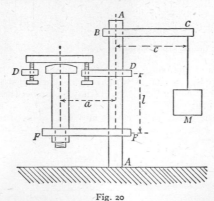

Fig. 20

(From Searle, *Miscellaneous Experiments* (Camb. Univ. Press))

examples of various experimental arrangements which have been used are given below.

(a) *Young's modulus by Searle's method.*

As fig. 20 shows, DF is a portion of a circular vertical rod AA under test. Two arms DD and FF carry an optically flat glass plate and a lens to give Newton's rings. A third arm BC is loaded by a force Mg, gradually applied, at a distance c from the axis of the rod. As the weight Mg is applied, a certain number of rings (N) will disappear at the centre of the interference pattern. The effect of the applied couple is to compress and bend the rod, and it is left as an exercise to the reader to show that Young's modulus is given by

$$q = \frac{2Mgl(4ac - r^2)}{N\pi\lambda r^4},$$

where r is the radius of the rod, a the distance of the centre of the lens from the axis of the rod, and λ the wave-length of the light used to produce the interference pattern.

(b) *Rigidity modulus by Searle's method.*

The apparatus (figs. 21 (a) and (b)) consists of the horizontal rod PQ under test, carrying clamped cross-pieces AB and DE at either end. The piece AB is pierced by a horizontal axis, so that the bar is free to turn and will consequently experience no bending moment when weights M are applied to either D or E. An ivory point C resting on a plane surface S supports the end Q of the bar and also serves as a fulcrum about which the torsion couple arising from the weight M acts. A glass test-plate rests on the centre of the bar.

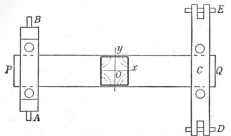

Fig. 21 *a*
(From Searle, *Miscellaneous Experiments* (Camb. Univ. Press))

Under the action of the couple, the central plane of the bar takes the form of a helicoid surface, the section of which by the horizontal plane gives rise to hyperbolic fringes, as shown in the figure. It may be proved that if $\tau = \frac{1}{2}(\tau_1 + \tau_2)$, where $\tau_1 = \lambda(n-1)/(u_n{}^2 - u_1{}^2)$ and $\tau_2 = \lambda(n-1)/(v_n{}^2 - v_1{}^2)$, and u and v are the distances from the centre O to fringes measured along directions at $45°$ and $-45°$ to the x- and y-axes,

$$n = \frac{Mgl}{\tau ab^3(\frac{16}{3} - 3 \cdot 361 b/a)},$$

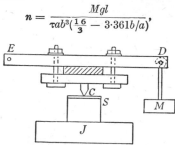

Fig. 21 *b*
(From Searle, *Miscellaneous Experiments* (Camb. Univ. Press))

where n is the coefficient of torsional rigidity, Mg the applied load, $2l$ the distance DE, and $2a$, $2b$ the width and thickness of the bar respectively.

(c) *Poisson's ratio.*

(1) Cornu's method.

The method is applicable only to a good reflector, such as glass or a metal which will take a high polish.

A rectangular bar of the material is taken and a plane optical test-plate is placed in contact with it. The bar is then loaded symmetrically as shown in fig. 22; the system of interference fringes produced between bar and test-plate is then observed. The fringes are rectangular hyperbolas (fig. 23), and it may be shown that if the asymptotes make an angle α with the x-axis, $\sigma = \rho/\rho' = \cot^2\alpha$. The angle may be measured directly with a goniometer eye-piece. Alternatively, if p_1, p_n, q_1, q_n are the distances of the first and nth fringes from the origin O

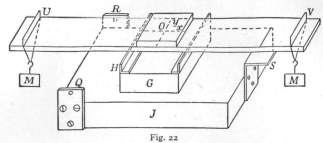

Fig. 22

(From Searle, *Miscellaneous Experiments* (Camb. Univ. Press))

measured along OX and OY respectively, the radii of curvature of the bar in these two directions are given by

$$\rho = \frac{(p_n{}^2 - p_1{}^2)}{\lambda(n-1)}$$

and

$$\rho' = \frac{q_n{}^2 - q_1{}^2}{\lambda(n-1)},$$

whence

$$\sigma = \rho/\rho' = \frac{(p_n{}^2 - p_1{}^2)}{(q_n{}^2 - q_1{}^2)}.$$

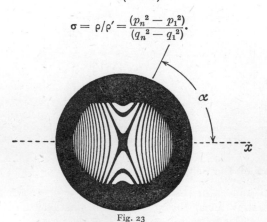

Fig. 23

(From *Handbuch der Physik*, Springer, Berlin)

The method is capable of many variations. For example, the optical test-plate may be replaced by a lens, giving Newton's rings. On bending the rod the rings will become increasingly elliptical in shape; finally, when the radius of curvature of the rod in one direction equals that of the lens, rectilinear fringes will be obtained.

(2) Method of diffraction haloes.

When lycopodium is dusted on a plane polished surface and illuminated by a small source placed in front of the surface, the illuminated particle and its image send secondary wavelets to the eye and the small source appears surrounded by a diffraction halo. If the surface is bent, the normal will rotate, the angle at which the light enters the eye will change, and the halo will appear deformed. In the experiment of Andrews * (fig. 24) a uniform rectangular brass plate P, one surface of which is polished and dusted with lycopodium, is bent by applied couples and placed a few feet from a small light source L_1. An observer at E measures the diameter of the elliptical haloes upon the superposed image of the screen S which is seen by reflection in the plate-glass plate G. The lengths of the major and minor axes are observed, the couple is increased, and the process continued. Let θ, φ be the angles subtended at the eye by the diameters in the plane of bending and perpendicular to it respectively. When the couple is increased, let these angles change to θ', φ'. Then Poisson's ratio is given by

$$\sigma = \frac{\dfrac{1}{\theta'} - \dfrac{1}{\theta}}{\dfrac{1}{\varphi'} - \dfrac{1}{\varphi}}.$$

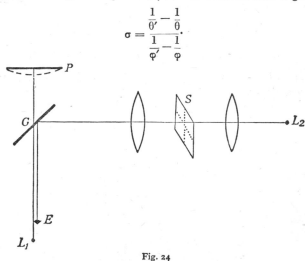

Fig. 24

The haloes are generally small and diffuse and do not improve when the plate is bent: great accuracy therefore cannot be attained.

24. Variation of Elasticity with Temperature.

For small ranges in the region of room temperature, there exists an approximately linear relation between elasticity and temperature. In general, as the temperature rises the elastic moduli fall, and for temperatures up to within 150° C. of the melting-point, Andrews † has found the general relation

$$q = q_1 e^{-bT},$$

where b takes some other value b_1 at an absolute temperature about half that of the melting-point. There is a general correlation

---

* Andrews, *Phil. Mag.* (2), Vol. 2, p. 945 (1926).

† Andrews, *Proc. Phys. Soc.*, Vol. 37, p. 3 (1925).

between degree of thermal expansion and change in the elastic modulus. Thus quartz, which has a negligible coefficient of expansion between 0° and 800° C., exhibits an almost constant value of q within this temperature range. Using a torsional oscillation method, Horton* has shown that the rigidity modulus, although showing approximately linear variation with temperature over small ranges, depends largely upon the previous treatment of the specimen. Irregular behaviour is also found at very low temperatures. The classical work of de Haas and Hadfield† has shown that the ductility of steel completely disappears at −252·8° C., whereas the mechanical properties of nickel, copper, and aluminium are much improved. In general, the effect is not permanent, the metal regaining its original elastic properties as the temperature returns to its original value.

25. Isothermal and Adiabatic Elasticities.

For small changes of temperature, the changes in the elastic properties of bodies are reversible; it is therefore possible to take e.g. a stretched wire through a Carnot cycle. Consider a wire of length l and cross-section A, subject to a strain e under a stress P and situated in a uniform temperature enclosure at a temperature T. Let the wire undergo an increase in strain δe: the work done on the wire is $PAl\,\delta e$. Now let the wire be transferred to another uniform temperature enclosure at temperature $T + \delta T$, the elastic properties changing so that the stress becomes $P + \delta P$. Finally, let the wire contract until it regains its original strain e, after which it is brought back to the first temperature enclosure to complete the cycle. The work done by the wire at the higher temperature is

$$(P + \delta P)Al\,\delta e,$$

and hence the net work done by the wire is

$$\delta PAl\,\delta e.$$

If h represents the heat given out reversibly by the wire on being stretched at temperature T, by a well-known thermodynamical relation

$$\frac{\text{Net work done during cycle}}{\text{Heat given out at temperature } T} = \frac{\delta T}{T},$$

or

$$\frac{\delta PAl\,\delta e}{h} = \frac{\delta T}{T},$$

or

$$h = T\left(\frac{\delta P}{\delta T}\right)_{e\text{ const.}} Al\,\delta e.$$

* *Phil. Trans.*, A, Vol. 204, p. 1 (1904).   † *Phil. Trans.*, A, Vol. 232, p. 297 (1933).

If ρ is the density of the material of the wire, C its specific heat, and J the mechanical equivalent of heat, the change in temperature due to the elongation is then

$$\delta\theta = \frac{T\left(\dfrac{\delta P}{\delta T}\right)_{e\ \text{const.}}}{\rho C J} \cdot \delta e.$$

The change in strain δe might have been produced by changing the temperature of the wire while maintaining the wire under constant stress. If a is the coefficient of linear expansion, the required temperature change is given by $\delta e = a\,\delta T$. If we represent Young's modulus by q, the wire may be brought back to its original length by decreasing the tension by δP, where $\delta P = -q\,\delta e = -qa\,\delta T$, or

$$\left(\frac{\delta P}{\delta T}\right)_{e\ \text{const.}} = -qa.$$

Hence

$$\delta\theta = -\frac{Tqa\,\delta e}{\rho C J}.$$

Now $q\,\delta e$ is the additional tension δP required to produce the change in strain δe. Hence the increase in temperature $\delta\theta$ produced by an increase in stress δP is given by

$$\delta\theta = -\frac{Ta\,\delta P}{\rho C J}. \qquad \ldots \ldots (46)$$

Equation (46) has been verified by Joule, using thermocouples inserted in loaded bars.

In general, the increase in strain δe due to the application of an increased strain δP is due partly to the increased stress and, if the heat does not escape, partly to the rise in temperature. The equation is

$$\delta e = \delta P/q + a\,\delta\theta.$$

Now $\delta\theta$ is given by equation (46); hence

$$\delta e = \frac{\delta P}{q} - \frac{a^2 T}{\rho C J}\,\delta P$$

or

$$\frac{\delta e}{\delta P} = \frac{1}{q} - \frac{a^2 T}{\rho C J}.$$

If we denote the adiabatic value of Young's modulus by q', we have

$$\frac{\delta e}{\delta P} = \frac{1}{q'} = \frac{1}{q} - \frac{a^2 T}{\rho C J}.$$

In agreement with theory, experiment shows that q' is always greater than q, but the numerical agreement is often far from satisfactory.

REFERENCES

G. F. C. Searle, *Experimental Elasticity* (Camb. Univ. Press).
Prescott, *Applied Elasticity* (Camb. Univ. Press).
Ewald, Pöschl and Prandtl, *The Physics of Solids and Fluids* (Blackie).
G. F. C. Searle, *Experimental Physics* (Camb. Univ. Press).

CHAPTER V

Compressibility of Solids and Liquids

1. Introduction. The Production of High Pressures.

The determination of the compressibility of liquids and solids presented for hundreds of years a problem of great experimental difficulty. In 1600, members of the Florentine Academy concluded that water was incompressible, since it was exuded through the pores of a hollow lead sphere when the latter was compressed in the jaws of a vice. Some years later Boyle demonstrated the compressibility of gases, communicating his results in a paper entitled "Touching the Spring of Air". Owing to the large magnitude of the effect in gases, work in this direction continued to progress satisfactorily.

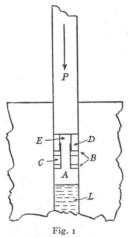

Fig. 1

(From Newman, *Recent Advances in Physics* (Churchill))

With liquids and solids, however, the effect is so small that it was not until 1762 that Canton first showed that water was definitely compressible. The experimental arrangement adopted was one which was used subsequently by the majority of experimenters until the recent work of Bridgman, when a new technique was devised. A large bulb fitted with a fine capillary is filled with the liquid, which is then subjected to pressure by a compression pump. The change in height of the liquid in the capillary indicates to a first approximation the change in the volume of the liquid. The method was developed by Regnault and is described in detail on p. 83.

The apparatus designed by Bridgman is shown in fig. 1. The liquid L is contained in a case of hardened steel, the pressure being applied by the advance of the steel piston P. The pressure is transmitted by the intermediary ring of steel D pressing on the soft rubber packing C, which is enclosed between the copper rings B, to the mushroom-shaped steel head A and thence to the liquid. The ingenuity of the apparatus lies in the fact that there can be no leak of liquid past the packing, since the pressure down the sides from above always becomes automatically greater than that up from the liquid. This action is achieved by

78

leaving a vacant space E behind the truncated stem of the head A; the whole of the downward force must then be supplied by the pressure on the rubber rings C, and this pressure will be greater than that in the liquid in the ratio of the area of the head A to the area of the rubber ring C. Pressures up to 20,000 Kgm. per sq. cm. can be used and measured with an accuracy of 0·1 per cent; in the interests of the economic life of the apparatus pressures above 12,000 Kgm. per sq. cm. were not often used, but owing to the absence of leak the only limit to the pressure is the cohesive strength of the walls of the container.

2. Measurement of High Pressures.

(i) *Primary gauges.*

The simplest type of primary gauge is some form of manometer, and the liquid commonly used is mercury. Such gauges were used by Regnault, Cailletet, and Amagat, but the height of the column which is practicable soon reaches a limit, and the method is not suitable for pressures above 1000 Kgm. per sq. cm.

The other type of primary gauge is the free piston gauge which was introduced by Amagat. This consists of a piston which is accurately fitted to a cylinder so that the leak along the sides is inappreciable. The pressure is then measured directly from the load which must be applied to the top of the piston in order to maintain it in equilibrium. The joint between piston and cylinder may be luted with molasses, but this treatment is effective only up to a pressure of 3000 Kgm. per sq. cm. The piston is rotated just before a measurement is made, to eliminate the effect of friction.

(ii) *Secondary gauges.*

The simplest of these is the Bourdon spring gauge, which consists of a plane spiral of metal or glass tubing which is flattened at the closed end. When the pressure is transmitted down the tubing, the spiral tends to straighten out and a pointer may be made to register the pressure. The gauge is useful up to pressures of 4000–5000 Kgm. per sq. cm.; its accuracy is limited by elastic hysteresis.

Bridgman has also used the variation of electrical resistance of a manganin coil with pressure as a secondary gauge. The method is particularly useful at high pressures.

3. Change in Volume of a Cylindrical Tube under Pressure.

As the change in volume of a cylindrical tube under pressure is involved in many determinations of the compressibility of solids and liquids, an expression for this quantity will now be obtained. Consider a cylindrical tube with flat ends, exposed to an external pressure p and an internal pressure P. Lamé has shown that the strains produced involve a *radial displacement* σ given by

$$\sigma = ar + \beta/r \quad \ldots \ldots \ldots \quad (1)$$

at a point in the cylinder wall a distance r from the axis, a and β being constants. There is also a *longitudinal displacement* parallel to the axis of the cylinder.

If X, Y, Z are the normal stresses along the radius, tangential to it, and along the axis respectively, the corresponding strains being e_{xx}, e_{yy}, e_{zz}, reference to Chapter IV, section 6, p. 50, shows that

$$\left.\begin{array}{l} X = (K + 4n/3)e_{xx} + (K - 2n/3)(e_{yy} + e_{zz}) \\ Y = (K + 4n/3)e_{yy} + (K - 2n/3)(e_{zz} + e_{xx}) \\ Z = (K + 4n/3)e_{zz} + (K - 2n/3)(e_{xx} + e_{yy}) \end{array}\right\} . \qquad (2)$$

Now since $e_{xx} = d\sigma/dr$ and $e_{yy} = \sigma/r$, we have from (1)

$$e_{xx} = a - \beta/r^2. \qquad \ldots \ldots \ldots (3)$$

and

$$e_{yy} = a + \beta/r^2. \qquad \ldots \ldots \ldots (4)$$

Hence from (2), (3) and (4), at the limits r_1 and r_2, where $X = -P$ and $X = -p$ respectively, we have

$$-P = 2Ka + 2n(a - 3\beta/r_1^2)/3 + (K - 2n/3)e_{zz} \qquad (5)$$

and

$$-p = 2Ka + 2n(a - 3\beta/r_2^2)/3 + (K - 2n/3)e_{zz}. \qquad (6)$$

Again, the force tending to stretch the cylinder parallel to its axis is $\pi(r_1^2 P - r_2^2 p)$, and the longitudinal stress is therefore

$$Z = \frac{(r_1^2 P - r_2^2 p)}{(r_2^2 - r_1^2)}. \qquad \ldots \ldots \ldots (7)$$

From equations (2), (3) and (4), however,

$$Z = (K + 4n/3)e_{zz} + (K - 2n/3)2a. \qquad \ldots \ldots (8)$$

Hence, from (7) and (8),

$$\frac{r_1^2 P - r_2^2 p}{(r_2^2 - r_1^2)} = (K + 4n/3)e_{zz} + (K - 2n/3)2a. \qquad (9)$$

Finally, from equations (5), (6), and (9),

$$a = e_{zz} = \frac{r_1^2 P - r_2^2 p}{(r_2^2 - r_1^2)} \frac{1}{3K} \qquad \ldots \ldots (10)$$

and

$$\beta = \frac{r_1^2 r_2^2 (P - p)}{(r_2^2 - r_1^2)} \frac{1}{2n}. \qquad \ldots \ldots (11)$$

The radial displacement σ is therefore given by

$$\sigma = \frac{r_1^2 P - r_2^2 p}{(r_2^2 - r_1^2)} \frac{r}{3K} + \frac{r_1^2 r_2^2 (P - p)}{(r_2^2 - r_1^2)} \frac{1}{2nr}. \qquad \ldots (12)$$

If L is the length of the unstrained tube, its internal volume is originally $v_1 = \pi r_1^2 L$, and hence the approximate change in internal volume is

$$\delta v_1 = 2\pi r_1 \sigma L + \pi r_1^2 e_{zz} L, \quad \ldots \ldots \quad (13)$$

since $\sigma = \delta r_1$ and $e_{zz} L = \delta L$.

From equations (10), (12) and (13) we have

$$\delta v_1 = \frac{\pi r_1^2 L}{(r_2^2 - r_1^2)} \left\{ \frac{r_1^2 P - r_2^2 p}{K} + \frac{r_2^2 (P - p)}{n} \right\}, \quad \cdot \quad (14)$$

and the change in external volume δv_2 is similarly given by

$$\delta v_2 = \frac{\pi r_2^2 L}{(r_2^2 - r_1^2)} \left\{ \frac{r_1^2 P - r_2^2 p}{K} + \frac{r_1^2 (P - p)}{n} \right\}. \quad \cdot \quad (15)$$

4. The Bulk Modulus of Solids.

The bulk modulus of solids may be determined as follows:

(i) Indirectly from the known relation (equation (5), Chapter IV, p. 52) between q, n and K, when q and n have been determined for the specimen. The disadvantage of the method is that the same specimen is rarely used for the determination of q and n and subsequently for the problem for which the value of K is required.

(ii) Many direct methods depend on the measurement of the strains of a thin hollow cylinder subject to given stresses. For example, Mallock has used an optical device to measure the longitudinal strain in a thin-walled tube under internal pressure. If the internal and external radii are r_1 and r_2 respectively, the pressure is P, and the longitudinal strain is l/L, from equation (10), putting $e_{zz} = l/L$ and p equal to zero, we have

$$K = \frac{P r_1 L}{6l(r_2 - r_1)}, \quad \ldots \quad (16)$$

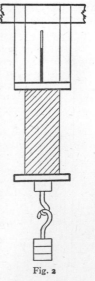

Fig. 2

since $(r_1 + r_2)$ is approximately equal to $2r_1$.

Alternatively, a load may be suspended from the end of the cylindrical tube arranged vertically and the change in internal volume registered by a liquid contained in the tube. The type of apparatus used by Amagat is shown in fig. 2; the change in volume is measured by means of the transparent graduated open capillary tube fixed to the top of the main tube. From equation (3), Chapter IV

(p. 51), or the theory given in section 3 of this chapter (p. 80), the change in volume is given by

$$\frac{\delta v_1}{v_1} = \frac{P(1 - 2\sigma)}{q} = \frac{P}{3K}, \quad \ldots \ldots \quad (17)$$

where P is the applied stress, σ is Poisson's ratio, and $\delta v_1/v_1$ is the volume strain.

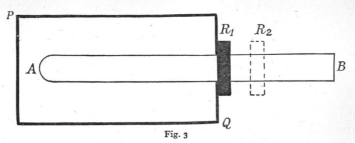

Fig. 3

(iii) Bridgman's methods are the most reliable; the general arrangement is shown in fig. 3.

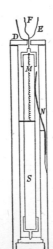

A heavy steel cylinder PQ encloses the specimen AB, which is in the form of a rod. A uniform external pressure is then applied hydrostatically by immersing the cylinder in a high-pressure chamber (fig. 1), and the contraction l_1 of the rod relative to the cylinder is measured by the movement of a loose-fitting ring R_1, which during the contraction moves to R_2, in which position it remains after the pressure is removed. Owing to the extension in length l_2 of the cylinder, the true contraction of the rod is given by $l = l_1 - l_2$. The change in length of the cylinder, which is only a few per cent of the change in the rod, is determined by comparator measurements. The volume strain is then given by $3l$, since the method actually measures the longitudinal strain. In place of the ring recorder R_1R_2, a sliding contact may be used, the change in length being determined in terms of a change in electrical resistance.

The absolute compressibility of one metal, for example iron, having been determined, relative and hence absolute compressibilities of other materials may be rapidly obtained.

In fig. 4, the specimen in the form of a long rod S is kept pressed against the bottom of the holder of iron by the spring M.

Fig. 4

(From Bridgman, *The Physics of High Pressure* (Bell).)

Attached to the upper end of the rod is a high-resistance wire sliding over a contact D, attached to the holder but insulated from it. The spring N keeps the wire pressed against its contact. The relative position of holder and wire is determined by a potentiometer measurement of the difference of potential between the sliding contact D and a terminal E fixed to the wire. One current terminal is at F and the other is earthed to the apparatus. The whole arrangement is placed in a high-pressure chamber and exposed to hydrostatic pressure; the relative linear compressibility is directly determined from the change in resistance.

5. Compressibility of Liquids.

(i) *Older Experiments.*—The early experiments are of historical interest only, owing to the uncertainty in the correction for the change of volume of the containing vessel. The instruments as a whole are termed *piezometers.* If δv_t is the apparent change in volume of the liquid contained in a piezometer under a pressure P applied simultaneously internally and externally, the true contraction will be

$$\delta v = \delta v_t + \delta v_1, \quad . \quad . \quad . \quad (18)$$

where δv_1 is the decrease in the internal volume of the container. For a cylinder of isotropic material, with flat ends, we obtain from equation (14), putting $p = P$,

$$\frac{\delta v_1}{v_1} = \frac{P}{k}, \quad . \quad . \quad . \quad (19)$$

and hence if k has been determined for the material by an independent experiment, δv_1 may be calculated. Finally, if K is the bulk modulus of the liquid, its value will be given by

$$\frac{\delta v_t}{v_1} = P\left(\frac{1}{K} - \frac{1}{k}\right). \quad . \quad . \quad (20)$$

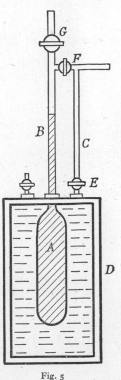

Fig. 5

The method has been used by Regnault and others to determine K. As fig. 5 shows, the liquid is contained in the bulb A and extends into the graduated capillary tube B, the upper end of which is connected to a compression pump and manometer. The pressure is transmitted to the outside of A by liquid contained in the outer vessel D, which can be placed in communication with the compressor by the side-tube C and the tap E. This tap, together with the remaining taps F and G, allows the pressure to be communicated (1) to the outside only, (2) to the inside only, or (3) to the outside and inside simultaneously. While the last arrangement is all that is required to obtain K from equation (20), if δv_o and δv_i represent the apparent contractions in volume under conditions (1) and (2), it may easily be shown, by applying equations (14) and (20), that

$$\delta v_o + \delta v_i = \delta v_t, \quad . \quad . \quad . \quad . \quad . \quad . \quad (21)$$

if the container is truly isotropic; a useful check on the applicability of equation (20) is therefore provided. In Regnault's experiments the container was actually a cylinder with *rounded* ends, and the corrections to be applied to equation (20) are of doubtful validity.

(ii) *Bridgman's Experiments.*—The classical experiments on the compressibility of liquids and the standard pressure-volume iso-thermals are due to Bridgman.

The liquid is contained in a steel cylinder similar to that shown in fig. 1, but fitted with an accurately-fitting steel piston carrying a contraction-measuring ring R_1 exactly like that shown in fig. 3 for the experiments on solids. The arrangement is then immersed in a high-pressure chamber of the type described on p. 78, the pressure being registered by means of a manganin resistance. The whole apparatus is placed in a thermostat; for water, isothermals up to 80° C. were obtained. To correct for the expansion of the containing vessel, the liquid is partially replaced by steel and the combined compressibility of the two is obtained.

6. Behaviour of Solids and Liquids at High Pressures.

The properties of matter at very high pressures are of fundamental importance, since atomic changes may be expected when forces of the order of the interatomic forces are applied. Pressures of 10^5 Kgm. per sq. cm. would be required to produce large effects: up to the present the maximum pressure attained is about 20,000 Kgm. per sq. cm., but even before this value is reached many interesting phenomena have been observed. A few of the more important observations of Bridgman will now be tabulated.

(1) Change in volume is entirely reversible with pressure; up to 25,000 Kgm. per sq. cm. no permanent change is produced.

(2) With liquids the volume change becomes relatively smaller; the compressibility at 12,000 Kgm. per sq. cm. is only about 1/20 of its value at moderate pressures.

(3) The coefficient of thermal expansion decreases, but to a lesser extent than the compressibility, and at very high pressures the same value is approached by all liquids.

(4) While a large part of the compressibility of liquids (and gases) is due to a decrease in the space between the atoms, with solids almost all the change of volume is produced by actual shrinkage of the atoms. The compressibility of solids is irregular, some decreasing and others increasing with increasing pressure.

(5) Anisotropic solids exhibit a great difference in the compressibilities along the different crystal axes. Tellurium actually expands along the trigonal axis when a uniform hydrostatic pressure is applied.

(6) There is no critical point between liquid and solid, and no maximum melting-point temperature above which only the liquid phase can exist, no matter how high the pressure.

(7) The coefficient of viscosity increases, and at enormously different rates for different substances. The approximate relation is $\eta = n \log p$, where n is a constant depending on the nature of the substance.

(8) The elastic moduli of some solids increase, while those of others decrease.

(9) The effect on thermal conductivity is irregular. Out of 48 metals, 39 show a decrease in electrical resistance; thermoelectric properties vary in both directions, while the Wiedemann-Franz ratio between thermal and electrical conductivities * increases in 9 examples out of 11. This behaviour indicates that the connexion between thermal and electrical conductivities cannot be completely explained on the existing electronic theory of metals and that there must be a considerable difference in the electron mechanisms giving rise to electrical resistance and thermoelectric effects.

REFERENCE

P. W. Bridgman, *The Physics of High Pressure* (G. Bell & Sons, Ltd., 1931).

* See Roberts, *Heat and Thermodynamics*, p. 232.

CHAPTER VI

Seismic Waves

1. Introduction.

Seismology deals with the problem of ascertaining the structure of the earth by means of the various waves which are produced by earthquakes. The source of these waves is the *focus* of the earthquake, that is, the place where the earth actually undergoes fracture. This region is some distance below the surface of the earth. The nearest point of the earth's surface to the focus is called the *epicentre*. By means of instruments called *seismographs*, records of the vibrations propagated from the focus to various points on the earth's surface are made. Great progress has been made in detecting and analysing these records and in assigning causes to the various types of vibrations.

2. Velocity of Longitudinal Waves.

After an earthquake has occurred, the first signal recorded by seismographs at distant stations is that due to the so-called *primary* or *P* wave (fig. 1). In this type of wave the vibrations are longitudinal,

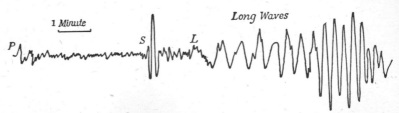

Fig. 1

that is, the particles of matter of which the earth is composed vibrate along the line of propagation of the energy. If the earth were a homogeneous sphere, these vibrations would travel along rectilinear paths, starting at the focus of the earthquake. The path between focus and recording station would be a chord of a great circle of the earth. In this book, this elementary view of the situation is adopted, and the velocity of the *P* waves through a homogeneous earth is calculated.

Consider the body undergoing strain, mentioned on p. 49. As in Chapter IV, p. 51, the three equations (1) hold, namely,

$$P_1 = \lambda\delta + 2n'e_{xx},$$
$$P_2 = \lambda\delta + 2n'e_{yy},$$
$$P_3 = \lambda\delta + 2n'e_{zz},$$

where

$$\lambda = \frac{\sigma q}{(1+\sigma)(1-2\sigma)} \quad \text{and} \quad 2n' = \frac{q}{(1+\sigma)}. \quad \cdots \quad (1)$$

Here q is Young's modulus of elasticity, σ is Poisson's ratio, and n' is n, the modulus of rigidity; e_{xx}, e_{yy}, e_{zz} are the strains and P_1, P_2, P_3 the stresses along the three axes respectively; and $\delta = e_{xx} + e_{yy} + e_{zz}$.

Consider the special case in which the only strain is $e_{xx} = \delta$ along the x-axis, e_{yy} and e_{zz} being each equal to zero. In this case P_1, the stress along the x-axis, is equal to $\lambda e_{xx} + 2n e_{xx}$.

That is,

$$P_1 = e_{xx}(\lambda + 2n)$$

$$= e_{xx}\left\{\frac{\sigma q}{(1+\sigma)(1-2\sigma)} + \frac{q}{(1+\sigma)}\right\}, \quad \cdots \quad (2)$$

$$= \frac{e_{xx}q(1-\sigma)}{(1+\sigma)(1-2\sigma)}, \quad \cdots\cdots\cdots \quad (3)$$

$$= je_{xx}, \text{ say,}$$

where

$$j = \frac{q(1-\sigma)}{(1+\sigma)(1-2\sigma)}. \quad \cdots\cdots\cdots \quad (4)$$

The coefficient j is called the *elongational elasticity*. As equation (3) shows, it is the modulus or factor connecting P_1 and e_{xx} when e_{yy} and e_{zz} are each equal to zero. In other words, equation (4) represents the relation between the stress and the strain in any direction, when lateral strains perpendicular to the first are prohibited. Now these are precisely the circumstances which arise when a longitudinal wave-train passes through a homogeneous medium which is practically unlimited in lateral directions. They are in sharp contrast with the circumstances attending the passage of longitudinal waves along a rod or wire.

Let a train of longitudinal waves of the above type traverse a homogeneous medium (fig. 2). Consider the forces on an element of matter AB, of uniform density ρ and unit cross-section, displaced longitudinally along the axis Ox to CD. Let the medium be unlimited laterally.

Let the displacement AC be l. Then BD is the same function of

$x + dx$ as l is of x. By Taylor's theorem, $f(x + dx) = f(x) + f'(x)\,dx$, if we neglect small terms. Here $BD = f(x + dx) = l + \dfrac{\partial l}{\partial x}\,dx$. Hence CD, which is equal to $BD - BC$, is equal to

$$l + \frac{\partial l}{\partial x}\,dx - l + dx = dx\left(\frac{\partial l}{\partial x} + 1\right).$$

Hence $CD - AB$, which is the extension of the element AB due to its displacement, is equal to $(\partial l/\partial x)\,dx$. The fractional extension is $\partial l/\partial x$. By equation (3) the average tensile force on the element CD is $j(\partial l/\partial x)$. If, however, equal tensions acted on the element at C and D, no longitudinal waves would be propagated. One tension must exceed the other. Only a small error of the second order is made by assuming $j(\partial l/\partial x)$ to be the tension at one end of the element CD,

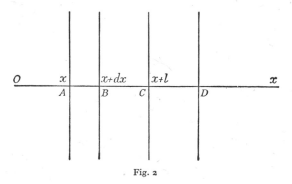

Fig. 2

say at C. The value of the tension at D is the same function of $x + dx$ as $j(\partial l/\partial x)$ is of x. Hence, by Taylor's theorem, it is

$$j\frac{\partial l}{\partial x} + j\,dx\,\frac{\partial^2 l}{\partial x^2},$$

approximately. At C the force on the element CD is $j(\partial l/\partial x)$, towards the origin O. At D the force is

$$j\frac{\partial l}{\partial x} + j\,dx\,\frac{\partial^2 l}{\partial x^2},$$

away from the origin. Now the mass of the element is $\rho\,dx$. Applying Newton's second law of motion to the element, we have

$$j\,dx\,\frac{\partial^2 l}{\partial x^2} = \rho\,dx\,\frac{\partial^2 l}{\partial t^2}$$

or

$$\frac{\partial^2 l}{\partial t^2} = \frac{j}{\rho}\frac{\partial^2 l}{\partial x^2}. \quad\cdot\quad\cdot\quad\cdot\quad\cdot\quad\cdot\quad\cdot\quad (5)$$

This type of differential equation is well known under the title of the " wave equation ". A general solution of it is $l =$ any function of $(x - v_1 t) = f(x - v_1 t)$, say, where

$$v_1^2 = j/\rho. \quad \cdots \cdots \quad (6)$$

This means that longitudinal waves travel along the x-axis with velocity

$$v_1 = \left(\frac{j}{\rho}\right)^{\frac{1}{2}} = \left\{\frac{q(1-\sigma)}{\rho(1+\sigma)(1-2\sigma)}\right\}^{\frac{1}{2}}. \quad \cdots \quad (7)$$

In a homogeneous earth, P waves would have this velocity. The adjectives *primary, irrotational, condensational*, and *push*, as well as *longitudinal*, are applied to these waves. In practice three distinct sets of P waves, arising in different ways, are often observed in the seismographic record of a single earthquake.

3. Velocity of Transverse Waves.

The second section of the vibrations recorded by distant seismographs after an earthquake is due to the so-called *secondary* or S waves (fig. 1). These vibrations have no component in the direction of propagation; they are transverse vibrations. In a homogeneous earth they too would pursue rectilinear paths starting at the focus of the earthquake, that is, chords of great circles. It will now be shown that the velocity of such transverse waves in homo-

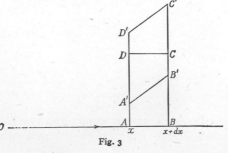

Fig. 3

geneous matter of density ρ is $v_2 = \left(\dfrac{n}{\rho}\right)^{\frac{1}{2}}$, where n is the modulus of rigidity.

Assume that the particles of matter vibrate in planes perpendicular to the direction of propagation, in rectilinear paths. Even if a transverse vibration is elliptical or circular, it can be resolved into two perpendicular rectilinear vibrations. Let Ox be the direction of propagation of a transverse plane wave (fig. 3). Consider a slice of matter $ABCD$ of thickness dx, normal to Ox. When a plane wave passes along, let every particle in the plane AD undergo the same lateral displacement in the plane of the figure, so that A goes to A' and D to D'. Let $AA' = DD' = y$. Similarly, let every particle in the plane BC undergo a lateral displacement $y + dy$. In this case $BB' = CC' = y + dy$. In such circumstances the slice undergoes shearing in the

y-direction. The angle of shear is the relative displacement dy divided by the thickness dx, that is, it is given by $\partial y/\partial x$. By Chapter IV, p. 48, the average tangential force per unit area producing this shear is $n\,\partial y/\partial x$. If the same tangential force were applied to both faces, AD and BC, a static shear would ensue, but no propagation of waves. Waves are propagated when there is a greater tangential force on one face, say on $B'C'$, than on $A'D'$. Assume, as a close approximation to the truth, that the tangential force per unit area acting on $A'D'$ is

$n\dfrac{\partial y}{\partial x}$, which is a function of x. This acts in the direction $D'A'$. The force per unit area acting on $B'C'$ is the same function of $x + dx$ as

$n\dfrac{\partial y}{\partial x}$ is of x. Hence it is given by $f(x + dx) = f(x) + f'(x)\,dx$, approxi-

mately, where $f(x) = n\dfrac{\partial y}{\partial x}$; that is, $f(x + dx) = n\dfrac{\partial y}{\partial x} + n\,dx\dfrac{\partial^2 y}{\partial x^2}$, ap-

proximately. This force acts in the direction $B'C'$. The net force per unit area tending to displace the slice in the y-direction is the difference

$n\,dx\dfrac{\partial^2 y}{\partial x^2}$. Let the length AD be 1 cm. and let the thickness of the slice

perpendicular to the plane of the figure also be 1 cm. Then the mass of the element $ABCD$ is $\rho\,dx$. Its equation of motion in the y-direction, derived from Newton's second law, is

$$\rho\,dx\frac{\partial^2 y}{\partial t^2} = n\,dx\frac{\partial^2 y}{\partial x^2},$$

which reduces to

$$\frac{\partial^2 y}{\partial t^2} = \frac{n}{\rho}\frac{\partial^2 y}{\partial x^2}, \quad \cdots \cdots \quad (8)$$

where t represents time.

This is a partial differential equation of the second order, of the same form as equation (5). A general solution of it is

$$y = f\left\{x - \left(\frac{n}{\rho}\right)^{\frac{1}{2}}t\right\},$$

where f means any function. This can be written in the form

$$y = f(x - v_2 t), \quad \text{where} \quad v_2 = \left(\frac{n}{\rho}\right)^{\frac{1}{2}}. \quad \cdots \quad (9)$$

This equation represents a disturbance travelling in the positive direction of x with velocity $v_2 = \left(\dfrac{n}{\rho}\right)^{\frac{1}{2}}$. The adjectives *secondary, equivoluminal, distortional* and *shake* are also applied to these waves as well as the adjective *transverse*. In practice the S waves arrived at the observing station in a direction inclined at some angle to the horizontal.

It is customary to consider the component vibrations in (a) the horizontal direction (the SH waves) and (b) the vertical plane containing the direction of propagation (the SV waves). Three different types of S waves, arising in different ways, are usually recorded in the seismogram of a single earthquake.

It may be noted that $v_2 = \left(\dfrac{n}{\rho}\right)^{\frac{1}{2}}$ is the expression for the velocity of transverse waves in any homogeneous elastic solid, and thus represents the velocity of light through the ether of space according to Fresnel's elastic solid theory. In that case n and ρ are the modulus of rigidity and the density of the ether respectively.

4. Rayleigh Waves.

There is a third type of wave, discovered by Lord Rayleigh, in which the vibrations are confined to a relatively thin layer close to the surface of the earth. In this case the waves do not arrive at the observing station along a chord starting from the focus of the earthquake, but along a great circle starting from the epicentre. Further, the displacement of particles of matter at any point on the earth's surface is in the vertical plane containing the direction of propagation, and can be resolved into (a) a vertical component, (b) a horizontal component in the direction of propagation. There is no horizontal component normal to the direction of propagation. No other kind of wave transmitted along the earth's surface would persist over long distances. The calculation of the velocity of Rayleigh waves is too long to reproduce here,* but it may be stated that the velocity would be constant if the earth were homogeneous. In the real earth, composed as it is of heterogeneous layers, a disturbance starting out as a single pulse becomes dispersed, that is, broken up into a set of waves with various periods and wave-lengths, all travelling with different velocities. At distant observing stations a series of oscillations is recorded, instead of a single throw such as would be observed if the earth were homogeneous.

5. Love Waves.

In the real heterogeneous earth a fourth type of surface waves, the Love waves, exists, in which the displacements of the particles of matter are horizontal and transverse to the direction of propagation. At any point on the earth's surface after an earthquake, a series of oscillations corresponding to Love waves of various velocities is produced. It can be deduced, from the fact that these waves actually exist, that their velocity is less in the surface layer of the earth's crust than in the subjacent matter. In actual seismograms recorded at distant stations the arrival of the P and S waves is well marked, but

* See Jeffreys, *The Earth* (Cambridge University Press).

the S wave is followed by a long series of oscillations, as in fig. 1. These are due to the Rayleigh and Love waves intermingled, and their complete interpretation is not yet settled. These complicated vibrations are referred to as the *long* or L waves, or as the *main shock*.

6. Seismographs.

The purpose of a seismograph is to register movements of the ground at the place where the instrument is situated. Any vibration of the ground may be resolved into three components, (a) vertical, (b) horizontal (say east and west), (c) horizontal (say north and south). Components (b) and (c) are of the same type, so that the problem is to record vertical and horizontal vibrations.

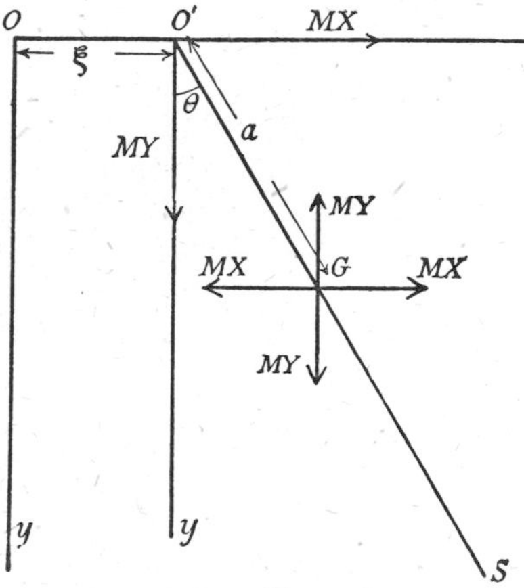

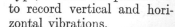

We first consider horizontal vibrations. To record these, one general method is to use some kind of pendulum, formed by a body suspended from a stand resting on the ground. It is instructive to consider the theory of the vibrations of a rigid " vertical " pendulum, when the ground and therefore the stand and the point of support are displaced horizontally.

Fig. 4

Case 1.—*Friction neglected.*

Let $O'GS$ (fig. 4) represent a rigid pendulum vibrating about a horizontal axis through O', perpendicular to the plane of the figure. By the horizontal displacement of the ground, O' itself has undergone a horizontal displacement ξ to the right, from a fixed point O. Let (x, y) be the co-ordinates of the centre of gravity G, referred to fixed axes Ox, Oy. Then $x = \xi + a \sin\theta$, $y = a \cos\theta$, where $O'G = a$. Let the forces on the pendulum be (a) the weight Mg, acting vertically downwards through G, and (b) certain other external forces acting at O', including the reactions of the supports, and let these forces be expressed in the form MX and MY, acting along $O'x$ and $O'y$ respectively. Add two pairs of equal and opposite forces MX, MX, and MY, MY, at the point G, parallel to the respective axes. The three forces MX now acting are equivalent to a force MX at G, to the right, and a clockwise couple of moment MXy, acting on the body. The three forces MY are equivalent to a force MY at G, vertically downwards, and a counterclockwise couple $MY(x - \xi)$, acting on the body. The equations of motion of the pendulum for translatory movements of G, if we neglect friction, are

$$M\ddot{x} = MX \quad \text{and} \quad M\ddot{y} = Mg + MY.$$

Hence

$$\ddot{x} = X \quad \text{and} \quad \ddot{y} = g + Y. \quad \ldots \quad \ldots \quad (10)$$

Taking moments about G, we obtain the equation of rotatory motion, namely,

$$MK^2\ddot{\theta} = MY(x - \xi) - MXy.$$

Hence

$$K^2\ddot{\theta} = Ya\sin\theta - Xa\cos\theta$$
$$= (\ddot{y} - g)a\sin\theta - \ddot{x}a\cos\theta, \quad \ldots \ldots \quad (11)$$

from (10), where K is the radius of gyration of the pendulum about an axis through its centre of gravity G. Now since

$$x = \xi + a\sin\theta,$$
$$\ddot{x} = \ddot{\xi} + a(\cos\theta.\ddot{\theta} - \sin\theta.\dot{\theta}^2).$$

Assume that θ is small and that $\dot{\theta}$ is negligibly small. Then

$$\ddot{x} = \ddot{\xi} + a\cos\theta.\ddot{\theta}. \quad \ldots \ldots \ldots \quad (12)$$

Further, y is approximately constant and $\ddot{y} = 0$. Equation (11) becomes

$$K^2\ddot{\theta} = -ga\theta - a\ddot{\xi} - a^2\ddot{\theta}. \quad \ldots \ldots \quad (13)$$

Hence

$$(K^2 + a^2)\ddot{\theta} + ga\theta + a\ddot{\xi} = 0. \quad \ldots \ldots \quad (14)$$

Let $(K^2 + a^2)/a = l$; l is the distance between O' and a certain point C, called the *centre of oscillation*. Then

$$l\ddot{\theta} + g\theta + \ddot{\xi} = 0. \quad \ldots \ldots \ldots \quad (15)$$

Put $g/l = n^2$. Then

$$\ddot{\theta} + n^2\theta + \frac{\ddot{\xi}}{l} = 0. \quad \ldots \ldots \ldots \quad (16)$$

The actual displacement ξ due to a distant earthquake is usually a complicated function of the time, but by Fourier's theorem it may be supposed to be resolved into a series of cosine terms, each of the form $\xi = \xi_0\cos\omega t$. Taking one of these terms, we insert $\xi = \xi_0\cos\omega t$ in equation (16). It becomes

$$\ddot{\theta} + n^2\theta - \frac{\omega^2\xi_0\cos\omega t}{l} = 0.$$

Hence

$$\ddot{\theta} + n^2\theta = \frac{\omega^2\xi_0\cos\omega t}{l}. \quad \ldots \ldots \ldots \quad (17)$$

The complete solution of this involves the complementary function and the particular integral. The complementary function is the solution of

$$\ddot{\theta} + n^2\theta = 0,$$

which is

$$\theta = A\cos(nt + \varphi).$$

The particular integral is found by writing

$$(D^2 + n^2)\theta = \frac{\omega^2\xi_0\cos\omega t}{l},$$

whence

$$\theta = \frac{\omega^2\xi_0\cos\omega t}{l(n^2 - \omega^2)}. \quad \ldots \ldots \ldots \quad (18)$$

The complete solution is

$$\theta = A\cos(nt + \varphi) + \frac{\omega^2\xi_0\cos\omega t}{l(n^2 - \omega^2)}. \quad \ldots \ldots \quad (19)$$

As the second term is the one produced by the earthquake, it is more interesting to us than the first. Write

$$\theta_1 = \frac{\omega^2 \xi_0 \cos \omega t}{l(n^2 - \omega^2)};$$

since $\xi = \xi_0 \cos \omega t$, we have

$$\xi = \frac{\theta_1 l (n^2 - \omega^2)}{\omega^2}. \quad \cdots \cdots \quad (20)$$

This represents one of the Fourier terms into which the actual displacement has been resolved. If a style or pen is mounted at the end S of the pendulum, such that $O'S = L$ cm., the apparent linear displacement of the style is $L\theta$, approximately, of which $L\theta_1$ is due to the earthquake:

$$L\theta_1 = \frac{L\omega^2 \xi_0 \cos \omega t}{l(n^2 - \omega^2)}$$

$$= \frac{L\omega^2 \xi}{l(n^2 - \omega^2)}, \quad \cdots \cdots \quad (21)$$

where $\xi = \xi_0 \cos \omega t$. The total displacement of the style is $L\theta + \xi$.

Case 2.—*Friction taken into account.*

Assume that a frictional force is present, which is proportional to the angular velocity of the pendulum. Insert a term of the form $\alpha \dot{\theta}$, to represent this retarding force, in equation (14). On reducing to the form of equation (16), and writing the frictional term as $2k\dot{\theta}$, we obtain the equation

$$\ddot{\theta} + 2k\dot{\theta} + n^2\theta + \frac{\ddot{\xi}}{l} = 0. \quad \cdots \cdots \quad (22)$$

Again assume that the actual seismic displacement ξ of the support can be expanded by Fourier's theorem in a series of cosine terms of the form $\xi = \xi_0 \cos \omega t$. Substitute $\xi = \xi_0 \cos \omega t$ in equation (22). It becomes

$$\ddot{\theta} + 2k\dot{\theta} + n^2\theta = \frac{\omega^2 \xi_0 \cos \omega t}{l}. \quad \cdots \cdots \quad (23)$$

As before, the complementary function represents that part of θ which is not produced by seismic displacements. To find the particular integral, assume a solution of the form $\theta = \theta_0 \cos(\omega t - \varphi)$. On substituting in equation (23) we have

$$-\omega^2 \theta_0 \cos(\omega t - \varphi) - 2k\omega \theta_0 \sin(\omega t - \varphi) + n^2 \theta_0 \cos(\omega t - \varphi) = \frac{\omega^2 \xi_0 \cos \omega t}{l},$$

which is true for all values of t. Substitute $\omega t = \frac{\pi}{2}$; then

$$(-\omega^2 + n^2) \sin \varphi = 2k\omega \cos \varphi$$

and

$$\tan \varphi = \frac{2k\omega}{n^2 - \omega^2}. \quad \cdots \cdots \quad (24)$$

Now put $\omega t = \varphi$. Then

$$(-\omega^2 + n^2)\theta_0 = \frac{\omega^2 \xi_0 \cos \varphi}{l} \quad \text{and} \quad \theta_0 = \frac{\omega^2 \xi_0 \cos \varphi}{l(n^2 - \omega^2)}.$$

From equation (24),

$$\cos \varphi = \frac{(n^2 - \omega^2)}{\{(n^2 - \omega^2)^2 + 4k^2\omega^2\}^{\frac{1}{2}}}$$

and

$$\theta_0 = \frac{\omega^2 \xi_0}{l\{(n^2 - \omega^2)^2 + 4k^2\omega^2\}^{\frac{1}{2}}}. \quad \cdots \cdots \quad (25)$$

The case when $k = n$ is of practical importance; for example, Galitzin's seismographs utilize this critical value of the damping. Then equation (25) becomes

$$\theta_0 = \frac{\omega^2 \xi_0}{l(n^2 + \omega^2)}. \quad \cdots \cdots \cdots \quad (26)$$

The quantity $l\theta_0$, which is the apparent maximum displacement of the centre of oscillation due to one Fourier term of the seismic displacement, is equal to

$$\frac{\omega^2 \xi_0}{n^2 + \omega^2}, \quad \cdots \cdots \cdots \quad (27)$$

that is, equal to ξ_0 multiplied by a constant factor. A pen at a distance L from the point of support or knife-edge has the apparent maximum displacement $L\theta_0$, which is also proportional to ξ_0. The pen faithfully reproduces the movements of the support with the same frequency, but on a different scale, provided the support moves with a definite frequency and amplitude for a sufficient number of oscillations. The magnification is the ratio of the pen's displacement to that of the support or ground. For a displacement $\xi = \xi_0 \cos \omega t$, the magnification is $L\theta_0/\xi_0$ (comparing maximum displacements). This is equal to $L\omega^2/l(n^2 + \omega^2)$ in the important case of critical damping.

7. Horizontal Pendulum Seismograph (Galitzin).

Seismographs belonging to the class of vertical pendulums just discussed are actually used to measure horizontal displacements, velocities, and accelerations of the earth's crust. They have, however, the disadvantage of being very heavy. Pendulums with masses up to 20 tons are required in order to reduce the friction involved in the registration of vibrations, when great magnification is needed. Another disadvantage is that the period of oscillation is small. To avoid these defects, seismographs belonging to the class of horizontal pendulum described in Chapter II, p. 29, are frequently used to measure horizontal movements.* The student should therefore refer to pp. 29–31 before proceeding further. Only slight additions are required to convert a horizontal pendulum into a very sensitive seismograph. When the earth moves horizontally, the supports of the pendulum do likewise and the " boom " of the latter is set in motion.

Various types of recording device are in use. In Galitzin's method, the boom of the horizontal pendulum extends beyond the bob. At a point on it beyond the bob a flat coil of copper wire is mounted, so that when the boom moves the coil moves in a strong magnetic field produced by a pair of horseshoe magnets. An induced current proportional to the angular velocity of the boom is produced in the coil, which is connected to a very sensitive galvanometer. The movements of the suspended part of the galvanometer are recorded by means of the usual

*For details of seismographs for measuring vertical displacements, see e.g. *Handbuch der Experimentalphysik*, Vol. XXV, Part II (1931).

mirror, lamp and sensitized paper device. The developed trace on the paper forms the seismogram. At a second place on the boom a copper plate is mounted. This also moves in a strong magnetic field produced by two other horseshoe magnets. The eddy currents induced in this plate introduce damping forces, which act on the pendulum. This damping is necessary in order that the seismogram obtained shall faithfully correspond to the movements of the earth, and that it shall be possible to calculate the horizontal displacement of the earth from the seismogram. The damping of both the pendulum and the galvanometer is arranged to be critical (dead beat). This arrangement simplifies the calculations. Galitzin's electromagnetic method of registration has the advantage of great magnification, of the order 1000, and also enables the recording apparatus to be housed in a different compartment from the pendulum.

8. Position of the Epicentre.

The shortest distance of the epicentre of an earthquake from a recording station, measured along the earth's surface, and reckoned as an angle subtended at the centre of the earth, is called the *epicentral distance*. In order to ascertain the position of the epicentre of a distant earthquake, use is often made of certain tables compiled by Zöppritz, Turner, and others. These contain values of epicentral distances of past earthquakes, the position of whose epicentre was known, tabulated alongside observed time intervals between the moments of arrival of the first P and S waves at the corresponding stations. The tables therefore show epicentral distances as a function of corresponding time intervals $S-P$. When a fresh earthquake occurs, examination of a seismogram gives the time interval $S-P$, and inspection of the tables then gives the epicentral distance. A similar procedure is applied to the data from two other stations recording the same earthquake, whose epicentral distances are thereby ascertained. On a suitable map or globe circles are drawn, whose centres are the stations and whose radii are the corresponding epicentral distances. The point of intersection of the three circles fixes the epicentre whose position is required. In practice the three circles do not give an exact point, but enclose a small area. Hence, data from a large number of stations are used, and the method of least squares is employed to ascertain the most likely position of the epicentre. The result is stated with a certain probable error.

9. Depth of Focus. Seebach's Method.

As earthquakes are probably caused by " fault slipping ", that is, breaking of the earth's rigid crust and slipping of the resulting portions, the focus is not a geometrical point but a more or less extended region. In the present elementary treatment, however, it is sufficient to regard the focus as a point source of seismic waves (fig. 5). As an example of methods of estimating the depth of the focus F vertically below the epicentre E, Seebach's method is selected. It is assumed that the medium between the earth's surface and a concentric sphere passing through F is homogeneous. Let the velocity of P waves in this medium be v cm. per sec. Let S be the position of any seismograph station on the surface. Let the distance FE be d cm. and ES x cm. The time τ required by the first P vibration to reach S is FS/v sec. $= (x^2 + d^2)^{\frac{1}{2}}/v$. Write $\tau = t - t_0$, where t is the actual time of arrival of the first P vibration, and t_0 is the time of occurrence of the earthquake at F. The quantity t_0 is unknown but is constant, and t varies when x varies. Hence

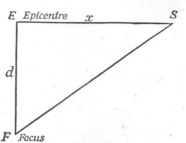

E *Epicentre* x S

d

F *Focus*

Fig. 5

$$\frac{(x^2 + d^2)^{\frac{1}{2}}}{v} = t - t_0 \quad . \quad (28)$$

and

$$x^2 + d^2 = v^2(t - t_0)^2. \quad (29)$$

The velocity v may be regarded as known, since it is obtained by other methods. A number of pairs of measured values of x and t are obtained from various stations. A graph connecting x and vt is plotted, giving a hyperbola from which d can be calculated; or, better, the method of least squares is employed to obtain the most probable values of d and t_0. It has been shown that the great earthquakes originate at depths of the order of 100 Km.

10. Geophysical Prospecting.

The modern technique of prospecting for minerals, oils, &c., makes use of methods arising out of the study of seismic waves and of the earth's gravitational field, as well as of electric and magnetic methods. The last two do not come within the scope of this book. As for gravitational methods, the Eötvös torsion balance (p. 24) has become a most useful instrument in the detection of ores. For example, if a large mass of a heavy or light mineral happens to be embedded in the earth, the variation of g in the neighbourhood reveals its presence. By a systematic survey, in which the various quantities discussed in Chapter III are measured, the mass of mineral can be located with considerable precision.

As an example of the application of seismic methods, the case of salt domes may be mentioned. These formations occur in Texas, North Germany, and elsewhere, and consist of large subterranean masses of rock salt. On their flanks valuable mineral oils are found, rendering their discovery highly profitable. One of the seismic methods of surveying for salt domes may be described as follows. Seismic waves of the P type are produced artificially by exploding a charge of guncotton or gelignite at a point S on the earth's surface (fig. 6). The time of the explosion is noted. Seismographs situated at other points

A, B, C and D, all in one plane, record the times of arrival of the first P waves. The distances SA, SB, SC, and SD, chords of the earth, are measured. The mean velocities along the various paths are calculated. Should one of the paths, for example SD, traverse a salt dome, the mean velocity along that path will be quite different from the mean

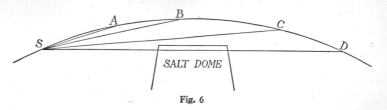

Fig. 6

velocity along the other paths. Similar measurements in a direction perpendicular to the first, using waves from a fresh source, confirm the first results. A more detailed survey then enables the position of the top and flanks of the dome to be accurately ascertained.

REFERENCES

Jeffreys, *The Earth* (Cambridge University Press, 1929).
Bouasse, *Séismes et Sismographes.*
Handbuch der Experimentalphysik, Vol. XXV, Part II.

CHAPTER VII

Capillarity

1. Elementary Principles.

It is assumed here that the student already has some elementary knowledge of capillary phenomena. The customary useful fiction is adopted, namely, that in every surface film separating a liquid and a gas, two liquids, or a solid and a liquid, a surface tension exists. This is defined as the force per centimetre exerted in the tangent plane to the surface, in a direction normal to an element of a line drawn in that surface through any point. This quantity is assumed to have the same value at every point in a given film, whatever the shape of the film may be. When a liquid and a solid meet along some line, a certain angle is included between a tangent plane to the surface of the liquid and a tangent plane to the surface of the solid at any point on the curve of contact. For the present this angle will be assumed to be the same at every point for any particular liquid-solid system. It is known as the *angle of contact* of that particular liquid and solid. For various difficulties connected with this, see § 25, p. 140.

Theorem.—The excess of pressure on one side of a film of constant surface tension over that on the other side is equal to $T(1/R_1 \pm 1/R_2)$, where T is the surface tension, and R_1, R_2 are the principal radii of curvature of the film at the point in question.

Proof.—Consider a surface film separating two regions containing fluids (fig. 1). In general it will be curved. Let a small curvilinear rectangle be drawn, enclosing any point O in the film, such that the sides are in " principal sections " of the film passing through A, B, C and D, the film being regarded as a geometrical surface.* Let the sides have lengths δl_1 and δl_2 respectively, and let the radii of curvature of these sides be R_1 and R_2 respectively. Let both centres of curvature lie on the same side of the film. Neglect slight differences in length and radius of curvature of opposite sides of the rectangle, and suppose that the film is in equilibrium with an excess of pressure p of the fluid on one side of the film over that on the other side. Let the film, pushed forward by the excess pressure p, undergo a small displacement δx cm. along the outward normal through O. As a result of this displacement,

---

* The two principal sections at a point are such that the curves of section have maximum and minimum radius of curvature.

let the sides of the rectangle be increased from δl_1 to $\delta l_1(1 + \alpha)$ and from δl_2 to $\delta l_2(1 + \beta)$ respectively, where α and β are small compared with unity. Thus the area of the rectangle is increased, and as this involves stretching of the film, work is done against the surface tension. Since the system was initially in equilibrium, it can be assumed that the work done by the excess pressure in pushing back the film is equal to the work done in stretching it. After the stretching, the new area of the element of film is

$$\delta l_1(1 + \alpha)\,\delta l_2(1 + \beta) = \delta l_1\,\delta l_2(1 + \alpha + \beta + \alpha\beta).$$

If we neglect the small term $\alpha\beta$, we have $\delta l_1\,\delta l_2(1 + \alpha + \beta)$. The initial area was $\delta l_1\,\delta l_2$, so that the increase in area is $\delta l_1\,\delta l_2(\alpha + \beta)$

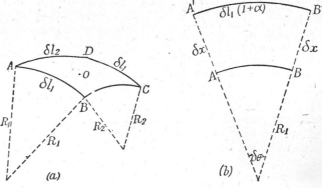

Fig. 1

sq. cm. Referring to fig. 1, we see that $\delta l_1(1 + \alpha) = (R_1 + \delta x)\,\delta\theta$ and also $\delta l_1 = R_1\,\delta\theta$, so that $\alpha = \delta x/R_1$. Similarly, $\beta = \delta x/R_2$. Hence the increase in area is

$$\delta x\,\delta l_1\,\delta l_2\left(\frac{1}{R_1} + \frac{1}{R_2}\right)\ \text{sq. cm.}$$

If we assume, as in elementary work, that the surface tension T may also be defined as the work required to stretch a surface film by one square centimetre under isothermal conditions,* and if we further assume that the stretching in the present case is isothermal, the work required to stretch the patch of film by the above amount is

$$T\,\delta x\,\delta l_1\,\delta l_2\left(\frac{1}{R_1} + \frac{1}{R_2}\right)\ \text{ergs.}$$

Now consider the work done by the excess pressure p in pushing forward the elementary area of film through δx cm. The initial thrust

* Strictly speaking, this definition requires correction by the theory of § 36, pp. 156, 157.

on the patch of film is the excess pressure multiplied by the area, i.e.
$p\,\delta l_1\,\delta l_2$ sq. cm. The final thrust is $p\,\delta l_1\,\delta l_2(1 + \alpha + \beta)$. As α and β
are small compared with unity, we may assume the thrust to be constant
and equal to $p\,\delta l_1\,\delta l_2$. When a force of this magnitude advances its
point of application through δx cm., the work done is $p\,\delta x\,\delta l_1\,\delta l_2$ ergs.
Equating the two quantities of work and cancelling factors, we have

$$p = T\left(\frac{1}{R_1} + \frac{1}{R_2}\right). \quad \cdots \cdots \quad (1)$$

If the centres of curvature of the sides AB and BC are on opposite
sides of the film and if $R_1 < R_2$, the equation has the form

$$p = T\left(\frac{1}{R_1} - \frac{1}{R_2}\right). \quad \cdots \cdots \quad (2)$$

2. Shape of an Interfacial Boundary.

Consider a system of two incompressible liquids in contact and in
equilibrium, the lighter one resting on the heavier. Fig. 2 represents
a principal section of such a system;
the curve AB is a section of the surface
of contact. It is required to find an
equation for the curve AB.

Take a point O far below the interface as origin of co-ordinates, and axes
Ox, Oy. Let the interface undergo an
elementary virtual displacement in which
each element of surface moves from its
initial position to its final position along
a normal to itself, the displacement at
a point P being δn cm. Let the element
of surface have sides of length δl_1 and
δl_2 cm., and let $\delta l_1 \times \delta l_2 = \delta S$. Let the
excess pressure on the concave side be
p dynes per sq. cm. Then, as in the

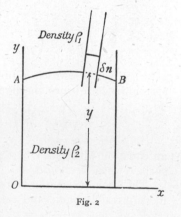

Fig. 2

last theorem, this pressure gives rise to a force $p\,\delta S$ dynes, which
does work on the element of interface amounting to $p\,\delta S\,\delta n = p\,\delta V$
ergs, where $\delta V = \delta S\,\delta n$ is an element of volume.

By the last theorem this work is equal to $T\left(\dfrac{1}{R_1} + \dfrac{1}{R_2}\right)\delta V$ ergs,

where R_1 and R_2 are the principal radii of curvature at P. The sum
of all such quantities taken over the whole of the interface is

$$\iiint T\left(\frac{1}{R_1} + \frac{1}{R_2}\right)dV \text{ ergs.}$$

As a result of the displacement, the system gains or loses potential energy. The gain of energy may be calculated as follows. Let the initial vertical co-ordinate of the typical element of surface just considered be y. Since the liquids are incompressible, the liquid removed from any one region is replaced by an equal volume from another. The displacement of the surface, δn, has the following effective result so far as gravitational potential energy is concerned. An element of volume δV of mass $\rho_1 \delta V$, with vertical co-ordinate y, is removed from its initial position and replaced by an element of volume δV of mass $\rho_2 \delta V$ with the same co-ordinate y. This particular element of volume gains potential energy $(\rho_2 - \rho_1) gy \, \delta V$ ergs, and the total gain of energy is

$$\iiint (\rho_2 - \rho_1) gy \, dV \text{ ergs,}$$

the integration being taken over the whole of the interface. Since the system is initially in equilibrium, the work done by the hydrostatic pressure is equal to the gain in potential energy. Hence

$$\iiint T \left(\frac{1}{R_1} + \frac{1}{R_2} \right) dV = \iiint (\rho_2 - \rho_1) gy \, dV;$$

that is,

$$\iiint \left\{ T \left(\frac{1}{R_1} + \frac{1}{R_2} \right) - (\rho_2 - \rho_1) gy \right\} dV = 0.$$

Now $\iiint dV$, which represents the total volume change of the system, is zero, since the liquids are incompressible; hence

$$T \left(\frac{1}{R_1} + \frac{1}{R_2} \right) - (\rho_2 - \rho_1) gy = \text{a constant,} \quad . \quad . \quad (3)$$

an equation which may be regarded as the differential equation of the surface whose section is AB.

The above reasoning holds in the case when one of the media is an incompressible liquid and the other a gas, for $\iiint dV$ will still be zero.

If we put $\rho_2 - \rho_1 = \rho$, we obtain equation (3) in a convenient form,

$$T \left(\frac{1}{R_1} + \frac{1}{R_2} \right) - g\rho y = \text{constant.} \quad . \quad . \quad . \quad (4)$$

Equation (4) is of great importance and forms the basis of many of the particular problems elucidated in the following sections.

3. Rise of a Liquid along the Side of an Inclined Plane Plate.

Let AB represent a transverse section of one face of a plane plate dipping into a liquid (fig. 3). The plate may be supposed to be of infinite length in the direction perpendicular to the plane of the figure. *BEC* represents a principal section of the free surface of the liquid. Assume that it is horizontal at a great distance from the plate. Let the angle of contact of the liquid with the plate be ψ, that is, let *DB*, the tangent to the curve *BEC* at the point of contact *B*, make an angle ψ with the plate. If we take an origin *O* below the surface, as in the last section, the equation of the curve *BEC* is

$$T\left(\frac{1}{R_1} + \frac{1}{R_2}\right) - g\rho y = \text{constant}, \quad \ldots \quad (5)$$

where $\rho = \rho_2 - \rho_1$ and the other symbols have their previous meanings. In the present problem all sections of the surface parallel to the plane

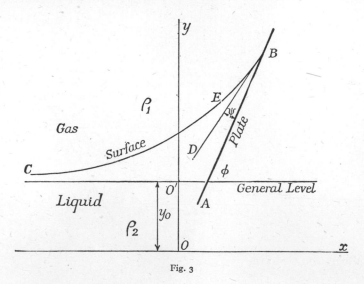

Fig. 3

of the figure are similar in shape, that is, the surface is cylindrical and one radius of curvature is infinite. Equation (5) therefore becomes

$$\frac{T}{R} = g\rho y + \text{constant}. \quad \ldots \quad \ldots \quad (6)$$

If we take O', in the "general level" of the free surface at a great distance from the plate, as origin, the constant becomes zero, for when $y = 0$ the free surface is plane and R is infinite.

Consider the tangents *PL*, *QM* and normals *PS*, *QS* drawn at *P* and *Q*, two points on the curve, an elementary distance δs apart (fig. 4). Let the ordinate of *P* be y. Let the tangents make angles θ and $\theta + \delta\theta$ with the axis $O'x$. The normals meet at *S*, the centre of curvature. The angle $PSQ = \delta\theta$; $PS = QS = R$, and $PQ = \delta s$. From the figure $R\,\delta\theta = \delta s$; hence $1/R = \delta\theta/\delta s$ and

$$\frac{T}{R} = T\,\frac{\delta\theta}{\delta s} = g\rho y.$$

Now

$$\frac{\delta y}{\delta s} = \sin\theta, \quad\text{and}\quad \frac{1}{\delta s} = \frac{\sin\theta}{\delta y};$$

hence

$$T\,\frac{\delta\theta}{\delta s}\,\delta y = T\sin\theta\,\delta\theta = g\rho y\,\delta y.$$

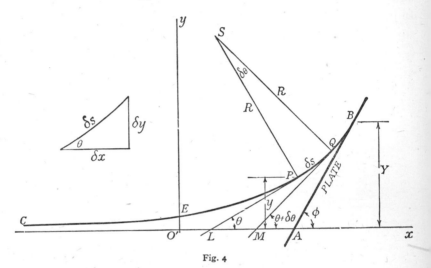

Fig. 4

On integration we have

$$-T\cos\theta = \tfrac{1}{2}g\rho y^2 + \text{constant,}$$

that is,

$$g\rho y^2 + 2T\cos\theta = \text{constant.}$$

When $y = 0$, $\theta = 0$, $\cos\theta = 1$, hence the constant is $2T$. That is,

$$g\rho y^2 = 2T(1 - \cos\theta). \quad \cdot \ \cdot \ \cdot \ \cdot \ \cdot \quad (7)$$

This is the equation of the curve BEC.

Comments.

(1) If the plate makes an angle φ with the horizontal, a tangent to the curve at B, where the liquid meets the plate, makes an angle $(\varphi - \psi)$ with the horizontal (ψ is the angle of contact), and the vertical co-ordinate Y of B is given by

$$g\rho Y^2 = 2T\{1 - \cos(\varphi - \psi)\}. \quad \cdot \ \cdot \ \cdot \ \cdot \ \cdot \ \cdot \quad (8)$$

(2) (a) If the plate is vertical, $\varphi = 90°$, and

$$g\rho Y^2 = 2T(1 - \sin\psi). \quad \ldots \ldots \ldots \quad (9)$$

(b) If $\psi = 0$ in addition,

$$g\rho Y^2 = 2T. \quad \ldots \ldots \ldots \ldots \quad (10)$$

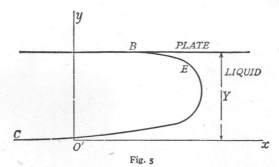

Fig. 5

(3) The general reasoning still holds if the plate is horizontal and the liquid is attached to the lower face; in fig. 5, for example, at a point of contact B we have $\varphi = 180°$. Hence

$$g\rho Y^2 = 2T(1 + \cos\psi).$$

When

$$\psi = 0, \quad g\rho Y^2 = 4T.$$

(4) The expression $T/g\rho$ is often called Laplace's constant * and is expressed by a^2.

(5) When a " sessile " drop or bubble, resting on or pendent from a horizontal plate, is large (fig. 6), a central portion of its surface, $HKYZ$, does not depart appreciably from the cylindrical shape, and the equation to

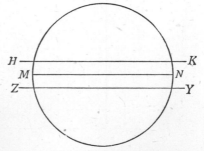

Fig. 6.—Plan of large sessile drop or bubble

a profile curve for a central section such as MN is given approximately by equation (8), with $\varphi = 180°$.

4. Rise of a Liquid between Two Vertical Plane Plates making a Small Angle with one another.

Fig. 7 shows the plates with the liquid between them. Let the angle of contact of the liquid with the plates be zero, and let the angle between the plates be α radians. YPQ and YSR represent the curves of contact of the upper surface of the liquid with the plates. Take an origin O, and horizontal and vertical axes Ox, Oy.

Consider the equilibrium of that element of liquid which is bounded by the vertical planes $PADS$ and $QBCR$, where $OA = OD = x$,

* Among the authors who use $T/g\rho = a^2$ are Ferguson, Rayleigh, and Dorsey. Among those who prefer $2T/g\rho = a^2$ are Sugden, Adam, and Lenard.

$PA = SD = y$, and $AB = \delta x$. The downward force on it, namely, its weight, is equal and opposite to the resultant force vertically upwards, due to surface tension. Assume that the upward force on the element due to displaced air is allowed for by using $\rho = \rho_2 - \rho_1$ as the density. The weight of the element = volume × density × g dynes = $y \,.\, AD \,.\, AB\rho g$ dynes, where $\rho = \rho_2 - \rho_1$. Now $PS = AD = xa$, approximately, since a is small. Hence the weight of the element is $yxa\,\delta x \,.\, \rho g$ dynes.

The forces due to surface tension are applied to the upper edges PS, SR, QR and PQ. Let PM, a tangent to the curve PQ at P, make

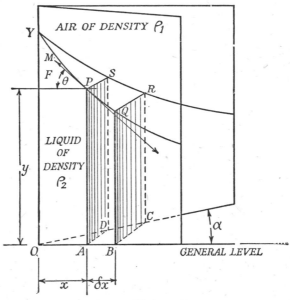

Fig. 7

an angle θ with the horizontal. There is a force $T \times PS$ acting on PS in a direction parallel to PM, due to the adjacent liquid. Resolved vertically upwards, the force becomes $Txa \sin\theta$. This force can be regarded as a function of x, say $f(x)$. Acting on QR there is a corresponding force downwards to the right, due to the adjacent liquid, which when resolved vertically is the same function of $x + \delta x$ as $Txa \sin\theta$ is of x. Since, by Taylor's theorem, any function of $x + \delta x$ can be written $f(x + \delta x) = f(x) + f'(x)\,\delta x$ plus small terms, the difference $f(x + \delta x) - f(x) = f'(x)\,\delta x$, very nearly. Since $f(x) = Tax \sin\theta$,

$$f'(x)\,\delta x = Ta\frac{d(x \sin\theta)}{dx}\,\delta x \text{ dynes.}$$

This difference gives us the resultant of the forces of surface tension on PS and QR resolved vertically downwards.

The two equal forces due to surface tension acting on PQ and SR act along normals to PQ and SR respectively, that is, in directions making angles θ with the vertical. Let $PQ = \delta s$. Each force has the value $T\,\delta s$ along the normal, i.e. $T\,\delta s \cos\theta$ vertically. Their resultant, resolved vertically upwards, is

$$2T\,\delta s \cos\theta = 2T\,\delta x.$$

Thus the four forces of surface tension give rise to a resultant upward force, which when equated to the weight gives

$$yx a\rho g\,\delta x = 2T\,\delta x - Ta\,\frac{d(x\sin\theta)}{dx}\,\delta x,$$

that is,

$$xy = \frac{2T}{a\rho g} - \frac{T}{\rho g}\frac{d(x\sin\theta)}{dx}. \qquad \ldots \ldots \text{(11)}$$

This may be regarded as the equation of the curve YPQ. As a first approximation the second term on the right may be neglected, giving

$$xy = \frac{2T}{a\rho g} = \text{a constant} = k, \text{ say.} \qquad \ldots \ldots \text{(12)}$$

The curve YPQ is approximately a rectangular hyperbola. Neglect of the second term on the right is equivalent to the assumption that the forces due to surface tension acting on PS and QR are equal and opposite.

Ferguson and Vogel * have shown how to obtain a more exact approximation to the shape of the curve YPQ, and have used it to devise an improvement in Grünmach's method of measuring surface tension. Their procedure is as follows:

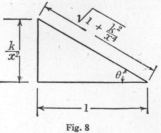

Fig. 8

Since $xy = k$, approximately,

$$y = \frac{k}{x}, \text{ approximately.}$$

Hence

$$\tan\theta = -\frac{dy}{dx} = \frac{k}{x^2}, \text{ approximately.}$$

From figs. 7 and 8 we see that $\sin\theta$ is positive. Hence

$$\sin\theta = \frac{k}{\sqrt{k^2 + x^4}} \quad \text{and} \quad x\sin\theta = \frac{kx}{\sqrt{k^2 + x^4}}.$$

* Ferguson and Vogel, *Proc. Phys. Soc.*, Vol. 38, p. 193 (1926).

On differentiating and then putting $k = xy$, we find that

$$\frac{d}{dx}(x \sin \theta) = \frac{y(y^2 - x^2)}{(y^2 + x^2)^{\frac{3}{2}}}.$$

Substitute in equation (11). This gives

$$xy = \frac{2T}{\alpha \rho g} - \frac{Ty(y^2 - x^2)}{\rho g(y^2 + x^2)^{\frac{3}{2}}}.$$

Put $T/\rho g = a^2$ in the first term on the right and $T = \frac{1}{2}g\rho\alpha xy$ in the small second term. This gives

$$xy = \frac{2a^2}{\alpha} - \frac{\alpha xy^2(y^2 - x^2)}{2(y^2 + x^2)^{\frac{3}{2}}}.$$

By choosing new variables

$$X = \frac{xy^2(y^2 - x^2)}{(y^2 + x^2)^{\frac{3}{2}}}, \quad Y = xy,$$

we can reduce the equation to the linear form

$$Y + \frac{\alpha X}{2} = \frac{2a^2}{\alpha}, \quad \ldots \ldots \ldots \quad (13)$$

whose intercept on the Y-axis is $2a^2/\alpha$.

5. Rise of a Liquid between Parallel Vertical Plates.

Let fig. 9 represent a vertical section of a system in which a liquid rises between two vertical parallel plates. The angle of contact is not assumed to be zero. The profile curve $ACPB$ is the same in all parallel sections perpendicular to the plates, and the surface of the liquid is cylindrical, i.e. one radius of curvature is infinite. Take an origin O in the general level of the external liquid, midway between the plates, and take horizontal and vertical axes Ox, Oy. The theory of § 3, p. 102, applies here; if y is the vertical co-ordinate of any point P on the profile curve, equation (5) holds, giving

$$T\left(\frac{1}{R_1} + \frac{1}{R_2}\right) - g\rho y = \text{constant, where } \rho = \rho_2 - \rho_1.$$

As in § 3, one radius is infinite and the origin lies in the general level, so that the equation becomes

$$\frac{T}{R} = g\rho y.$$

From fig. 4, p. 104, we have $R\,\delta\theta = \delta s$. Further, $\delta y = \delta s \sin \theta$, hence

$$T\,\delta y/R = T \sin \theta\,\delta\theta = g\rho y\,\delta y.$$

Integrating, we have

$$-T \cos \theta = \frac{1}{2}g\rho y^2 + \text{constant.}$$

At C let $y = y_0$ and $\theta = 0$; then

$$-T = \tfrac{1}{2}g\rho y_0^2 + \text{constant.}$$

By subtraction,

$$2T(1 - \cos\theta) = g\rho(y^2 - y_0^2), \quad \cdots \quad (14)$$

which can be written

$$y^2 = \frac{2T}{g\rho}(B - \cos\theta), \quad \cdots \cdots \quad (15)$$

where

$$B = 1 + \frac{g\rho y_0^2}{2T}.$$

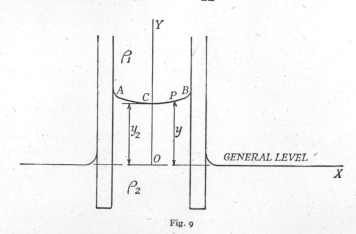

Fig. 9

The profile curve $ACPB$ may either be concave or convex upwards or it may have a point of inflection, according as the liquid makes an acute angle of contact with both plates, with neither, or with one plate only. Thus when the constant B of equation (15) exceeds $+1$, y^2 is positive, and y may be either positive or negative, but not zero. The equation then gives the profile curve when the liquid makes an acute angle of contact with both or neither of the plates.

Equation (15) is the differential equation of the profile curve. A rigorous integration is difficult, but the co-ordinates of various points can be obtained by a method of successive approximation, of which a sketch is now given.

At C (fig. 10), the radius of curvature is given by equation (6), that is, $T/R_0 = g\rho y_0$ or $R_0 = T/g\rho y_0$.

Near C, it may be assumed that an elementary portion CD of the profile curve is circular and of radius R_0. Let K be the centre of this circle; then $KC = KD$. Let CKD be a small angle 2ϕ.

In fig. 10,

$$CE = FD = CD \cos \phi = 2R_0 \phi \cos \phi,$$
$$DE = CD \sin \phi = 2R_0 \phi \sin \phi.$$

The ordinate of D is $y_0 + DE$
$$= y_0 + 2R_0 \phi \sin \phi.$$

If $y = y_0 + 2R_0 \phi \sin \phi$ is now substituted in the equation $T/R = g\rho y$, a value of $R = R_1$, say, is obtained, which may be taken as the radius of curvature of the next element DH of the profile curve. Thus

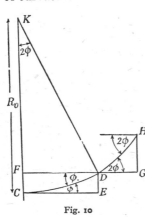

Fig. 10

$$R_1 = \frac{T}{g\rho(y_0 + 2R_0 \phi \sin \phi)}.$$

By an argument similar to the one used in obtaining DE and CE, the increments DG and GH may now be found:

$$DG = 2R_1 \phi \cos 2\phi \quad \text{and} \quad GH = 2R_1 \phi \sin 2\phi.$$

To obtain the relation between the ordinates of the points of contact, we proceed as follows. Let the liquid make angles of contact Q_1, Q_2 with the plates on the left and right respectively, and let the ordinates of the points of contact be Y_1 and Y_2 respectively.

By equation (14),

$$g\rho(Y_1^2 - y_0^2) = 2T(1 - \cos\theta_1) = 2T(1 - \sin Q_1),$$
$$g\rho(Y_2^2 - y_0^2) = 2T(1 - \cos\theta_2) = 2T(1 - \sin Q_2).$$

By subtraction we obtain

$$g\rho(Y_1^2 - Y_2^2) = 2T(\sin Q_2 - \sin Q_1), \quad . \quad . \quad . \quad (16)$$

which is the required relation.

6. Rise of a Liquid between Two Parallel Vertical Plates close together.

In determining the height of the lowest point of the surface, let us assume the plates (fig. 11) to be of the same material, the angle of contact to be zero, and the distance between the plates to be X cm., where X is very much less than a, that is, than $\sqrt{T/g\rho}$. As the plates are close together and the length of the profile curve is small, it may be assumed to be semicircular. The elevated portion of the liquid is in equilibrium. Consider a column of it, 1 cm. thick, measured at right angles to the plane of fig. 11. The downward force on it, i.e. its weight, is equal to the sum of the two upward forces due to surface tension. The area between the sections of the meniscus and the tangent plane at its lowest point is equal to the area of a rectangle minus the area of a semicircle, that is, its area is $X^2/2 - \pi X^2/8$.

Hence the volume of the slice of unit thickness is

$$Xy_0 + \frac{X^2}{2} - \frac{\pi X^2}{8}.$$

The equation of equilibrium is

Weight of slice of unit
thickness $= 2T$,

or

$$Xy_0 g\rho + g\rho X^2 \left(\frac{1}{2} - \frac{\pi}{8}\right) = 2T;$$

hence

$$y_0 = \frac{2T}{X\rho g} - 0{\cdot}107\,X, \quad \ldots \ldots \quad (17)$$

which is the required height. It is left to the student to calculate y_0 when the angle of contact is not zero.

7. Horizontal Force on One Side of a Vertical Plane Plate Dipping in a Liquid.

Take an origin O in the general level (fig. 12). Let the liquid under consideration extend indefinitely to the left of the figure. Take any point K on the left-hand face of the plate; let OK be y. Consider the horizontal force on an elementary area of the plate, whose section is $KQ = \delta y$, and whose length, measured at right angles to the plane of the paper, is 1 cm. Since K is y cm. above O, the pressure there is the atmospheric pressure P minus the quantity $g\rho y$; accordingly, the force on KQ towards the right is $(P - g\rho y)\,\delta y$ dynes. On the whole surface up to A, where $OA = Y$, the whole force acting horizontally to the right is

$$\int_0^Y (P - g\rho y)\,dy = PY - \tfrac{1}{2}g\rho Y^2 \text{ dynes.}$$

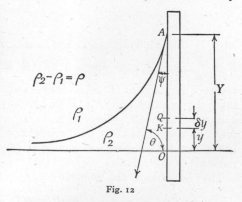

Fig. 12

Further, at the top there is a force $T \sin \psi$ acting horizontally to the left, where ψ is the angle of contact. The resultant force to the left is $T \sin \psi - PY + \frac{1}{2} g \rho Y^2$ dynes.

Now by equation (9), p. 105,

$$g\rho Y^2 = 2T(1 - \sin \psi).$$

Hence the net force to the left is $T - PY$, provided we neglect any forces acting on the plate above A.

8. Horizontal Force on One of Two Parallel Vertical Plates Dipping in a Liquid.

In fig. 13 let the point K be y cm. above the general level. If the atmospheric pressure is P, the pressure at K is $P - g\rho y$. Consider

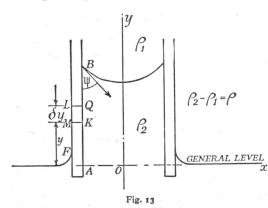

Fig. 13

the forces on a strip of plate of height δy between two horizontal planes LQ and MK, per centimetre length measured at right angles to the plane of the figure. On LM there is a force $P \delta y$ dynes to the right. On QK there is a force $(P - g\rho y)\delta y$ dynes to the left. The net force is therefore $g\rho y\, \delta y$ dynes to the right. The total force of this kind acting on the plate to the right up to the level of B is $\int_0^Y g\rho y\, dy$ dynes, where $Y = AB$, that is, $\frac{1}{2} g \rho Y^2$ dynes. If the angle of contact at B is ψ, there is another force $T \sin \psi$ acting to the right, making $\frac{1}{2} g\rho Y^2 + T \sin \psi$ altogether. Outside the plate and acting to the left, there is a force which by the theory of the previous section is $T - PZ$, where Z is the height of the point F. If, as usually happens, Z is negligible compared with Y, this force reduces to T. Hence, if we take into consideration forces both inside and outside, the resultant force acting to the right is

$$\frac{1}{2} g\rho Y^2 + T \sin \psi - T \text{ dynes.} \quad \ldots \quad (18)$$

9. Rise of a Liquid in a Vertical Circularly Cylindrical Tube. (Narrow Tube: Angle of Contact not Zero.)

Fig. 14 represents a central vertical section of a circularly cylindrical tube dipping into a liquid. The profile or meridional curve is represented by LMN. Let the angle of contact be ψ. In the present case of a narrow tube the profile curve is short in length and may be assumed to be nearly circular, that is, the surface may be assumed to be nearly spherical.*

Let $\rho = \rho_2 - \rho_1$. Let r and R be the radii of the tube and of the meniscus respectively, and let H be the height of M, the lowest point of the meniscus, above the general level. It is assumed that the same atmospheric pressure P exists above the liquid inside and outside the tube. Since the

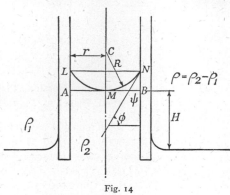

Fig. 14

elevated portion of the liquid is in equilibrium, its weight is equal to the upward force due to surface tension, acting around the circle whose section is LN. Hence

$$2\pi r T \cos\psi = \pi r^2 H \rho g + \text{weight of liquid lens between} \left.\begin{array}{c} \\ LMN \text{ and } AMB \end{array}\right\} \quad . \quad (19)$$

If the weight of the liquid lens is neglected, equation (19) reduces to

$$2\pi r T \cos\psi = \pi r^2 H \rho g,$$

whence

$$T = \frac{r H \rho g}{2 \cos\psi}.$$

When the volume of the liquid lens $LMNBA$ is not negligible, it is calculated by elementary mensuration and is found to be

$$V = \pi r^3 \{\sec\psi + \tfrac{2}{3} \tan^3\psi - \tfrac{2}{3} \sec^3\psi\},$$

expressed in terms of the angle of contact and the radius of the tube. In this case the equation of equilibrium is

$$2\pi r T \cos\psi = \pi r^2 H \rho g + \pi r^3 \rho g \{\sec\psi + \tfrac{2}{3} \tan^3\psi - \tfrac{2}{3} \sec^3\psi\},$$

* Rayleigh, *Collected Papers*, Vol. 6, p. 351.

which gives

$$T = \frac{rH\rho g}{2\cos\psi} + \frac{r^2\rho g}{2}\{\sec^2\psi + \tfrac{2}{3}\sec\psi\tan^3\psi - \tfrac{2}{3}\sec^4\psi\}.$$

When

$$\psi = 0, \ T = \frac{rH\rho g}{2} + \frac{r^2\rho g}{6}.$$

If we put $T/\rho g = a^2$, we may write this equation in the form

$$H = \frac{2a^2}{r} - \frac{r}{3}. \qquad \cdots \cdots \quad (20)$$

10. Rise of a Liquid in any Vertical Circularly Cylindrical Tube Dipping into an Open Vessel of Liquid (Angle of Contact not Zero).

Fig. 15 represents a central vertical section. The surface of the liquid is not assumed spherical, nor is the profile curve assumed circular. By symmetry, however, the surface must be a surface of revolution.

Equation of the Meridional Profile Curve.—Take an origin O at the point where the axis of the tube meets the general level. The vertical co-ordinate y of any point P is given by equation (4) of § 2, namely,

$$T\left(\frac{1}{R_1} + \frac{1}{R_2}\right) - g\rho y = \text{constant}, \qquad \cdots \quad (21)$$

where in this case neither R_1 nor R_2 is infinite. One of these principal radii is the radius of curvature of the meridional profile curve. Let it be R_1.

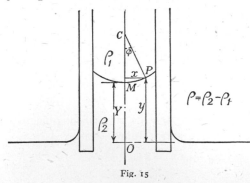

Fig. 15

The other principal radius R_2 is equal to PC, where PC is the normal at P, because of the symmetry about the axis OC. Thus $R_2 = PC = x/\sin\phi$, where $MCP = \phi$.

Further, if we note that at M, which is one of those points which in solid geometry are known as umbilics, the radii of curvature are equal, they may each be denoted by b, say, and if we put $OM = Y$, equation (21) becomes

$$\frac{2T}{b} - g\rho Y = \text{constant.} \qquad \cdots \cdots \quad (22)$$

Hence at any point P, by equations (21) and (22), we have

$$T\left(\frac{1}{R_1} + \frac{\sin\phi}{x}\right) - g\rho y = \frac{2T}{b} - g\rho Y. \quad \dots \quad (23)$$

Divide throughout by T/b and put $y - Y = z$; then

$$\frac{1}{R_1/b} + \frac{\sin\phi}{x/b} = 2 + \frac{z\rho g}{T/b}. \quad \dots \quad (24)$$

Write $T/g\rho = a^2$ and

$$\frac{b^2}{a^2} = \frac{b^2 g\rho}{T} = \beta. \quad \dots \quad (25)$$

Then

$$\frac{1}{R_1/b} + \frac{\sin\phi}{x/b} = 2 + \frac{\beta z}{b}. \quad \dots \quad (26)$$

If R_1 and $\sin\phi$ are expressed in terms of x and z, this equation takes the form of a differential equation of the second order, which has not yet been integrated by rigorous methods. However, Bashforth and Adams * devised a special method of obtaining numerical values of x/b and z/b corresponding to various values of ϕ from 0° to 180° and of β from $+0.1$ to $+100$. To use the important tables published by them, values of β and ϕ are chosen and then the tables give the corresponding values of x/b and z/b. The value of x/b fixes that of β, and vice versa.

11. Application to the Measurement of Surface Tension.

Sugden † has described what some authorities regard as the best form of the capillary rise method of obtaining surface tensions of liquids in the presence of their own vapours. He makes the substitution $2T/g\rho = a_1^2$. The theoretical part of the determination involves three cases, (1) $r/a_1 < 0.25$, (2) $0.25 < r/a_1 < 2.24$, (3) $r/a_1 > 6$. There is a hiatus between (2) and (3), referred to again on p. 117.

We begin by considering the second case.

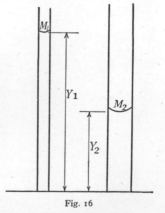

Fig. 16

Case (2), $0.25 < r/a_1 < 2.24$. The liquid is placed in a vertical U-tube (fig. 16) with one narrow limb and one wide limb, the radii being r_1 and r_2 respectively. Further, $0.25 < r/a_1 < 2.24$ for the

* *An Attempt to Test the Theory of Capillary Action* (Cambridge University Press, 1883).

† Sugden, *Journ. Chem. Soc.*, Vol. 119, p. 1483 (1921).

narrow limb. The limbs are regarded as two separate tubes standing in an open vessel. We see that equation (5) or (22) holds for each umbilic, that is,

$$\frac{2T}{b_1} - g\rho Y_1 = \text{constant,}$$

$$\frac{2T}{b_2} - g\rho Y_2 = \text{the same constant,}$$

where b_1, b_2 are the radii of curvature at the points M_1, M_2 and Y_1, Y_2 are the heights.

On subtraction,

$$2T\left(\frac{1}{b_1} - \frac{1}{b_2}\right) = g\rho(Y_1 - Y_2) = g\rho H, \text{ say.} \quad . \quad . \quad (27)$$

Tube (1) is narrow and tube (2) is wide. As a first approximation, put $b_1 = r_1$ and $b_2 = \infty$; then, if we use the measured value of H, which is easy to obtain, an approximate value of $2T/g\rho = a_1^2$ is calculated.

From the measured values of r_1 and r_2, r_1/a_1 and r_2/a_1 are calculated.

Assume that the angle of contact, ψ, of the liquid has been measured; ψ is 90° minus the ϕ of Bashforth and Adams, when the point P is on the line of contact of liquid and tubes, and their tables give the corresponding β.

Now, by the definition of a_1, equation (25) becomes

$$\frac{2b^2}{a_1^2} = \beta; \quad . \quad . \quad . \quad . \quad . \quad . \quad (28)$$

hence

$$\frac{1}{a_1}\sqrt{\frac{2}{\beta}} = \frac{1}{b},$$

and

$$\frac{r}{a_1}\sqrt{\frac{2}{\beta}} = \frac{r}{b}. \quad . \quad . \quad . \quad . \quad . \quad (29)$$

Sugden has constructed a table of corresponding values of β, r/b, and r/a_1 obtained from equation (29), for values of r/a_1 between 0·25 and 2·24.

Using the approximate values of r_1/a_1 and r_2/a_1 obtained above, Sugden's table gives values of r_1/b_1 and r_2/b_2, and hence $1/b_1$ and $1/b_2$ are calculated. Substitute these new values of $1/b_1$ and $1/b_2$ in equation (27) and calculate a more accurate value of $2T/g\rho = a_1^2$ and hence of r_1/a_1 and r_2/a_1. Again use Sugden's table to get more accurate values of r_1/b_1 and r_2/b_2, and again use equation (27) to get a new value of a_1^2 and a_1. After a few repetitions of this process the value of a_1

obtained becomes practically constant and an accurate value of T is derived from it. This is the value of the surface tension of the liquid in contact with its own vapour.

Case (1), $r/a_1 < 0.25$. Consider a narrow vertical capillary standing in an open vessel of liquid. The equation $2T(1/b_1 - 1/b_2) = g\rho H$ holds, but, since one tube is infinitely wide, we may neglect $1/b_2$ and write, for the narrow tube, $2T/b = g\rho H$, or

$$a_1{}^2 = \frac{2T}{g\rho} = bH. \qquad \cdots \cdots \quad (30)$$

This value of $a_1{}^2$ is substituted in Rayleigh's formula * for very narrow tubes, namely,

$$a_1{}^2 = r\left(H + \frac{r}{3} - 0.1288\,\frac{r^2}{H} + 0.1312\,\frac{r^3}{H^2}\right),$$

the proof of which is too long to give here. Then, by equation (30),

$$\frac{b}{r} = 1 + \frac{r}{3H} - 0.1288\,\frac{r^2}{H^2} + 0.1312\,\frac{r^3}{H^3},$$

from which b can be calculated. Substituting in (30), we obtain a numerical value of $a_1{}^2$, and hence find T.

Case (3), $r/a_1 > 6$. Consider a wide vertical tube standing in an open vessel of liquid. In this case Rayleigh's formula for very wide tubes is used, namely,

$$\frac{r}{a} - \log_e \frac{a}{H} = 0.8381 + 0.2798\,\frac{a}{r} + \frac{1}{2}\log_e\frac{r}{a}, \quad \cdots \quad (31)$$

where

$$a = \frac{a_1}{\sqrt{2}} = \sqrt{\frac{T}{g\rho}}.$$

The proof of (31) is also too long to reproduce here.

From experimental values of r and H, a and T can be calculated.

For tubes in which $2.24 < r/a < 6$ no exact formula giving the capillary rise seems to have been put forward, but Sugden gives an approximate graphical method of extrapolation for use in this case.

12. Measurement of the Surface Tension of a Liquid Available only in very Small Quantity.

If the volume of liquid available is only about two cubic millimetres, the method of Ferguson and Kennedy † is very suitable, especially as a knowledge of the density of the liquid is not required.

---

* Rayleigh, *Proc. Roy. Soc.*, A, Vol. 92, p. 184 (1915).

† Ferguson and Kennedy, *Proc. Phys. Soc.*, Vol. 44, p. 511 (1932).

Some of the liquid under test is placed in a clean glass capillary tube C, mounted vertically, with an open end downwards. This tube is connected at the top to a manometer system which enables the air pressure above the liquid to be varied and measured. The liquid is thus contained in the capillary as a short vertical column. The pressure above is adjusted until the lower end of the liquid, at the mouth of the tube, is plane and horizontal. Since the liquid is in equilibrium, the resultant upward force on it is equal to the resultant downward force. Assuming that the angle of contact is ψ, we get

$$2\pi r T \cos\psi = \text{Weight of liquid} + \text{Thrust on the top}$$

$$= g\rho\{\pi r^2 h_1 + \pi r^3/n\} + g\rho_3 h_2 \pi r^2,$$

where $\rho = \rho_2 - \rho_1$ is the excess density of the liquid under test, ρ_3 is the excess density of the manometer liquid measuring the pressure at the top, and h_1 and h_2 are the heights of the liquid and manometer columns respectively; the term $g\rho\pi r^3/n$ represents the weight of the plano-concave liquid lens under the meniscus,

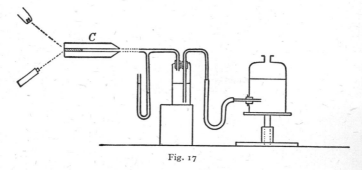

Fig. 17

n being a pure number whose value is 3 when ψ is zero and the meniscus is hemispherical. On reduction, we have

$$\frac{2T\cos\psi}{gr} = \rho\left(h_1 + \frac{r}{n}\right) + \rho_3 h_2. \quad \cdots \quad (32)$$

The tube C (fig. 17) with the liquid in it is next mounted in a horizontal position, and the air pressure is altered until the meniscus at the open end of C is exactly plane. The liquid is again in equilibrium, and the pressure on the plane end is atmospheric. The excess pressure on the other end is again given by the manometer and is $g\rho_3 h_3$, say, that is, there is a thrust $g\rho_3 h_3 \pi r^2$ acting to the left. There is also a force towards the right of value $2\pi r T \cos\psi$, due to surface tension. For equilibrium we must have

$$2\pi r T \cos\psi = g\rho_3 h_3 \pi r^2. \quad \cdots \cdots \quad (33)$$

This assumes that the capillary tube is so narrow that the gravitational forces causing a distortion of the right-hand meniscus from the spherical shape are small compared with the forces due to surface tension. In other words, it is assumed that the distortion is negligible.

Comparing equations (32) and (33), we see that

$$\rho_3 h_3 = \rho\left(h_1 + \frac{r}{n}\right) + \rho_3 h_2. \quad \cdots \cdots \quad (34)$$

Having found, by experiment, that the two sides of this equation are equal, we need only use equation (33) to get

$$T = \frac{g\rho_3 h_3 r}{2\cos\psi}. \qquad \dots \dots \dots \quad (35)$$

Ferguson and Kennedy show by experiments with liquids for which $\psi = 0$ that equation (34) is satisfied by tubes for which $r < 0.05$ cm. They have also used the method to determine interfacial surface tensions.

13. Pendent Drop at the End of a Tube.

Fig. 18 shows a pendent drop of liquid in equilibrium at the lower end of an open vertical tube. Let there be a column of liquid in the tube above the drop. Let its total height above the bottom of the meniscus be H. This height is usually so great that the effect of the curvature of the meniscus at the top on the pressure at any point in the drop is negligible. Here we shall assume that this is the case.

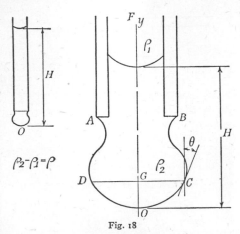

Fig. 18

Consider the equilibrium, as regards vertical forces, of the portion of liquid whose meridional section by a central vertical plane is $CODG$. It is subject to the following forces. Vertically downwards there are the weight mg and a force due to hydrostatic pressure on the plane DC, namely,

$$\pi GC^2\{P + g\rho(H - OG)\},$$

where P is the atmospheric pressure. Vertically upwards there are the forces $\pi GC^2 P$ due to atmospheric pressure below the drop and $2\pi TGC\cos\theta$ due to surface tension. If we restrict the discussion to cases in which DC is not much above O, we may assume that the profile curve is parabolic and has the equation $y = kx^2$. If the co-ordinates of C are $(x, y,)$ i.e. if $GC = x$, $OG = y$, then the mass of $CODG$, regarded as the sum of the masses of elementary horizontal slices, is

$$\int_0^y \rho\pi x^2\, dy = \int_0^y \frac{\rho\pi y}{k}\, dy = \frac{\rho\pi y^2}{2k},$$

and its effective weight is $\pi\rho g y^2 / 2k$, where $\rho = \rho_2 - \rho_1$.

The equation representing the equilibrium of $CODG$, on which the total downward forces are equal to the total upward forces, is

$$\frac{\pi \rho g y^2}{2k} + \pi x^2 \rho g(H - y) = 2\pi T x \cos \theta. \quad \ldots \quad (36)$$

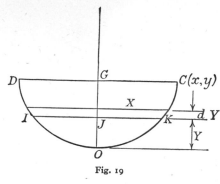

Fig. 19

Next, consider the equilibrium, with respect to horizontal forces, of that half of $CODG$ which is convex towards the reader. There is a horizontal force equal to $T \times$ length of arc COD away from the reader. Another horizontal force $T \sin \theta$ per cm. length acts normally to the circumference of the circle whose diameter is DC. This amounts to a resultant $T \times DC \sin \theta = 2xT \sin \theta$ towards the reader. The hydrostatic thrust of the other half of the bottom of the drop, acting towards the reader, is calculated as follows (fig. 19):

Thrust on an elementary strip IJK

     = pressure at $J \times$ area of strip

     = (pressure at O — pressure due to OJ) $\times$ area of strip

     = $g\rho(H - Y)2XdY$.

Hence total thrust on section $CGDO = \int_0^y 2g\rho(H - Y)XdY$.

If we put $Y = kX^2$, the integral becomes

$$\int_0^x 2g\rho(H - kX^2)X \, 2kX \, dX$$

$$= 4g\rho k\left(\frac{Hx^3}{3} - \frac{kx^5}{5}\right),$$

and if we put $y = kx^2$, this becomes $4g\rho\left(\dfrac{Hxy}{3} - \dfrac{xy^2}{5}\right)$ dynes towards the reader.

Let the length of the arc COD be l. The horizontal forces on the front half of $CODG$ balance. Hence

$$Tl = 2xT \sin \theta + 4g\rho\frac{Hxy}{3} - 4g\rho\frac{xy^2}{5}. \quad \ldots \quad (37)$$

On eliminating H from equations (36) and (37), we find that

$$T = \frac{2g\rho xy^2}{15\left\{2x\sin\theta + \dfrac{8y\cos\theta}{3} - l\right\}} . \quad \ldots \quad (38)$$

Ferguson has applied this formula to the measurement of T. The method is of particular use in measuring T for molten metals.

14. Sentis's Method of Measuring the Surface Tension of a Liquid.

A piece of clean glass capillary tubing (fig. 20) is drawn out to a fine jet and dipped into a liquid. The latter is sucked up inside the tube and is then allowed to fall gently. A drop forms around the end and rises a little way up the outside of the tube. Inside, the level is at A. While the drop is in equilibrium its radius R in a certain horizontal plane DC is measured by an optical method. A dish containing more of the same liquid is placed on the table of a spherometer underneath the drop, and is raised until the liquid just touches the bottom of the drop; the spherometer is then read. The liquid is now raised until the level of the liquid inside the tube is at A once more, and the spherometer is again read.

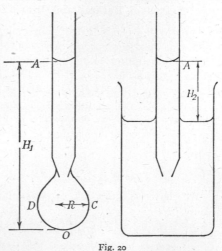

Fig. 20

The assumption is made that the portion of the drop below the plane DC is hemispherical. Then the upward forces on this portion are equal to the downward forces. Let P be the atmospheric pressure. Then

$$2\pi RT + P\pi R^2 = \frac{2\pi}{3}R^3\rho g + \pi R^2 \text{ (hydrostatic pressure at level } DC\text{),}$$

where $P\pi R^2$ is the effective upward force due to atmospheric pressure acting on the underside.

Substitution for the hydrostatic pressure gives

$$2\pi RT + P\pi R^2 = \frac{2\pi}{3}R^3\rho g + \pi R^2\left\{P + \rho g(H_1 - R) - \frac{2T}{r}\right\},$$

where r is the radius of curvature at the lowest point of the meniscus. That is,

$$2T = \frac{2}{3}R^2\rho g + g\rho R(H_1 - R) - \frac{2TR}{r}.$$

The second part of the experiment, for a liquid making zero angle of contact with the walls of the tube, gives

$$2\pi rT = g\rho\pi r^2 H_2,$$

$$\frac{T}{r} = \tfrac{1}{2}g\rho H_2,$$

approximately, if we assume that the meniscus is hemispherical and neglect the liquid lens immediately below the meniscus. Hence

$$2T = \{\tfrac{2}{3}R^2 + R(H_1 - R) - RH_2\}g\rho.$$

Putting $a^2 = \dfrac{T}{g\rho}$, we have

$$2a^2 = \tfrac{2}{3}R^2 + R(H_1 - R) - RH_2$$

or

$$2a^2 = R(H_1 - H_2) - \frac{R^2}{3}. \qquad \ldots \ldots \ldots \quad (39)$$

15. Drop Weight Method of Measuring the Surface Tension of a Liquid. Method of Harkins and Brown.

Instead of a pendent drop, consider a drop of liquid of volume V c.c. which has just ceased to make contact with the lower end of a rod or tube and is falling under gravity. Such a lower end is called a " tip ". Let its external radius be r cm. The shape of the drop is complicated, but its weight Mg may be regarded as a function of the surface tension T of the liquid, the radius r of the tip, the volume V of the drop, and other variables. Now the products Mg and Tr have the dimensions of a force. Hence, applying the method of dimensions, we have

$Mg = Tr \times$ a non-dimensional function of the various variables,
     $= Tr \times f_1(x, y, z, \ldots)$, say.

We may take the non-dimensional factor 2π out of the function, leaving

$$Mg = 2\pi Tr f_2(x, y, z, \ldots).$$

Since the function must be non-dimensional, we may try the special cases

$$Mg = 2\pi Tr f_3\left(\frac{r}{V^{\frac{1}{3}}}\right) \qquad \ldots \ldots \quad (40)$$

or

$$Mg = 2\pi Tr f_4\left(\frac{r}{a}\right), \text{ where } a^2 = \frac{T}{g\rho}, \text{ the capillary constant.} \quad (41)$$

The constant a has the dimensions of a length.

For any particular drop, $f_3(r/V^{\frac{1}{3}})$ and $f_4(r/a)$ will be numerically equal.

In their researches with water and benzene, Harkins and Brown [*] weighed the drops of a liquid falling from a given tubular tip. The density was known and hence $V^{\frac{1}{3}}$ was calculated, and thus, from a measured value of r, $r/V^{\frac{1}{3}}$ was obtained. By the capillary rise method, a value of T was obtained experimentally and a value of r/a was calculated. The value of $Mg/2\pi rT$, that is, of $f_3(r/V^{\frac{1}{3}}) = f_4(r/a)$,

[*] Harkins and Brown, *Journ. Amer. Chem. Soc.*, Vol. 1, p. 499 (1919).

was then computed. Thus, corresponding to each value of $r/V^{\frac{1}{3}}$, a value of $f_3(r/V^{\frac{1}{3}})$ was obtained, and corresponding to each value of r/a, a value of $f_4(r/a)$. Repetition of the experiment with the same liquid but other tips gave sets of such values. Curves connecting (1) $r/V^{\frac{1}{3}}$ and $f_3(r/V^{\frac{1}{3}})$ and (2) r/a and $f_4(r/a)$ were plotted. The actual determinations of Harkins and Brown dealt with values of r/a ranging from 0·025 to 2·60. The corresponding values of $f_4(r/a)$ did not remain constant, but varied from 0·924 to 0·5352. Precisely the same curves connecting r/a and $f_4(r/a)$ were obtained for four liquids of such varying densities and viscosities as water, benzene, carbon tetrachloride, and ethylene dibromide. That is, the curves were absolutely superposed on one another when plotted on the same sheet of paper. A similar result was found for the curves connecting $r/V^{\frac{1}{3}}$ and $f_3(r/V^{\frac{1}{3}})$. The curves were almost exactly those of a cubic equation.

The unchanging form of the function $f_4(r/a)$ for four dissimilar liquids justifies the belief that from such a curve as the one connecting $r/V^{\frac{1}{3}}$ and $f_3(r/V^{\frac{1}{3}})$, together with a simple drop experiment, the surface tension of any liquid can be found. All that is necessary to carry out a drop weight experiment with the liquid, measure M and r, and calculate $r/V^{\frac{1}{3}}$; in the tables of Harkins and Brown or on the appropriate graph determine $f_3(r/V^{\frac{1}{3}})$, which is equal to $f_4(r/a)$, and on the other graph find the corresponding value of r/a and calculate a and T.

Practical Details.—The apparatus is placed in a thermostat. If a drop were allowed to form and fall under gravity alone, it would take its full " drop time " of more than three minutes. A large part of it is therefore formed by suction on the part of the operator and it is then allowed to complete its growth and fall under gravity. Usually a thirty-drop run is taken, which requires about 30 min. A run involves the following operations: (1) the cleaning, mounting and levelling of the tip; (2) the adjustment of the liquid in the supply bottle to a suitable level; (3) the forcing of the liquid back through the capillary so that no drop is on the tip; (4) the placing of a clean weighing bottle around the tip; (5) the adjustment of the protecting box in the thermostat; (6) a pause for a period up to 40 min. to allow the liquid to reach the proper temperature; (7) the drawing over of a drop and keeping it a full size for 5 min. before falling, to saturate the receptacle for weighing with vapour; (8) the drawing over and weighing of 29 other drops; (9) the forcing back of the residual drop into the supply cup; (10) the removal of the apparatus from the thermostat; (11) the cooling of the weighing bottle with ice-water for half a minute; and (12) the stoppering and weighing. The radii of the tips vary from 0·09946 cm. to 1·0028 cm.

Comments.—(1) The equation $Mg = 2\pi rT$, sometimes called Tate's law, is seen to be incorrect.

(2) The ratio of the surface tensions of two liquids is not equal to the ratio of the weights of drops falling from a given tip, as is often assumed.

(3) Any departure from a circular shape of the edge of the tip introduces error. Hence a special method of grinding is used.

(4) The method can also be applied to interfacial surface tensions; indeed, Harkins and Brown consider the drop weight method to be the most accurate and convenient method of measuring interfacial tensions between liquids, as distinct from the commoner case of a liquid in contact with a gas. The capillary rise method is superior in the latter case, but for interfacial tensions it is inferior in that it involves some uncertainty about the angle of contact.

16. Force on a Horizontal Disc Pulling a Liquid Upwards.

Elementary Treatment.—Consider the extra forces on the underside of a counterpoised horizontal circular disc, which has made contact with a liquid below it and has been raised through a short distance

H cm. Assume that the liquid spreads to the edge of the disc, as it does in many cases. Contact will then be made at the edge of the disc. Fig. 21 represents the meridional curves bounding a central section of the liquid. Let the tangent to the curve at any point B make an angle θ with the horizontal, and let the tangent at S, a point of contact, make an angle θ_s with the horizontal. This is not assumed to be equal to the angle of contact with the disc. In addition to its weight, the following forces act upon the disc: (1) a downward atmospheric thrust of $P\pi R^2$ dynes; (2) a downward pull of $2\pi RT \sin \theta_s$ dynes due to surface tension round the edges; (3) an upward thrust due to liquid pressure on the under face, of value $(P - g\rho H)\pi R^2$ dynes, making a total force

$$F = 2\pi RT \sin \theta_s + g\rho H \pi R^2 \text{ vertically downwards.} \qquad (42)$$

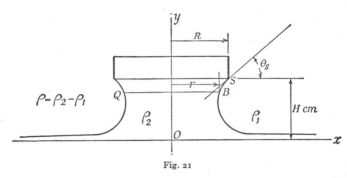

Fig. 21

When the disc is raised from the position $H = 0$, the angle θ_s has the initial value 180°, and decreases to zero, and then detachment takes place. The maximum value of H is that corresponding to $\theta_s = 0$. The maximum value of F occurs when H has a smaller value, and may be calculated approximately as follows.

From equation (42),

$$dF = 2\pi RT \cos \theta_s d\theta_s + g\rho \pi R^2 dH.$$

When R is large, the surface film is approximately cylindrical in the sense of § 3, p. 103, and the approximate equation (7) of § 3 may be used, namely,

$$g\rho H^2 = 2T(1 - \cos \theta_s). \quad \ldots \ldots \quad (43)$$

Differentiating this, we have

$$g\rho H \, dH = T \sin \theta_s d\theta_s.$$

Substitute for dH in the equation for dF. Then

$$dF = 2\pi RT \cos \theta_s d\theta_s + \frac{T \sin \theta_s \pi R^2 d\theta_s}{H}. \quad \ldots \quad (44)$$

Now $dF/d\theta_s = 0$ when F has a maximum value. Hence F has a maximum when $\tan\theta_s = -2H/R$, and this value of θ_s, which is small, is a root of the equation $\cos\frac{1}{2}\theta_s/\cos\theta_s = -2a/R$, obtained by substituting for H from equation (43) above and using the relation $T/g\rho = a^2$.

17. Liquid Pulled Upwards by a Horizontal Flat Ring.   Extra Downward Force on the Ring.

Fig. 22 represents a central vertical section of a horizontal flat ring pulling a liquid upwards. The two cross-sections of the material of the ring are rectangular. Let the tangents to the profile curves make an angle θ_s with the horizontal at A, B, C and D respectively.

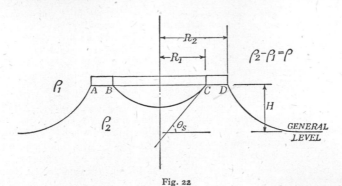

Fig. 22

As the surface tension acts around the circumference of each circle, the extra downward pull due to surface tension is $2\pi(R_1 + R_2)T\sin\theta_s$ dynes. The upward force due to liquid pressure on the lower face is $\pi(R_2^2 - R_1^2)(P - g\rho H)$ dynes, since this face is raised H cm. above the general external level at which the pressure P is atmospheric. The downward force on the upper face is $P\pi(R_2^2 - R_1^2)$ dynes. Thus the total extra downward force, in addition to the weight of the ring, is

$$F = 2\pi(R_1 + R_2)T\sin\theta_s + \pi g\rho H(R_2^2 - R_1^2) \text{ dynes.} \quad (45)$$

A special case occurs when $\theta_s = 90°$ and R_1 and R_2 are nearly equal. In this case

$$F = 4\pi RT, \text{ approximately,} \quad \cdots \quad (46)$$

where R is the mean radius.

The approximate expression $F = 4\pi RT$ is often used to measure the surface tension of liquids for which $\theta_s = 90°$. It gives $T = F/4\pi R$, F being taken to mean the maximum extra force required to detach the ring of rectangular ribbon or circular wire.

A more accurate expression * for the surface tension when the ring is made of material with a rectangular section, and when $\theta_s = 90°$, is

$$T = \frac{F}{4\pi R}\left[1 - \left\{2\cdot8284 + 0\cdot6095\sqrt{\frac{h}{R}}\right\}\frac{\delta}{\sqrt{hR}} + \left\{3 + 2\cdot585\sqrt{\frac{h}{R}} + 0\cdot371\frac{h}{R}\right\}\frac{\delta^2}{hR}\right],$$

where F is the maximum extra force, R is the mean radius of the ring, $h = \dfrac{F}{\pi R^2 \rho g}$, $\rho = \rho_2 - \rho_1$, and 2δ is the thickness of the ring, measured vertically.

18. Measurement of Surface Tension by the Ring Method.

The ring method is particularly useful in studying the progressive changes which occur in the surface tensions of various liquids with the passage of time.

(1) *Lecomte du Noüy's apparatus* † will now be described. A ring of platinum containing 10 per cent of iridium hangs from an inverted V frame of the same wire, to which it is "sweated". This system can be cleaned by heating. It is suspended from an arm A of a special horizontal torsion balance, called a *tensimeter*. The wire of the ring is of circular section, about 0·3 mm. in diameter, its mean circumference being about 4 cm. The torsion wire is steel piano wire of diameter 0·25 mm. The liquid lies in a clock glass. In the experiment a pointer F attached to the torsion wire rotates over a fixed circular scale as the ring is raised. The beam A is kept horizontal by lowering the support carrying the liquid. The maximum angular reading θ of the pointer is noted. The scale is calibrated in the absence of liquid by attaching known weights to the ring, so that θ corresponds to a certain maximum extra pull P. The ring is of such thin wire that du Noüy assumes that

$$P = 4\pi RT. \qquad \ldots \ldots \ldots (47)$$

The method has the following advantages: (1) Only a small quantity of liquid is required. (2) Each reading takes only about 20 sec. (3) The pull is measured to within 0·1 dyne. (4) Comparisons with standard liquids are quickly made.

(2) *The Ring Method of Harkins, Young and Cheng.*‡—Consider a metal ring of circular wire, suspended horizontally in a liquid. As the ring is gradually raised out of the liquid, the extra downward pull on it in addition to the weight passes through a maximum value. If the ring is made of thin wire, the maximum pull is given approximately by $P = 4\pi RT$, where R is the mean radius of the ring and T is the surface tension. More accurately, $FP = 4\pi RT$, where F is a non-dimensional factor. To avoid difficulties connected with the calculation of F, Harkins, Young and Cheng proceeded, in effect, as follows. Since $4\pi RT/P$ is a non-dimensional function of the variables connected with the experiment, they assumed that

$$\frac{4\pi RT}{P} = f_1\left(\frac{R}{r}\right) \qquad \ldots \ldots (48)$$

or

$$\frac{4\pi RT}{P} = f_2\left(\frac{R^3}{V}\right), \qquad \ldots \ldots (49)$$

where V is the volume of liquid held up by the maximum pull of the ring (which is equal to $P/\rho g$, where ρ is the density) and r is the radius of the wire.

---

* Verschaffelt, *Comm. Leiden, Suppl.* No. 42d, (1918).
† Lecomte du Noüy, *Journ. Gen. Physiol.*, Vol. 1, p. 521 (1919).
‡ Harkins, Young and Cheng, *Science*, Vol. 64, p. 333 (1926).

Using water, benzene and bromobenzene, liquids of known surface tension, they measured the maximum pull on three rings of different R and r but constant R/r. They plotted graphs in which the abscissæ were values of R^3/V and the ordinates were values of $4\pi RT/P$. The points for all three liquids were found to lie on one smooth curve. They inferred that if the same rings and other liquids had been used, the values of R^3/V and $4\pi RT'/P$ would have given points on the same curve.

To obtain an accurate value of the surface tension of another liquid, the procedure is as follows. Take a ring of the same metal and same R/r as one of those used by Harkins, Young and Cheng. Use it to measure the maximum pull as it is raised out of the given liquid. Calculate $R^3/V = R^3 g\rho/P$. Find the point on the graph of Harkins, Young and Cheng, for rings of the same R/r as that used, which has the abscissa R^3/V. Read off the value of the ordinate y, which is $4\pi RT/P$, and from it calculate T, the surface tension, which is given by $yP/4\pi R$.

The practical precautions employed may be summarized as follows:

(1) The whole apparatus is enclosed in a thermostat to keep the temperature constant.

(2) The surface of the liquid is swept by barriers to clean it before an experiment.

(3) The liquid is covered by an inverted glass funnel to reduce evaporation.

(4) The thermostat is supported independently of the rest of the apparatus, to prevent agitation of the liquid under test.

(5) The dish containing the liquid is made wide, to prevent errors due to the curvature of the meniscus.

19. Measurement of the Rate of Spreading of a Substance over the Surface of a Liquid.

The ring method has been applied to measure the rate of spreading of a substance over the surface of a liquid, by Cary and Rideal.* A crystal of a fatty acid, e.g. myristic acid, is brought into contact with the surface of an N/100 solution of hydrochloric acid in water. A film of solution of the myristic acid is formed, which spreads out from the crystal. More acid continues to dissolve and to spread until the strength of the solution forming the film reaches a certain value, when spreading ceases. The direct object of Cary and Rideal's experiment is to compare the surface tension at points on the circumference of a circle at whose centre the crystal touches the liquid, at various instants following contact, with that of the N/100 hydrochloric acid before contact, measured at points on the same circle. From the values of the surface tension thus obtained, the mean strength of the solution at points on the circumference of the circle at various instants can be calculated, and hence

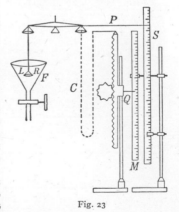

Fig. 23

the rate of spreading of the molecules of the myristic acid.

In the experiment the actual quantity measured is the force required to detach a horizontal platinum ring from the surface of the liquid, and this force is proportional to the surface tension (see equation (47)).

The apparatus is shown in fig. 23. The platinum ring LR is suspended from one arm of a balance, so as to hang just below the surface of the liquid, which

* Cary and Rideal, *Proc. Roy. Soc.*, A., Vol. 109, p. 306 (1925).

is contained in a funnel *F*. The ring is counterpoised by a light eye-glass chain *C*, so supported at one end that weights can be gradually added to that side of the balance. The weight contributed by this chain at any time is known from a previous calibration experiment in which the ring is replaced by weights, and in which a pointer *Q*, attached to the chain, moves over a calibrated scale *M*. The instant when the ring is on the point of being detached is registered by the movement of a long pointer *P* on an arbitrary scale *S*.

The experimental procedure is as follows. Some N/100 hydrochloric acid is poured into the carefully cleaned funnel, and the force required to detach the ring is measured. The ring is again dipped in the liquid. The end of a glass rod 1 mm. in diameter, coated with myristic acid, is then lowered into the surface of the liquid, and at the moment of contact a stop-watch is started. Before long the surface tension falls and the pointer *P* begins to move down. The time is noted. The chain is raised to bring the pointer *P* above the zero, but it soon falls past the zero again. The time and the force are noted as it passes through the zero. The chain is again raised and the process repeated. The temperature of the liquid is recorded.

Results.—Myristic acid and similar substances are found to spread in two stages.

Stage I. The surface is covered by a unimolecular " expanded " film* under zero compression, and if a crystal of constant circumference is used the time required for the spreading is proportional to the area of surface of the hydrochloric acid solution covered. From a crystal of myristic acid of circumference 2·51 mm., used by Cary and Rideal, at 25° C. it was found that $9·06 \times 10^{13}$ molecules left the crystal per second, i.e. $36·1 \times 10^{13}$ molecules per sec. per cm. length of crystal face.

Stage II. The expanded film of stage I becomes packed more closely with molecules of myristic acid, although it remains unimolecular, that is, one molecule thick. The pressure in the surface increases until there is equilibrium at the surface of the crystal between surface solution and recondensation, that is, until as many molecules return to the crystal per second as leave it.

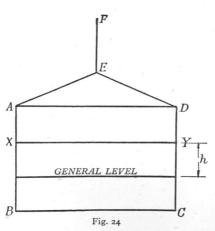

Fig. 24

20. Lenard's Frame Method for Surface Tension.†

In this method the experiment consists in the measurement of the maximum pull required to detach a frame *ABCDE* (fig. 24) with a cross wire *XY* from the surface of a liquid. In particular, as the frame is being dragged out, a film of liquid attached

*See p. 168.   † Lenard, *Ann. d. Phys.*, Vol. 74, p. 381 (1924).

to the wire XY along its whole length pulls downwards on the frame. It is the maximum value of this pull which is measured.

Regard XY as a horizontal cylinder of length l cm. and radius r cm. Fig. 25 shows a section of the cylinder and film below it. Let the angle of contact be zero, and let θ be the angle made with the horizontal by tangent planes to the liquid and wire at the points of contact K and M. In addition to the weight which the frame has, when XY is dry and just not touching the surface, the downward pull on the frame in the position shown in fig. 24, will be

$$P = 2Tl \sin \theta + hlbg\rho - W_1 + W_2, \quad \cdot \quad \cdot \quad (50)$$

where ρ is the density of the liquid, b is KM in the figure, h is the height of KM above the general level of the liquid, W_1 the weight of the portion KLM of fig. 25 considered as liquid, and W_2 the downward pull due to the removal of the upthrust on the immersed portions of XB and YC which occurs when XY is raised through a height h. The expression $hlbg\rho - W_1$ is the weight of the elevated liquid, which pulls downwards on XY. The shape of the surface films

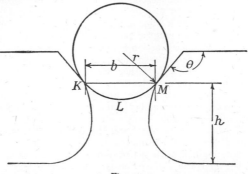

Fig. 25

is cylindrical in the sense of § 3, p. 103, and the theory of that section, and in particular equation (8), applies here. The original form of equation (8) is $g\rho Y^2 = 2T\{1 - \cos(\varphi - \psi)\}$. Now the left-hand side of fig. 25 is comparable with fig. 4. Here $Y = h$, $\psi = 0$, and $\varphi = 180° - \theta$. Hence we have

$$g\rho h^2 = 2T\{1 - \cos(180° - \theta)\} = 2T(1 + \cos\theta) \quad . \quad (51)$$

and

$$1 + \cos\theta = \frac{g\rho h^2}{2T} = \frac{h^2}{a_1{}^2}, \text{ say.}$$

Hence, in the general case,

$$\sin\theta = (1 - \cos^2\theta)^{\frac{1}{2}} = \left\{ 1 - \left(\frac{h^2}{a_1{}^2} - 1\right)^2 \right\}^{\frac{1}{2}}.$$

Also $b/2r = \sin\theta$ and $b = 2r \sin\theta$. If the two vertical wires of the frame each have a radius R cm., $W_2 = 2\pi R^2 g\rho h$. We may now write

$$P = 2Tl \sin\theta + 2hlrg\rho \sin\theta - W_1 + 2\pi R^2 g\rho h$$

$$= 2l(T + g\rho hr)\left\{ 1 - \left(\frac{h^2}{a_1{}^2} - 1\right)^2 \right\}^{\frac{1}{2}} - W_1 + 2\pi R^2 g\rho h. \quad (52)$$

The position of the first (and more important) of the two maxima of P is found as follows. Differentiate P with respect to h, treating W_1 as a constant, since the influence of W_1 on the position of the maximum is very slight. Substitute $h = a_1(1 + x)$, where x is a small quantity compared with unity. Neglect powers of x higher than the first. It is found that the first maximum occurs when

$$h = a_1\left\{1 + \frac{(lr + \pi R^2)}{2l(a_1 + 2r)}\right\}, \quad \ldots \ldots \quad (53)$$

and the corresponding maximum value of the pull * is

$$P_{\max} = 2lT + 2g\rho a_1(lr + \pi R^2)\left\{1 + \frac{(lr + \pi R^2)}{2l(a_1 + 2r)}\right\} - \tfrac{1}{2}\pi r^2 g\rho l. \quad (54)$$

In the actual experiment, two series of weighings are carried out. With the frame immersed to a definite depth in the liquid, one weighing is performed in the absence of a film, and one weighing with a film attached to the wire XY. The difference gives the quantity P. By repetition at various depths $P_{\max}$ is found. An important correction is applied for the vertical force due to surface tension of the film, which acts on the vertical wire AB at X and on DC at Y, when a film is attached to XY. Other effects, of small importance, near the points X and Y are taken into consideration. In experiments described by Lenard, the length XY varied from 3 to 5 cm., and XY was made of wire of various metals of diameters between 0·03 mm. and 0·1 mm. The frame $ABCDE$ was made of wire of diameter from 0·5 mm. to 0·6 mm. In an experiment with earth-nut oil at 21° C., when XY was made of iron wire, the uncorrected value of T was 3·78 mg./mm. and after correction 3·35 mg./mm. Lenard and his collaborators have improved the frame method until the results are, in their opinion, correct to $\pm 0·044$ per cent. They give the surface tension of water as 72·86 dynes/cm. at 18° C. Lenard asserts that no method in use up to 1924 gave results accurate to ± 1 per cent.

The measurements in the frame method of Lenard are those of length and weight. Lengths can be measured with very great accuracy. Accuracy of weighing depends on the type of balance. A delicate Hartmann and Braun torsion balance is used. By means of a sinker attached beneath the frame, it is arranged that the weight of the system with no film is approximately zero, and that with a film the whole of the scale of the balance is used. Maximum sensitiveness is thus obtained.

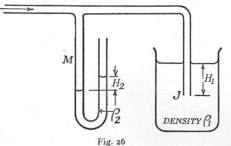

Fig. 26

21. Determination of the Surface Tension of a Liquid from the Maximum Pressure in Bubbles (often called Jäger's Method).

(i) *Elementary Theory.*— A glass jet J (fig. 26), cut off squarely at the tip, is mounted vertically so that the tip is immersed

---

* Here the approximate value $W_1 = \tfrac{1}{2}\pi r^2 g\rho l$, corresponding to $\theta = 90°$, which is nearly correct, is used in the last (and small) term.

at a depth H_1 in a liquid whose surface tension is to be found. By means of a dropping funnel, air bubbles are blown at the tip and then break away. A manometer M containing a light liquid of density ρ_2 shows the maximum pressure $g\rho_2 H_2 + P$ in the bubbles before they break away. P is the atmospheric pressure. The elementary theory assumes that the maximum pressure is reached when the bubble reaches a hemispherical shape of radius r equal to the radius of the bore of the jet, and that then the bubble becomes unstable and breaks away. The excess pressure inside the bubble over that outside when on the point of breaking away is assumed to be $2T/r$. This gives the equation

$$\frac{2T}{r} = P + g\rho_2 H_2 - P - g\rho_1 H_1$$

and
$$T = \tfrac{1}{2} gr\{\rho_2 H_2 - \rho_1 H_1\}. \quad . \quad . \quad . \quad . \quad (55)$$

The method is used to measure T at various temperatures. The assumption that instability and detachment occur when the bubble is hemispherical would seem to be unsound. This difficulty is avoided in Sugden's discussion, which we shall now describe.

(ii) *Sugden's Discussion.*[*]—Fig. 27 represents a bubble forming at the end of a jet below the surface of a liquid whose surface tension is required. The figure represents a central section, showing a meridional profile curve. At a point P on the

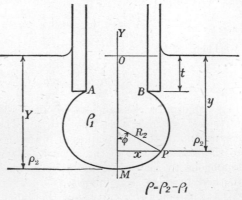

Fig. 27

surface of the bubble, the general equation (4) holds, with a plus sign before $g\rho y$, because P is below the general level ($\rho = \rho_2 - \rho_1$). Thus

$$T\left(\frac{1}{R_1} + \frac{1}{R_2}\right) + g\rho y = \text{a constant},$$

if the origin is taken at O in the general level. Alternatively, the same equation may be derived almost from first principles. It expresses the fact that the pressure inside the bubble near P exceeds that outside the bubble near P by $T(1/R_1 + 1/R_2)$. The internal pressure at O

* Sugden, *Journ. Chem. Soc.*, Vol. 121, p. 858 (1922).

is regarded as constant. At M, if each radius of curvature is called b and the depth Y, we get

$$\frac{2T}{b} + g\rho Y = \text{the same constant.} \quad \cdots \quad (56)$$

Combining these, we get an equation which holds at any point P:

$$T\left(\frac{1}{R_1} + \frac{1}{R_2}\right) + g\rho y = \frac{2T}{b} + g\rho Y.$$

Also

$$\frac{1}{R_2} = \frac{\sin\phi}{x}.$$

Divide throughout by T/b and put $Y - y = z$. Then

$$\frac{1}{R_1/b} + \frac{\sin\phi}{x/b} = 2 + \frac{zg\rho}{T/b}.$$

Put

$$\frac{2T}{g\rho} = a_1{}^2 \quad \text{and} \quad \frac{2b^2}{a_1{}^2} = \frac{b^2 g\rho}{T} = \beta. \quad \cdots \quad (57)$$

Then

$$\frac{1}{R_1/b} + \frac{\sin\phi}{x/b} = 2 + \frac{\beta z}{b}. \quad \cdots \cdots \quad (58)$$

This equation is the same as equation (26) of § 10, p. 115, and Bashforth and Adams's tables apply to it. They give values of x/b and z/b corresponding to given values of β and ϕ. Sugden applies these tables to the measurement of the surface tension of the liquid in a manner analogous to that which he used in his capillary rise method. His method, in effect, is as follows.

At the point B, t cm. below the general level, $x = r$, the radius of the tube, and

$$\frac{1}{R_1/b} + \frac{\sin\phi}{r/b} = 2 + \frac{\beta z}{b},$$

the ϕ and z now corresponding to the point B, i.e. to $z = Y - t$. The pressure inside the bubble at the level of B is

$$\frac{2T}{b} + g\rho_2 Y - g\rho_1(Y-t) + \text{atmospheric pressure.}$$

The pressure outside at the level of B is

$$g\rho_2 t + \text{atmospheric pressure.}$$

The pressure inside minus the pressure outside, if we put $\rho = \rho_2 - \rho_1$, is

$$\frac{2T}{b} + g\rho(Y - t),$$

$$= \frac{2T}{b} + g\rho z,$$

which can be written in the form $g\rho h$, where h is a positive depth; that is,

$$g\rho h = \frac{2T}{b} + g\rho z$$

or

$$h = \frac{a_1^2}{b} + z.$$

Multiply throughout by r/a_1^2;

$$\frac{hr}{a_1^2} = \frac{r}{b} + \frac{rz}{a_1^2}$$

$$= \frac{r}{b} + \frac{r}{a_1}\frac{z}{b}\frac{b}{a_1}$$

$$= \frac{r}{b} + \frac{r}{a_1}\frac{z}{b}\sqrt{\beta/2}. \quad \ldots \ldots \quad (59)$$

Write $hr/a_1^2 = r/X$, that is,

$$X = \frac{a_1^2}{h}; \quad \ldots \ldots \ldots \quad (60)$$

then

$$\frac{r}{X} = \frac{r}{b} + \frac{r}{a_1}\frac{z}{b}\sqrt{\beta/2}. \quad \ldots \ldots \quad (61)$$

For a given liquid and orifice, there are fixed values of r, T, and ρ, i.e. a fixed value of r/a_1. If the excess pressure in the bubble alters, so will the shape and size of the latter. For any one pressure there is one value of h, of X, and of r/X, and corresponding to that value of r/X there is one value of ϕ, that is, one value of β. Bashforth and Adams's tables give the corresponding values of β, $x/b = r/b$, and z/b, and enable r/X to be calculated by equation (61). Then $T = g\rho a_1^2/2 = g\rho h X/2$.

Calculation reveals that for a given value of r/a_1 and for steadily increasing values of ϕ, r/X passes through a maximum which can readily be determined. The reciprocal X/r passes through a minimum. It is assumed that the bubble breaks away when r/X has a maximum value, that is, when the excess pressure inside has a maximum value. Sugden gives four-figure tables of minimum values of X/r and corresponding values of r/a_1.

22. Experimental Details of Jäger's Method.

By means of the apparatus in fig. 28 the pressure required to liberate bubbles from the lower ends of two tubes of different radii, immersed to the same depth in a liquid, is measured.

The manometer is used to measure these maximum pressures, which exceed atmospheric pressure by p_1 and p_2. These excess pressures may be written in the form $p_1 = g\rho H_1$ and $p_2 = g\rho H_2$, where ρ is the density of the liquid under test less that of air.

Let the radii of the tubes be r_1 cm. and r_2 cm.

Then $g\rho H_1$ is equal to pressure due to depth of the lower end of the first tube below the surface + excess pressure of inside over outside at level of the lower end, from fig. 27. Hence

$$g\rho H_1 = g\rho t + g\rho h_1,$$

or

$$H_1 = t + h_1$$

$$= t + \frac{a_1{}^2}{X_1}, \text{ by (60).} \quad \ldots \ldots \quad (62)$$

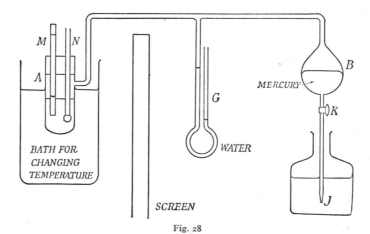

Fig. 28

Similarly,

$$H_2 = t + \frac{a_1{}^2}{X_2}. \quad \ldots \ldots \ldots \quad (63)$$

Hence

$$H_1 - H_2 = a_1{}^2\left(\frac{1}{X_1} - \frac{1}{X_2}\right)$$

or

$$a_1{}^2 = \frac{(H_1 - H_2)}{\left(\dfrac{1}{X_1} - \dfrac{1}{X_2}\right)}. \quad \ldots \ldots \ldots \quad (64)$$

Start with the approximate values $X_1 = r_1$, $X_2 = r_2$ given by elementary theory, and the experimental value of $H_1 - H_2$, and solve for $a_1{}^2$. Then calculate r_1/a_1 and r_2/a_1. Use Sugden's table to get better values of X_1/r_1 and X_2/r_2 and hence of X_1 and X_2. Substitute these values in equation (64) and again solve for $a_1{}^2$. Obtain new values of r_1/a_1 and r_2/a_1 and again use the tables to get X_1/r_1 and X_1, X_2/r_2 and X_2. Insert these in equation (64). After a few repetitions of this process the values of $a_1{}^2$ obtained remain constant and give T.

Practical Details.—Two clean glass tubes, one of internal diameter about 3 mm., the other a similar tube drawn out to a fine capillary at the lower end, pass vertically through the rubber stopper of a vessel A and dip into the liquid whose surface tension is required, with their lower ends at the same depth. The lower end in each case is cut off square, without ragged inner edges when viewed under the microscope. The upper part of A is connected to a water manometer G and a mercury suction bulb B with a capillary jet J. A is surrounded by a water-bath, which is screened from the rest of the apparatus.

In taking readings the upper end of one of the tubes, M, say, is closed by a stopper, and the tap K is opened. Air enters the open tube N and a train of bubbles forms and breaks away at its lower end. The maximum pressure is read, the rate of bubble formation being kept slow. In this way H_1 is calculated. The experiment is then repeated with M open and N closed. This gives the value of H_2. If the jet J has the correct size, the rate of formation of bubbles can be controlled. The maximum pressure shown by the gauge is independent, as it should be, of the rate of bubble formation, except for very high rates, when the experimental conditions are not in agreement with the theoretical conditions discussed above. The inner diameters of the lower ends of M and N must be measured carefully.

In experiments quoted by Sugden, pairs of tubes with the following radii were used:

$$r_1 = 0.007796 \text{ cm.} \qquad\qquad r_2 = 0.162 \text{ cm.}$$
$$r_1 = 0.009934 \text{ cm.} \qquad\qquad r_2 = 0.159 \text{ cm.}$$
$$r_1 = 0.007525 \text{ cm.} \qquad\qquad r_2 = 0.0600 \text{ cm.}$$

Sugden's Results.

$$\text{Water} \quad T_{20°} = 72.91 \text{ dynes/cm.}$$
$$\text{Benzene} \quad T_{20°} = 28.86 \text{ dynes/cm.}$$

These values are in good agreement with those obtained by other observers and methods.

Comments.—(1) The method does not require a very large quantity of liquid. It can be used to find T at various temperatures.

(2) Sugden's table of values of X/r reveals that the assumption used in the elementary form of Jäger's experiment, namely, that the maximum pressure in a bubble occurs when it is hemispherical, that is, when $\varphi_B = 90°$, is true only for tubes of infinitely small diameter. For a tube of radius 0.35 cm. the maximum pressure occurs when $\varphi_B = 160°$.

23. Excess Pressure Inside a Spherical Bubble or Drop.

We consider a bubble of gas, assumed to be spherical, in equilibrium when totally submerged in a liquid. We neglect local pressure differences at various points inside and also outside the bubble, and also the effect of the force of gravity on its shape. Let the radius be r cm. and let the internal pressure exceed the external pressure by p dynes/sq. cm., and let the surface film have a tension T. Let the bubble undergo a slight virtual increase in size, that is, let the radius change from r to $r + dr$, and let the excess pressure change from p to $p + dp$. By the principle of virtual work, the total work done in this change by all the forces keeping the bubble in equilibrium is zero. The work done by the pressure in pushing out the surface = force $\times$ distance = $p \times 4\pi r^2 dr$ ergs, small terms being neglected, and the work done by the surface tension in stretching the surface isothermally is $-T\, d(4\pi r^2) = -8\pi Tr\, dr$ ergs. (This assumes the definition of surface tension given on p. 100.)   Hence

$$p \times 4\pi r^2 dr - 8\pi Tr\, dr = 0$$

and

$$p = \frac{2T}{r}. \quad \cdots \cdots \cdots \quad (65)$$

In the case of a soap bubble surrounded by a gas, there are two surface films and

$$p = \frac{4T}{r}. \quad \cdots \cdots \cdots \quad (66)$$

In large bubbles, local pressure differences become more important, the shape is no longer spherical, and the above equations become rougher approximations.

24. Surface Tension of a Liquid found by Measurements on Stationary Drops and Bubbles.

We consider the general appearance of (a) a sessile drop of liquid resting on a horizontal plate, the medium above the drop being a gas; (b) a bubble of gas resting on a plate or projecting from the upper end of a tube, the medium above it being a liquid; (c) a pendent drop of liquid projecting from the lower end of a tube, the medium below it being a gas; (d) a pendent bubble of gas resting under a plate or projecting from the lower end of a tube, the medium below it being a liquid. In all these cases the interface is a surface of revolution about a certain vertical axis, by symmetry.

The accompanying figures, 29 (a), (b), (c) and (d), represent central sections. A and B, O and D are pairs of points close to the surface but on opposite sides of it.

In case (a) the following equations for pressure differences can be written down:

$p_A - p_B = T(1/R_1 + 1/R_2)$, where R_1 and R_2 are the principal radii of curvature near A;

$p_O - p_A = -g\rho_2 y$, where y is the difference in level of O and A;

$p_O - p_D = 2T/b$, where b is the (only) radius of curvature near O;

$p_B - p_D = g\rho_1 y$.

Combining these, we get

$$T\left(\frac{1}{R_1}+\frac{1}{R_2}\right)=\frac{2T}{b}+gy(\rho_2-\rho_1). \quad . \quad . \quad . \quad (67)$$

Case (d) gives the same final equation. Cases (b) and (c) give

$$T\left(\frac{1}{R_1}+\frac{1}{R_2}\right)=\frac{2T}{b}-gy(\rho_2-\rho_1). \quad . \quad . \quad . \quad (68)$$

These are the differential equations of the meridional curves, that is, profile curves of central sections, and their integrals, if obtainable, would be the equations to these curves. They are not integrable in the general case by rigorous methods. In the special cases of very large drops and bubbles, they are integrable.

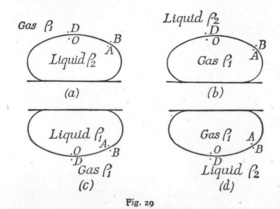

Fig. 29

The theory giving T for large drops and bubbles placed as in (a) and (d) may be stated as follows. Equation (67) reduces to

$$T\left(\frac{1}{R_1}+\frac{1}{R_2}\right)=g\rho y, \text{ where } \rho=\rho_2-\rho_1,$$

since b, the radius of curvature near O, is very great. Further, one of the two radii of curvature near A is very great, since the drop is large, and the equation becomes $T/R=g\rho y$. The theory then proceeds as in § 3, p. 102. Take axes Ox and Oy as shown in fig. 30. Put $R=ds/d\theta$, where θ is the angle made by the tangent at A with Ox, and we have

$$T\frac{d\theta}{ds}=g\rho y.$$

Now

$$\sin\theta=\frac{dy}{ds}.$$

Hence

$$T \sin \theta \frac{d\theta}{dy} = g\rho y,$$

and, multiplying by dy and integrating, we have

$$-T \cos \theta = \tfrac{1}{2}g\rho y^2 + \text{constant.}$$

When $y = 0$, $\theta = 0$, $\cos \theta = 1$, hence the constant is $-T$. Hence

$$g\rho y^2 = 2T(1 - \cos \theta) \quad \ldots \quad \ldots \quad (69)$$

is the equation to the meridional curve in terms of y and θ.

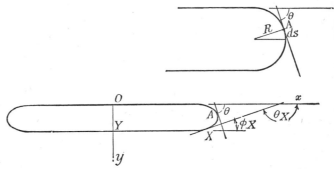

Fig. 30

Put $T/g\rho = a^2$. Since

$$\frac{dy}{dx} = \tan \theta,$$

$$\cos \theta = \frac{1}{\sqrt{1 + \left(\dfrac{dy}{dx}\right)^2}},$$

and equation (69) can be written in the form

$$y^2 = 2a^2 \left\{ 1 - \frac{1}{\sqrt{1 + \left(\dfrac{dy}{dx}\right)^2}} \right\}.$$

Hence

$$\frac{1}{\sqrt{1 + \left(\dfrac{dy}{dx}\right)^2}} = \frac{2a^2 - y^2}{2a^2}.$$

On inverting and squaring, we have

$$1 + \left(\frac{dy}{dx}\right)^2 = \left(\frac{2a^2}{2a^2 - y^2}\right)^2,$$

$$\left(\frac{dy}{dx}\right)^2 = \frac{y^2(4a^2 - y^2)}{(2a^2 - y^2)^2},$$

$$\frac{dy}{dx} = + \frac{y\sqrt{4a^2 - y^2}}{(2a^2 - y^2)}, \quad \cdots \quad (70)$$

taking the positive root, since dy/dx is positive when $y^2 < 2a^2$. This may be seen from fig. 30, according to which dy/dx is positive if $\theta < 90°$, and by equation (69), $y^2 < 2a^2$ when $\theta < 90°$.

There are two methods of obtaining a^2 and hence T.

Method (1) arises out of the fact that

$$dy/dx = \infty \quad \text{when} \quad y^2 = 2a^2 = a_1{}^2, \text{say.} \quad \cdots \quad (71)$$

This holds for very large or infinite drops. For drops or bubbles which are nearly plane at the vertex, a condition which holds in most practical cases, Ferguson * gives the more accurate formula

$$\frac{dy}{dx} = \infty \quad \text{when} \quad y^2 = a_1{}^2 + \cdot 606\,\frac{a_1{}^3}{r}, \quad \cdots \quad (72)$$

where r is the maximum horizontal radius of the drop.

In the experiment, the values of y and r at the greatest horizontal section are measured with the aid of a microscope, and the value of $a_1{}^2$ is obtained by the method of successive approximations.

In one case of a bubble of air in tap water, Ferguson obtained $y = \cdot4051$, $r = 2\cdot540$ cm. by experiment. As a first approximation he put $a_1 = \cdot4051$ in the small second term on the right of the equation $y^2 = a_1{}^2 + \cdot606\,a_1{}^3/r$ and calculated a better value of $a_1{}^2$ in this way.

The value of a_1 derived from this was substituted in the small term, and a new value of $a_1{}^2$ was found. The process was repeated until a constant value of $a_1{}^2$ was found, namely, $a_1{}^2 = \cdot1502$, whence T $(=\frac{1}{2}a_1{}^2 g\rho)$ was found to be $73\cdot65$ dynes/cm. for tap water at 8° C.

Method (2) arises from the fact that for large drops or bubbles

$$g\rho y^2 = 2T(1 - \cos\theta).$$

At X, $\theta = 180° - \psi$, where ψ is the angle of contact. Let OY, the full height of the bubble, be H. Then

$$g\rho H^2 = 2T(1 + \cos\psi). \quad \cdots \cdots \quad (73)$$

To obtain the surface tension with the aid of this formula, H must be measured by means of a microscope and ψ must be measured in some special way. Since this method involves a knowledge of ψ, the determination of which always involves a certain amount of doubt, it is not considered as good as the other.

* *Phil. Mag.*, Vol. 25, p. 509 (1913).

25. Contact of Solids, Liquids, and Gases.

Consider a system (fig. 31) consisting of a solid S and a liquid L. Suppose that they are initially in contact, and are then separated, Let the work per square centimetre required to separate them, that is, the work performed by the operator who separates them, be W_{SL} ergs, say. Before separation there is potential energy in the interface, amounting to T_{SL} ergs per sq. cm., the surface tension of the interface. After separation there is energy T_{SG} ergs per sq. cm. on the surface between the solid and a gas, for example, air, and T_{LG} ergs per sq. cm. on the surface between the liquid and the gas.

The initial energy of the system plus the work of separation which is given to or done on the system is equal to the final energy after separation. Hence we have Dupré's equation

$$T_{SL} + W_{SL} = T_{SG} + T_{LG}. \quad \cdots \quad (74)$$

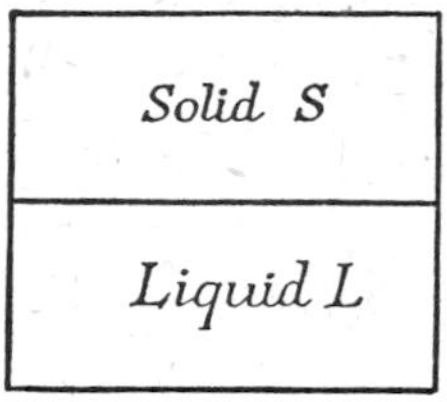

Fig. 31 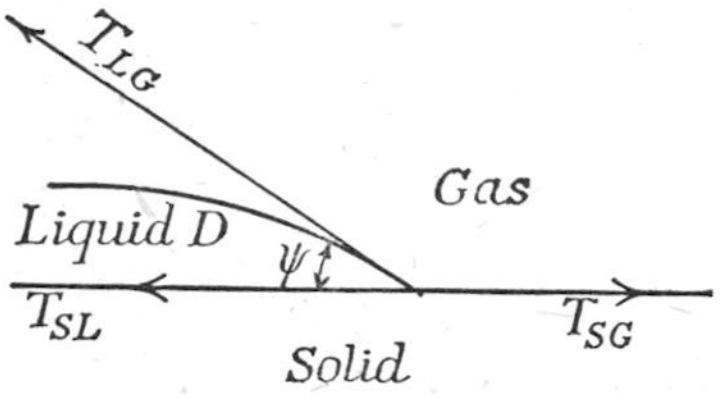   Fig. 32

Next consider a system consisting of a liquid, a solid, and a gas all in contact and in equilibrium. Assume that they meet along a common line of contact. The molecules in this line are in equilibrium. Hence, from fig. 32, since the net horizontal force per centimetre to the left is equal to the net horizontal force per centimetre to the right,

$$T_{SL} + T_{LG} \cos \psi = T_{SG}, \quad \cdots \quad (75)$$

where ψ is the angle of contact between liquid and solid. If $T_{SG} - T_{SL}$ is eliminated from equations (74) and (75), we have Young's equation

$$W_{SL} = T_{LG}(1 + \cos \psi). \quad \cdots \quad (76)$$

If $\psi = 0$, $W_{SL} = 2T_{LG}$.

Now the work required to separate two portions of the same liquid, by reasoning analogous to that at the beginning of this section, is $W_{LL} = 2T_{LG}$ ergs per sq. cm. Hence the meaning of the fact that $\psi = 0$ is that the attraction between solid and liquid is equal to the attraction between two parts of the same liquid.

Effect of Friction.—In practice, when measuring angles of contact, it is necessary, according to Adam and Jessop,* to take into account the friction which

* *Journ. Chem. Soc.*, p. 1865 (1925).

always exists between a liquid and a solid in contact. In other words, equation (76) is incomplete and requires an extra term for the frictional force. Moreover, according to the same authors, this friction causes the angle of contact to have one value ψ_A when the liquid is on the point of advancing over the solid, and another value ψ_R when it is on the point of receding. When the liquid is about to advance, the equilibrium of the liquid molecules along the line of contact in fig. 33 gives

$$T_{SL} + T_{LG} \cos \psi_A + F = T_{SG}, \quad \ldots \ldots \text{(77)}$$

where F is the frictional force per cm. Similarly, when the liquid is about to recede,

$$T_{SL} + T_{LG} \cos \psi_R - F = T_{SG}. \quad \ldots \ldots \text{(78)}$$

If we add (77) and (78), F is eliminated, and by combination with (75) we get

$$\cos \psi_A + \cos \psi_R = 2 \cos \psi, \quad \ldots \ldots \text{(79)}$$

where ψ is the true equilibrium angle of contact.

Neumann's Triangle.—The question arises, what happens when a drop of a liquid L_1 is placed on the flat surface of another liquid L_2, with which it does not mix? In particular, does the drop spread?

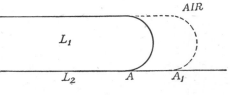

Fig. 33

In fig. 33 let the drop have a point of contact A with L_2. At a given instant let the drop be in the position shown. Whether it is in equilibrium or not will appear later. Let the area of contact of drop and liquid be increased by an amount S sq. cm., so that A proceeds to A_1. The area of contact of drop and air also increases by S sq. cm. Let the tension of the surface between liquids L_1 and L_2 be T_{12}, between liquid L_1 and air, T_1, and between liquid L_2 and air, T_2. On account of the alteration in the areas of contact, the potential energy of the system increases by $(T_{12} + T_1 - T_2)S$ ergs. Now a system like the above tends to reach a state of equilibrium in which the potential energy has a minimum value, that is, the system tends to move so that the potential energy becomes less. Thus the drop will spread if $(T_{12} + T_1 - T_2)S$ is negative, that is, if $T_2 > (T_{12} + T_1)$. In this case spreading will continue until liquid L_1 covers liquid L_2. There will be no point where three liquids meet. If a drop of liquid L_2 is placed on liquid L_1, the condition for spreading is that $T_1 > (T_{12} + T_2)$. If in the first case $T_2 < (T_{12} + T_1)$, or in the second $T_1 < (T_{12} + T_2)$, it will be possible to place a drop of one of the liquids on the other so as not to spread, that is, so as to remain in equilibrium, and then there will be a line of contact round the drop, where three fluids, two liquids and a gas, meet. The condition that this may happen may be expressed thus: if a triangle can be drawn whose sides are proportional to T_1, T_2 and T_{12}, it will be possible for three fluids to meet. This accounts for the name " Neumann's triangle ".

In practice it has not yet been found possible to draw such a triangle. For all liquids tried either $T_2 > (T_{12} + T_1)$ or $T_1 > (T_{12} + T_2)$, and yet it is possible to find many cases where a drop of one liquid will lie in equilibrium on another. These exceptions are regarded as only apparent, that is, it is supposed that in each case the surface of one of the liquids is rendered impure by contamination with the other. When a drop of oil apparently stands on water, it is really standing on a film of oil, so that although there appear to be three fluids meeting, this is not really the case.

26. Measurements of the Angle of Contact between a Solid and a Liquid.

(1) *Adam and Jessop's Method.*—This method is suitable when the solid can be obtained in the form of a flat plate. Such a plate is supported (so as to dip in the liquid) by a clamp which can be moved vertically upwards or downwards.

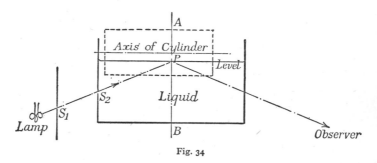

Fig. 34

The rectangular trough containing the liquid is of plate glass, with the tops of the sides ground flat and coated with a suitable non-contaminating substance, e.g. paraffin wax if the liquid is water. Before an experiment is carried out the liquid surface is swept free of contamination by a barrier, that is, a scraper coated with non-contaminating material. This is very important. Then a rough value ψ_A is determined by lowering the plate gently into the liquid so that the latter " advances " over the plate. If the angle of setting is correct, the liquid will continue horizontal right up to the plate. A rough setting is made by eye. By raising and again lowering the plate into the liquid until the correct condition is fulfilled, an accurate setting is made. After each setting a period of about a minute should elapse before the profile of the surface is examined for horizontality. The authors consider that as the angle of contact varies from point to point of a plate, it is sufficiently exact to measure the angle between the edge of the plate and the horizontal by a protractor. The angle ψ_R is measured in a similar way to ψ_A, except that just before observations are made, the plate is raised slightly to make the liquid recede. The equation

$$2 \cos \psi = \cos \psi_A + \cos \psi_R$$

then gives the true angle of contact.

(2) *Angle of Contact between Paraffin Wax and Water. Ablett's Method.**—In this method it is recognized that an angle of contact varies according as the liquid is advancing over the solid, receding, or stationary, and corresponding measurements are made. The effect of varying the speed of the liquid relative to the solid is also investigated.

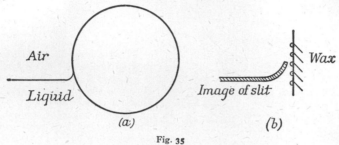

Fig. 35

The main part of the apparatus (fig. 34) is a solid glass cylinder about three inches in diameter and three inches long, which is carefully coated with paraffin wax. After cooling, the surface of the wax is turned smooth. The cylinder is mounted and geared so as to rotate about its own axis, which is horizontal, with various linear surface velocities, up to about 4 mm. per sec. It is partly immersed in water in a special glass tank. One end of the tank is covered with dull black paper, in which a narrow horizontal slit S_2 is made. Parallel light from a lamp passes obliquely upwards through an adjustable slit S_1, then through S_2 and the liquid, and falls on the under side of the surface of the liquid, whence it is

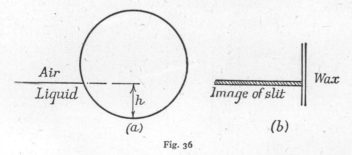

Fig. 36

reflected downwards towards an observer. The observer sees a horizontal image of the slit S_2 adjoining the silhouette of the surface of the cylinder, and that end of the image near the cylinder is in general curved. The depth of the liquid can be altered, but the lamp and S_1 are always arranged so that the point P is in a fixed vertical plane AB. When the cylinder is at rest and the level of the liquid is not specially selected, the general end view of the system, as seen by the unaided eye, is as in fig. 35(*a*), and when the above optical system is used, the image seen is as in fig. 35(*b*).

The experiment consists in adjusting the depth of water until the general view is as in fig. 36(*a*) and the special image as in fig. 36(*b*). The difference between

* Ablett, *Phil. Mag.*, Vol. 46, p. 244 (1923).

the depth in this position and in that when the liquid just touches the lowest point of the cylinder gives h.

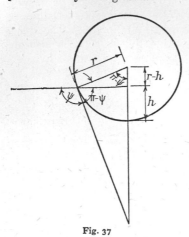

Fig. 37 shows that

$$- \cos \psi = \cos(\pi - \psi) = \frac{r - h}{r}$$

or

$$\cos \psi = \frac{h - r}{r}. \quad . \quad . \quad (80)$$

Ablett's mean value of ψ is 104° 32′.

Analogous experiments are carried out with the cylinder rotating in clockwise and anticlockwise directions; in each case the depth is adjusted until a perfect image is seen right up to the line of contact. Ablett found that for surface speeds up to about 0·44 mm./sec. the angles of contact varied in a definite way, but for speeds exceeding 0·44 mm./sec. they became constant. The mean value of ψ_1, the angle of contact for anticlockwise rotation, observed on the left-hand side of the cylinder and therefore corresponding to the case of a liquid ad-

Fig. 37

vancing over a solid, was 112° 56′. The mean value of ψ_2 corresponding to liquid receding was 96° 16′. Within the limits of experimental error $\psi = \frac{1}{2}(\psi_1 + \psi_2)$.

27. Measurement of Interfacial Surface Tensions.

Some of the methods previously described may be used to measure interfacial surface tensions. Mack and Bartell * describe a method of measuring the ten-

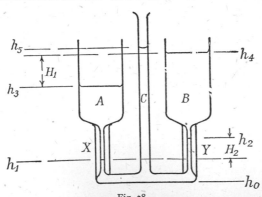

sion of the surface between water and various organic liquids, which has the advantage of precision and of not requiring more than about 2 c.c. of organic liquid. The case when the liquid is denser than water is discussed here.

Fig. 38

(From *Journ. Amer. Chem. Soc.* (1932), with slight alterations)

The apparatus, which is made of glass, is shown in fig. 38. It consists of two wide cups A and B, sealed to capillaries X, Y of different radii r_1, r_2, and through them joined to a central wide tube C. This arrangement is set up vertically. Water is first poured into A (which is connected to the narrow capillary X) to avoid entrapping bubbles of air. A larger quantity of water is then poured into B. Both

* Mack and Bartell, *Journ. Amer. Chem. Soc.*, Vol. 54, p. 936 (1932).

capillaries are filled with water and a little extra is added. The organic liquid is introduced into the central tube C and rises up the two capillaries. By a certain method of manipulation, the levels are brought near two etched marks on the capillary tubes, and the system is allowed to attain equilibrium. The five different levels are accurately measured. Assume that the interface in X at level h_1 is convex upwards. The vertical cylinder of liquid above the interface is at rest. Hence, equating vertical forces, we have

$$\pi r_1^2 g \left\{ \left(h_2 - h_1 + \frac{r_1}{3} \right) \rho_0 - \left(h_3 - h_1 + \frac{r_1}{3} \right) \rho_W \right\} = 2\pi r_1 T_{12}, \quad . \quad (81)$$

where ρ_0, ρ_W are the densities of the organic liquid and of water respectively. Similarly, for the interface in Y,

$$\pi r_2^2 g \left\{ \left(h_5 - h_2 + \frac{r_2}{3} \right) \rho_0 - \left(h_4 - h_2 + \frac{r_2}{3} \right) \rho_W \right\} = 2\pi r_2 T_{12}. \quad . \quad (82)$$

Subtracting equation (82) from equation (81), and putting $h_4 - h_3 = H_1$, $h_2 - h_1 = H_2$, $r_2 - r_1 = R$, we find that, if we assume that R is small compared to r_1 or r_2, and neglect certain terms,

$$T_{12} = \frac{g}{2(1/r_1 - 1/r_2)} \{ (H_1 - H_2)\rho_W + H_2 \rho_0 - \tfrac{1}{3} R(\rho_0 - \rho_W) \}. \quad . \quad (83)$$

It is to be noted that in the above equations the approximate expression corresponding to a hemispherical meniscus is used, and r is taken to mean the radius of the capillary in each case. This assumption is justified if we use narrow capillaries. The radius of the larger capillary is less than 1 mm. One advantage of the method is that ρ_0 need not be known more accurately than to two places of decimals, as this quantity only occurs in the small terms of equation (83). One example of a result obtained by Mack and Bartell is that the surface tension of the interface nitrobenzene-water at $15 \cdot 13°$ C. is $26 \cdot 65$ dynes/cm.

28. Capillary Waves or Ripples. Velocity of Gravity Waves on a Liquid.

One method of measuring the surface tension of a liquid depends on the phenomenon of ripples excited upon the surface of a liquid. It is convenient to introduce this subject by studying the mechanism of a certain type of wave passing over the surface of a deep liquid. In this particular type of wave, the surface of the liquid is traversed by transverse vertical vibrations controlled by the force of gravity. It will be assumed in the present elementary treatment that every drop of liquid in or near the surface describes a circular path in a vertical plane; this is very nearly the actual state of affairs for waves of small amplitude.*

Fig. 39 represents a section of a liquid traversed by such waves, in a vertical plane parallel to the direction of motion. Let c be the velocity of the waves in a horizontal direction. Assume that every drop of liquid describes a circle of radius r in an anticlockwise direction. Let τ be the time taken to describe a circle. This is also the time taken by the waves in moving forward through a distance equal to the wave-

---

* Ewald, Pöschl and Prandtl, *The Physics of Solids and Liquids*, p. 232 (Blackie & Son, Ltd., 1936).

length λ. At a point on the crest, such as X, the instantaneous horizontal velocity of a drop ($= q_1$, say) is

$$c - \frac{2\pi r}{\tau}. \quad \ldots \ldots \quad (84)$$

Similarly, at a point Y in a trough, q_2, the horizontal velocity of a drop, is

$$c + \frac{2\pi r}{\tau}. \quad \ldots \ldots \quad (85)$$

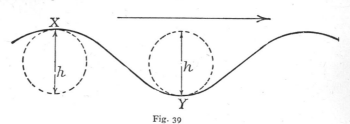

Fig. 39

By Bernoulli's theorem, or by the assumption that the change in velocity of a drop is due to the fall in height, we have

$$q_2{}^2 = q_1{}^2 + 2gh,$$

where $h = 2r$. Hence

$$q_2{}^2 = q_1{}^2 + 4gr. \quad \ldots \ldots \quad (86)$$

By squaring (84) and (85) and subtracting one from the other, we have

$$q_2{}^2 - q_1{}^2 = \frac{8\pi c r}{\tau}.$$

Hence

$$4gr = q_2{}^2 - q_1{}^2 = \frac{8\pi c r}{\tau},$$

and

$$c = \frac{g\tau}{2\pi} = \frac{g\lambda}{2\pi c},$$

since $\lambda = c\tau$. Hence

$$c = \left(\frac{g\lambda}{2\pi}\right)^{\frac{1}{2}}. \quad \ldots \ldots \quad (87)$$

29. Effect of Surface Tension on the Velocity of Gravity Waves.

By § 28, the velocity of waves travelling over the surface of a deep liquid and depending only on the force of gravity is $c = \sqrt{g\lambda/2\pi}$.

In order to allow for the effect of surface tension, it is to be noted that wherever the surface film of a liquid is curved, there is, by § 1, p. 100, a pressure directed from the concave side to the convex side equal to $T(1/R_1 + 1/R_2)$, where T is the surface tension and R_1, R_2 are the principal radii of curvature at the point considered.

Consider simple harmonic waves travelling over a liquid; the position of any point on the surface in a given vertical plane section, parallel to the direction of propagation, at any given moment may be represented by

$$y = a \sin\left(\frac{2\pi x}{\lambda} + b\right),$$

where y is the ordinate of the point above the undisturbed level, λ the wave-length, a the constant amplitude, x the abscissa of the point measured from some arbitrary origin, and b another constant. If we assume that in all sections parallel to the one under consideration

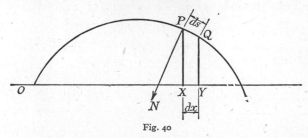

Fig. 40

the profile curve is the same, the system of waves is cylindrical and R_1, say, is infinite. Also

$$R_2 = \frac{\left\{1 + \left(\dfrac{dy}{dx}\right)^2\right\}^{\frac{3}{2}}}{\dfrac{d^2y}{dx^2}} = \frac{1}{\dfrac{d^2y}{dx^2}}$$

if dy/dx is small compared with unity, as is the case in practical experiments on ripples.

If $y = a \sin(2\pi x/\lambda + b)$,

$$\frac{d^2y}{dx^2} = -\frac{4\pi^2 y}{\lambda^2}.$$

Thus at a point such as P in fig. 40 the surface tension causes an excess pressure, directed along NP, of T/R_2, or along PN of $-T/R_2$, that is, of $4\pi^2 T y/\lambda^2$ dynes per sq. cm.

The excess force on an element of area whose profile curve is PQ ($= ds$), and whose thickness is 1 cm. measured perpendicularly to the plane of the figure, is $4\pi^2 T y \, ds/\lambda^2$ dynes, acting along PN, or $4\pi^2 T y \, dx/\lambda^2$ resolved vertically downwards. The principal downward (restoring) force on the element $PQYX$ is its weight $g\rho y\,dx$ dynes. The total downward force on it is therefore

$$g\rho y\,dx + \frac{4\pi^2 T}{\lambda^2}\,y\,dx \text{ dynes} = y\rho\,dx\left(g + \frac{4\pi^2 T}{\lambda^2\rho}\right) \text{ dynes.}$$

Thus the effect of surface tension is, as it were, to change g to $g + 4\pi^2 T/\lambda^2\rho$.

Now the velocity of "gravity waves" on deep liquids has been shown to be $c = \sqrt{\lambda g/2\pi}$.

Hence the velocity of waves controlled by gravity and surface tension is

$$c = \sqrt{\frac{\lambda}{2\pi}\left(g + \frac{4\pi^2 T}{\lambda^2\rho}\right)}. \quad \ldots \quad \ldots \quad (88)$$

In this equation we put $c = n\lambda$, where n is the frequency; after squaring, we may rewrite the equation in the form

$$T = \frac{\lambda^3 n^2 \rho}{2\pi} - \frac{g\lambda^2\rho}{4\pi^2}. \quad \ldots \quad \ldots \quad (89)$$

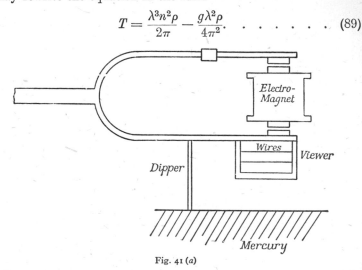

Fig. 41 (a)

30. Measurement of Surface Tension by the Ripple Method.

This method, introduced by Lord Rayleigh,* has been used by various authors. A recent improvement of the method by Ghosh, Banerji and Datta † possesses several advantages and will now be described.

The liquid whose surface tension is required is placed in a shallow porcelain rectangular trough of dimensions 10 in. × 6 in. × 1·5 in. Above the liquid (fig. 41 (a) and (b)) is mounted an electrically-maintained tuning-fork of frequency

---

* *Scientific Papers*, Vol. 3, pp. 383–396.

† Ghosh, Banerji and Datta, *Phil. Mag.*, 7th Series, Vol. 1, p. 1252 (1926).

about 100 vibrations per sec. Its prongs are horizontal, one above the other, when at rest, and they vibrate in a vertical plane. To the lower prong are attached two objects. First, a blade, 3 in. long, of polished silver or aluminium, called a dipper; this by its up and down vibrations, in and out of the liquid, excites ripples on the surface. The plane of the dipper is vertical, but perpendicular to the plane of vibration of the prongs. The two trains of ripples excited by the dipper are reflected by the ends of the trough and give rise to stationary ripples. Secondly, a rectangular framework of metal, called the viewer, having two steel wires running horizontally along its length, is attached to the same prong as the dipper, but nearer the tip. The plane of the viewer is vertical, and parallel to the plane of vibration of the prongs. The purpose of the viewer is to enable the wave form of the ripples to be seen and photographed and the wave-length to be measured.

This is done by causing a parallel beam of light, proceeding in planes perpendicular to the plane of vibration of the prongs, to be reflected by the ripple-curved surface of the liquid and to pass obliquely upwards past the wires of the viewer. An observer receiving this light sees that the shadows of the two steel wires are not straight but have the clear wave-like form of the ripples, for the light is proceeding in planes parallel to the crests of the real stationary ripples. A metal plate with two fine notches at a measured distance apart is fixed in the same plane as the wires of the viewer. This is photographed along with the shadow - ripples and enables the exact wave-length to be calculated from the micrometric measurement of the wave-length of the shadows.

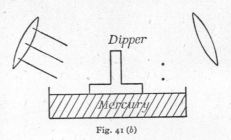

Fig. 41 (b)

It is assumed that the wave-length of the shadows is equal to the wave-length λ of the real ripples on the liquid. The whole device is thus a stroboscopic arrangement for measuring λ, using one fork only. When the amplitude of the ripples is below a certain limit and the depth of liquid in the trough is above a certain limit, the value obtained is constant. The frequency of the fork is determined by the aid of an accurate chronographic recorder tuned in unison with the fork, which also records signals from a standard clock at intervals of one second. The surface tension is calculated from equation (89):

$$T = \frac{\lambda^3 n^2 \rho}{2\pi} - \frac{g\lambda^2 \rho}{4\pi^2}$$

where T is the surface tension of the liquid, ρ its density, λ the wave-length of the ripples, and n the frequency of the fork.

31. Stability of a Cylindrical Film.

It is required to show that a circular cylinder of liquid, or a circularly cylindrical film, in equilibrium under the action of surface tension begins to be unstable when the wave-length of a disturbance imposed upon it exceeds the circumference ($\lambda > 2\pi a$).

We neglect the weight, and assume that initially the liquid (fig. 42) is in the form of a circular cylinder of radius a. Let its surface undergo a periodic disturbance such that the radius of the disturbed cylinder at any point A is $y = a + b\cos 2\pi x/\lambda$, where λ is the wave-length. Thus circular symmetry about the axis Ox is assumed. In the disturbed cylinder, equilibrium is stable if the pressure in the swollen parts, e.g. near Y, is greater than the pressure in the constricted parts, e.g. near C. For then the fluid inside tends to flow back to the constricted parts, thus restoring the initial shape of the film. The excess pressure over the external pressure at any point inside the film is $T(1/R_1 + 1/R_2)$. One of these radii of curvature is y itself (R_1, say). If we assume that dy/dx is small, then

$$\frac{1}{R_2} = \frac{\dfrac{d^2y}{dx^2}}{\left\{1 + \left(\dfrac{dy}{dx}\right)^2\right\}^{\frac{3}{2}}} = \frac{d^2y}{dx^2} \text{ approximately.}$$

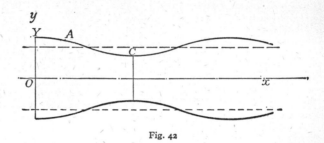

Fig. 42

Now

$$\frac{dy}{dx} = -\frac{2\pi b}{\lambda}\sin\frac{2\pi x}{\lambda},$$

$$\frac{d^2y}{dx^2} = -\frac{4\pi^2 b}{\lambda^2}\cos\frac{2\pi x}{\lambda}.$$

Hence

$$\frac{1}{R_1} + \frac{1}{R_2} = \frac{1}{a + b\cos\dfrac{2\pi x}{\lambda}} \pm \frac{4\pi^2 b}{\lambda^2}\cos\frac{2\pi x}{\lambda},$$

the positive sign being taken at Y, the negative sign at C. At points such as Y,

$$\frac{1}{R_1} + \frac{1}{R_2} = \frac{1}{a + b} + \frac{4\pi^2 b}{\lambda^2}.$$

At C,

$$\frac{1}{R_1} + \frac{1}{R_2} = \frac{1}{a - b} - \frac{4\pi^2 b}{\lambda^2}$$

The pressure at Y exceeds that at C by

$$T\left(\frac{1}{a+b} + \frac{4\pi^2 b}{\lambda^2} - \frac{1}{a-b} + \frac{4\pi^2 b}{\lambda^2}\right)$$

$$= T\left(\frac{8\pi^2 b}{\lambda^2} - \frac{2b}{a^2 - b^2}\right); \quad \cdots \cdots \cdots \quad (90)$$

and if $b \ll a$, $a^2 - b^2 = a^2$ approximately, and this reduces to

$$T\,\frac{2b}{a^2}\left(\frac{4\pi^2 a^2}{\lambda^2} - 1\right). \quad \cdots \cdots \cdots \quad (91)$$

This is positive, and the cylinder is stable, so long as $4\pi^2 a^2 > \lambda^2$, that is, when $2\pi a > \lambda$. The cylinder ceases to be stable when $2\pi a = \lambda$.

It can be shown that maximum instability occurs when $9\cdot02\,a = \lambda$.

32. Jets.

We now attempt to find an expression for the wave-length of a jet of liquid, using the method of dimensions. The symbol S is used here for surface tension to avoid confusion with T, representing time. The study of liquid jets gives useful information about the surface tension of the liquid. When a jet of liquid emerges horizontally from an orifice under pressure, its surface shows peculiar recurrent forms. This phenomenon is partly due to surface tension. Under ordinary conditions the motion of the liquid is " steady " in the hydrodynamical sense, that is, the velocity at any point remains constant and the surface of the jet is fixed in space, though made up of moving drops. The distance between consecutive corresponding points of the recurrent figure may be called the wave-length λ. It is the distance described by the stream during one complete vibration. When the shape of the orifice is given, the wave-length of the jet may be regarded as a function of S, the surface tension, ρ the density of the liquid, A the area of the orifice, and P the pressure at which the jet emerges. Viscosity is assumed to play only an unimportant part. The direct analytical determination of λ in terms of S, ρ, A, and P is laborious in the general case, but the method of dimensions gives a certain amount of information about λ.

Assume that $\lambda = $ a constant $\times S^v \rho^w A^x P^y$, where v, w, x and y are to be found. The dimensions of S are those of force per unit length, i.e.

$$S = MLT^{-2}\,.\,L^{-1} = MT^{-2}.$$

Those of ρ are mass per unit volume, hence

$$\rho = ML^{-3};$$
$$A = L^2;$$
$$P = \text{force/area} = MLT^{-2} . L^{-2} = ML^{-1}T^{-2}.$$
$$\lambda = \text{constant} \times S^v \rho^w A^x P^y,$$
$$\lambda = (MT^{-2})^v (ML^{-3})^w (L^2)^x (ML^{-1}T^{-2})^y,$$

i.e. $L^1 = M^{v+w+y} L^{-3w+2x-y} T^{-2v-2y},$

whence

$$v + w + y = 0$$

$$-3w + 2x - y = 1$$

$$-2v - 2y = 0, \text{ on comparing indices.}$$

Solving for w, x and y in terms of v, we get

$$y = -v$$

$$w = 0$$

$$x = \tfrac{1}{2}(1 - v)$$

and

$$\lambda = \text{constant} \times S^v A^{\frac{1-v}{2}} P^{-v},$$

which may be written in the form

$$\lambda = \text{constant} \times A^{\frac{1}{2}} (SA^{-\frac{1}{2}} P^{-1})^v.$$

Thus v is undetermined.

We may write

$$\lambda = A^{\frac{1}{2}} \times \text{a function of } (SA^{-\frac{1}{2}} P^{-1}). \quad \ldots \quad (92)$$

33. Measurement of Surface Tension by means of Jets.

The surface of a jet of liquid emerging from an orifice is being constantly renewed, and hence contamination of the surface due to standing, such as occurs in sessile drops, is absent. This is a considerable advantage from the point of view of accurate measurements of surface tension. Expressions for the surface tension in terms of the wave-length λ of the recurrent form of the jet, the velocity of the jet, and certain constants of the liquid have been calculated by Rayleigh and Bohr, for the case where the amplitude of the wave form of the section of the jet is small compared with λ. Rayleigh, Pedersen, Bohr and Stocker have carried out experiments to measure * T, based on these expressions.

* We now revert to the use of T to represent surface tension.

Stocker's Method.[*]—The full expression for the surface tension T of a liquid in the form of a jet emerging in a horizontal direction from an orifice is

$$T = \frac{4\pi^2 c^2 a^3 (\rho_1 + \rho_2)\left\{1 + \frac{37}{24}\left(\frac{b}{a}\right)^2\right\}}{\lambda^2\left\{6 + 10\left(\frac{\pi a}{\lambda}\right)^2 + 2.5\left(\frac{\pi a}{\lambda}\right)^4\right\}}. \quad \ldots \quad (93)$$

Here c is the velocity of emergence, λ the wave-length, ρ_1 and ρ_2 are the densities of the liquid and of the surrounding air respectively, and

$$\frac{b}{a} = \frac{r_{\max} - r_{\min}}{r_{\max} + r_{\min}},$$

where $r_{\max}$ and $r_{\min}$ are the maximum and minimum radii of the sections of the jet (fig. 43), and

$$a = \tfrac{1}{2}(r_{\max} + r_{\min})\left\{1 - \tfrac{1}{6}\left(\frac{b}{a}\right)^2\right\}.$$

Stocker's experiments are devoted to the measurement of the various quantities on the right-hand side of equation (93). In his case the liquids are transparent, e.g. water and aqueous solutions, and flow out of an elliptical aperture in the end of a piece of thermometer tubing of elliptical bore. The jet is so arranged that its two perpendicular planes of symmetry are horizontal and vertical respectively. The steady pressure is provided by a column of water about one metre high.

To obtain λ, the jet itself is made to serve as an optical system forming an image of an infinitely distant point-source of light, situated in the horizontal plane of symmetry of the jet. In practice a horizontal parallel beam of light, travelling at right angles to the axis of the jet, is refracted by it (fig. 43).

Rays passing through such sections as SS', or $S_1 S_1'$, where the horizontal width of the jet has a maximum value, give rise to real images at B, B_1, &c., which have the form of narrow vertical bright lines. No such real images are formed at other places. As the jet gets farther from the aperture, internal friction causes its sectional profile to become flatter, $S_1 S_1'$ is less than SS', and the image B_1 is

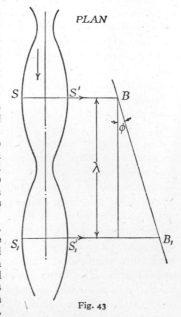

Fig. 43

farther away from the axis of the jet than B. The photographic plate of a camera is inclined so as to give clear images of B, B_1, and other focal lines. Up to eight such sharp images can be obtained on a single plate. The distance

---

[*] Stocker, *Zeits. f. phys. Chem.*, Vol. 94, p. 149 (1920).

6*

BB_1 is measured on the plate, and it is easy to calculate $\lambda = BB_1 \cos\varphi$, since φ is easily obtained. In a certain case, $BB_1 = 5\cdot89$ mm., $\varphi = 27°\cdot78$, $\lambda = \cdot521$ cm.

The velocity c of the jet is obtained by measuring the volume of liquid Q emerging per second and then using the formula $c = Q/\pi r^2$, where r is the mean radius. To obtain Q, an electromagnetic device is arranged so that the jet is permitted to pass through an aperture in a circular disc for a known period of time and is then cut off sharply by the rotation of the disc through part of a revolution. During the time when flow is permitted, the liquid passing is collected; it is then weighed. $Q = W/\rho_1 t$, where W is the mass in grammes collected in t sec., and ρ_1 is the density of the liquid. The greatest and least diameters of the jet, $2r_{max}$ and $2r_{min}$, are measured directly by means of a microscope with a micrometer eyepiece, the jet being illuminated over a length of 5 cm. The quantities b/a and a are then calculated; ρ_1 and ρ_2 are measured in the usual way.

Result. $T_{18°} = 72\cdot43 \pm 0\cdot15$ dyne/cm. for water.

This method is not suitable for an opaque liquid like mercury.

34. Criticism and Comparison of Various Methods of Measuring Surface Tension.

(i) *Capillary Rise Method.*—This method, as originally carried out, has the following disadvantages. (1) The angle of contact of the liquid and tube, (2) the internal radius of the tube at a distance from the end, and (3) the temperature of the meniscus, are required. It is difficult to measure these quantities with a very high degree of precision. (4) The experiment is static and contamination inside the tube is not improbable. (5) According to Dorsey, the cleaning of a small tube is not easy. (6) A correction for the curvature of the liquid in the reservoir is required. Recent modifications of the original method eliminate some of these difficulties, but not others. Sugden's method, described in § 11, p. 115, eliminates the reservoir correction (6), but retains (2), (3) (4) and (5), even when the angle of contact may be taken as zero. Ferguson's modification (p. 117) enables the surface tension of a very small quantity of a liquid to be measured with precision.

(ii) *Sessile Drop and Bubble Method.*—Theoretically, this method would seem free from objections, except that the drops have to stand while measurements are being made, and the film runs a certain risk of contamination. In addition, to avoid the introduction of the angle of contact, it is necessary to measure the distance from the plane of maximum diameter to the vertex. Measurements of this quantity appear to involve errors of several per cent (Lenard). To get accurate results it is necessary to carry the approximations rather far. A fair amount of liquid is required. The method is convenient for the determination of the surface tension of molten metals near the melting point.

(iii) *Maximum Bubble Pressure Method (Jäger's Method).*—This method, as used by Sugden, has the following advantages. (1) It does not involve the angle of contact explicitly, i.e. that angle need not be measured. (2) The internal radius of the tube has only to be measured at the end, where it is easily accessible. (3) Temperature control is good; the bubbles are formed in the middle of a body of liquid of known temperature.   (4) Contamination is avoided by continual renewal of the surface involved.   (5) A large quantity of liquid is not required.

The theory assumes (1) that static conditions exist, (2) that the internal circumference of the tube on which the bubble forms is circular and horizontal. Dorsey asserts that no attempt has been made to determine how far these conditions may be departed from without introducing appreciable errors.

(4) *Ring Method.*—The ring method has the advantages of rapidity and facility and, as applied by Harkins and his collaborators, great accuracy. It is becoming increasingly important in applied physics.

35. Temperature Relations of Surface Tension.

In considering the way in which the surface tension of a liquid is affected by temperature changes, we must distinguish between " associated " and " unassociated " liquids. An unassociated liquid is one which contains nothing but individual molecules of that liquid, so that if the molecules were further subdivided, the chemical nature of the liquid would be changed. An associated liquid contains groups consisting of individual molecules attached to one another, each group acting like a molecule of another species. There is evidence that at ordinary temperatures water contains groups consisting of two H_2O molecules, in addition to single H_2O molecules. In these circumstances water is an associated liquid. At ordinary temperatures benzene and carbon tetrachloride are unassociated. There is evidence that, as might be expected, the groups of an associated liquid break up as the temperature rises.

The surface tension of unassociated liquids decreases as the temperature rises. The changes may be represented over a wide range of temperature by Ferguson's empirical formula,

$$T = T_0 \left(1 - \frac{\theta}{\theta_c}\right)^n, \quad \cdots \cdots \quad (94)$$

where T is the surface tension of a liquid in contact with its own vapour, θ the absolute temperature, θ_c the critical temperature of that liquid (in the sense of Andrews*), T_0 a constant, and n a constant for a single liquid, but varying slightly from liquid to liquid. The mean value of n is about 1·2.

Equation (94) is equivalent to one given by Van der Waals. From it we can deduce directly that the surface tension of an unassociated

* See Roberts, *Heat and Thermodynamics*, p. 87.

liquid is zero at the critical temperature. By differentiation,

$$\frac{dT}{d\theta} = -\frac{nT_0}{\theta_c}\left(1 - \frac{\theta}{\theta_c}\right)^{n-1}. \quad \ldots \quad (95)$$

Eötvös' Law.—The variation of surface tension of both associated and unassociated liquids with temperature is represented by an equation, due in a simple form to Eötvös, but corrected by Ramsay and Shields, namely,

$$T(Mvx)^{\frac{2}{3}} = K(\theta_c - \theta - d), \quad \ldots \quad (96)$$

where T is the surface tension at $\theta°$ absolute; d is a constant term introduced by Ramsay and Shields, which has a value between 6 and 8 for most liquids; θ_c is the critical temperature; x is a number called the *coefficient of association* of the liquid at θ, equal to the effective molecular weight of the associated liquid divided by the molecular weight of an unassociated liquid with the same molecules; and K is a constant which is approximately equal to 2·12 for associated liquids and has a mean value of 2·22 for unassociated liquids, for which, of course, $x = 1$. M is the molecular weight of the unassociated liquid and v its specific volume.

From this law it follows that the surface tension is zero when $\theta = \theta_c - d$, that is, at a temperature a few degrees below the critical temperature. According to Callendar, water has a critical temperature of 653° absolute, but its surface tension vanishes near 647° absolute.

36. Thermodynamics of a Film.

To understand this section some knowledge of thermodynamic formulæ and the use of perfect differentials is required.* Let an elementary quantity of heat dH be given to a portion of a film of liquid which has the surface tension T. Some of the energy is used in increasing the internal energy U by dU, and some in performing external work dW. By the first law of thermodynamics,

$$dH = dU + dW.$$

Now the external work dW done *by* the film as the result of the addition of heat is $-T\,dA$, where dA is the increase in area. For when a film is stretched by dA, work $+T\,dA$, which is numerically positive, is done *on* the film by the operator, that is, $-T\,dA$ is done *by* the film. Hence

$$dH = dU - T\,dA. \quad \ldots \quad (97)$$

By the second law of thermodynamics,

$$dH = \theta\,d\phi, \quad \ldots \quad (98)$$

* For a detailed exposition see Roberts, *Heat and Thermodynamics*, Chaps. XII and XIII.

where $d\phi$ is the increase in entropy, if we suppose the heat to have been used up in performing reversible processes only. Now U, θ and ϕ may be regarded as functions of any pair of variables connected with the film which we care to select, and hence $U - \theta\phi = F$, say, is also a function of any pair of variables. Differentiate F. Then

$$dF = dU - \theta d\phi - \phi d\theta = T dA - \phi d\theta. \quad . \quad . \quad (99)$$

Since dF is a perfect differential of F with respect to A and θ, it follows from equation (99) that

$$\left(\frac{\partial T}{\partial \theta}\right)_{A\text{ const.}} = -\left(\frac{\partial \phi}{\partial A}\right)_{\theta\text{ const.}} \quad . \quad . \quad . \quad (100)$$

Since $d\phi = dH/\theta$,

$$\left(\frac{\partial H}{\partial A}\right)_{\theta\text{ const.}} = -\theta\left(\frac{\partial T}{\partial \theta}\right)_{A\text{ const.}} \quad . \quad . \quad . \quad (101)$$

Physically, this equation means that when a film is stretched isothermally, heat must be added to keep the temperature constant, and this heat, reckoned per unit increase in area, is equal to the product of the absolute temperature and the temperature coefficient of surface tension, with its sign changed. The product, with the sign changed, is numerically positive. Now when the area of a film is increased isothermally by 1 sq. cm., work equal to T ergs is required to perform the stretching, and energy equal to $-\theta(\partial T/\partial\theta)_A$ must be supplied to keep the temperature constant. We may suppose that both these amounts of energy are contained in the new portion of film, 1 sq. cm. in area. The total energy in that 1 sq. cm., as far as surface tension is concerned, is U_1, say, and is equal to

$$T - \theta\left(\frac{\partial T}{\partial \theta}\right)_{A\text{ const.}} \quad . \quad . \quad . \quad . \quad (102)$$

Every square centimetre of a large film may be supposed to be produced by stretching, starting from a film of negligible area. Hence $U_1 = T - \theta(\partial T/\partial\theta)_{A\text{ const.}}$ is the total surface energy per square centimetre of a film of any size. T, the surface tension, is called the "free" or "available" energy and $-\theta(\partial T/\partial\theta)_{A\text{ const.}}$ is called the "bound" energy. In the case of water at 15° C., T is approximately 74 dynes per cm., and $-\theta(\partial T/\partial\theta)_{A\text{ const.}}$ is approximately $+43$ dynes per cm. The second term is important. (On pp. 100 and 136, we neglected it, thereby assuming that the energy it represents is taken by the film from its surroundings, to maintain a constant temperature.)

When a film, like a soap film in an ordinary soap bubble, has two faces, the total energy has the form

$$U_1 = 2\left\{T - \theta\left(\frac{\partial T}{\partial \theta}\right)_{A\text{ const.}}\right\}. \quad . \quad . \quad (103)$$

37. Relations connecting Surface Tension and Other Quantities.

(1) *Macleod's Relation.*—A large number of non-associated substances, with a wide range of chemical properties, obey the empirical law

$$T = K(\rho_1 - \rho_2)^4 \quad \ldots \quad (104)$$

over a wide range of temperature. Here T is the surface tension, K is a constant for a given substance, and ρ_1, ρ_2 are the densities of a liquid and its saturated vapour at the temperature at which T is measured.

(2) *Sugden's Parachor.*—Even more important than Macleod's relation is that of Sugden, namely,

$$\frac{MT^{\frac{1}{4}}}{\rho_1 - \rho_2} = \text{a constant,} \quad \ldots \quad (105)$$

where T, ρ_1 and ρ_2 have their previous meanings and M is the atomic weight of certain elements or the molecular weight of certain molecules or groups of molecules. The constant is called the *parachor* of the particular atom, molecule or group concerned, and is proportional to the molecular volume. The constancy is maintained (1) during temperature variations of a single substance, (2) when the atom, molecule or group concerned is transferred from one compound to another. For example, atomic hydrogen, represented by H, has the same parachor, 17·1, in a large number of compounds. For substances which are saturated in the chemical sense, the parachor is an additive function. Thus, as we proceed along the paraffin series, the parachor of the whole substance changes by about 39·0 when the group CH_2 is added, that is, the parachor of the group CH_2 is 39·0. The parachor of molecular hydrogen, H_2, is obtained by subtracting n times the parachor of CH_2 from the parachor of a paraffin with the formula C_nH_{2n+2}, and has the value 34·2. For a large number of compounds it has been found that the parachor derived from the expression $\dfrac{MT^{\frac{1}{4}}}{(\rho_1 - \rho_2)}$ can also be calculated by adding together two sets of constants, one for the parachors of the atoms in the molecule, the other for the constitutional influences of unsaturation and ring closure. Thus constitutional factors such as double bonds, triple bonds, and rings have a definite parachor which is independent of the atoms or groups concerned. For example, a double bond has the same parachor when it exists between C and C, C and O, or N and O. Provided the bonds of a six-membered ring remain constant, the total parachor of the bonds remains constant, even though the identity of the groups changes.

38. Molecular and Other Theories of Capillarity.

From time to time attempts have been made to explain capillary phenomena in terms of some fundamental property of matter, e.g. a law of force between particles, without introducing arbitrary *ad hoc* hypotheses. One of the most celebrated is that of Laplace, a brief account of which will be given here.

(I) *Laplace's Theory.*—It is assumed that every particle of matter in the universe attracts every other particle with a force which is some function of the distance apart. The precise value of this force

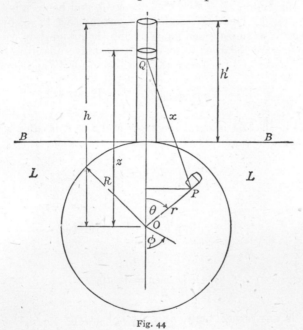

Fig. 44

is not stated, but it is assumed that when the distance apart exceeds a certain limiting value, called the range of molecular action, the value of the force becomes negligibly small and is reckoned as zero.

Attraction of a Sphere on a Cylinder resting on it.—Consider the attraction of a sphere of matter of density ρ on a cylinder of the same matter resting upon its surface as in fig. 44.

Let the cylinder have a cross-section of area 1 sq. cm., and let its height be $(h - R)$ cm. $= h'$. In particular, consider the attraction between an element of matter, of volume $r^2 \sin \theta \, dr \, d\theta \, d\phi$, near the point P, and an element of the vertical cylinder near the point Q. Assume the law of force to be such that particles, each of unit mass, whose distance apart is x cm., exert a force on one another, in the direction of increasing x, of value $-dV_1(x)/dx$ dynes, or, in other words, that the potential at a point x cm. from unit mass has the value $+V_1(x)$. Let $PQ = x$ cm. and let $OQ = z$ cm. The potential energy of unit mass at Q, due to the element of volume $r^2 \sin\theta \, dr \, d\theta \, d\phi$ near P, is therefore $+V_1(x)\rho r^2 \sin\theta \, dr \, d\theta \, d\phi$. The total potential energy V of unit mass at Q due to the whole sphere is

$$+\rho \int_0^{2\pi} d\phi \int_0^R r^2 \, dr \int_0^\pi V_1(x) \sin\theta \, d\theta.$$

From the figure, $x^2 = z^2 + r^2 - 2zr\cos\theta$, and hence x is a function of both r and θ. Treating z and r as constants, we have, by differentiation, $x\,dx = zr \sin\theta \, d\theta$, and since during the integration with respect to θ, r and z are regarded as constant, we may substitute for $\sin\theta \, d\theta$ the value $x\,dx/zr$ and rearrange the expression for V, as follows:

$$V = +\rho \int_0^{2\pi} d\phi \int_0^R \frac{r\,dr}{z} \int_{z-r}^{z+r} V_1(x)x\,dx. \quad . \quad . \quad (106)$$

The limits in the last integral are $z + r$ and $z - r$, because x has these values when $\theta = \pi$ and $\theta = 0$ respectively. Further,

$$\int_0^{2\pi} d\phi = 2\pi.$$

Hence

$$V = +2\pi\rho \int_0^z \frac{r\,dr}{z} \int_{z-r}^{z+r} V_1(x)x\,dx.$$

Let

$$\int_\beta^\infty V_1(x)x\,dx = V_2(\beta), \quad . \quad . \quad . \quad . \quad (107)$$

where β is any lower limit, and let $\int_x^\infty V_1(x)x\,dx = V_2(x)$. Assume that when x exceeds a certain limiting value c, the potential energy of two molecules or particles due to their proximity vanishes. In symbols, $V_1(x) = 0$ when $x > c$. In this case $V_2(x) = 0$ when $x > c$. Assume that the radius of the sphere is so great that $z + r$ is always greater than c; $z - r$ is sometimes greater than c, sometimes less than c. Then

$$\int_{z-r}^{z+r} V_1(x)x\,dx = \int_{z-r}^\infty V_1(x)x\,dx,$$

since $z + r$ and ∞ are both above the limiting value c. Hence

$$\int_{z-r}^{z+r} V_1(x)x\,dx = V_2(z - r),$$

by (107), and

$$V = +2\pi\rho \int_0^R \frac{V_2(z-r)r\,dr}{z}. \quad \ldots \quad (108)$$

The force on unit mass at Q acting towards O is $+\partial V/\partial z$. The force on an element of the cylinder, of height dz, of cross-section 1 sq. cm., and of mass $\rho\,dz$ is

$$+\frac{\partial V}{\partial z}\rho\,dz, \quad \ldots \quad \ldots \quad (109)$$

acting towards O.

The total force F acting on the whole cylinder of height $h - R$, say, is

$$\int_R^h \frac{\partial V}{\partial z}\rho\,dz$$

$$= +2\pi\rho^2 \int_0^R \int_R^h \frac{\partial}{\partial z}\left\{V_2(z-r)\frac{r}{z}\right\}dz\,dr$$

$$= -2\pi\rho^2\left\{\int_0^R \frac{V_2(R-r)r\,dr}{R} - \int_0^R \frac{V_2(h-r)r\,dr}{h}\right\}$$

$$= -2\pi\rho^2\left\{\frac{1}{R}\int_0^R V_2(R-r)r\,dr - \frac{1}{h}\int_0^R V_2(h-r)r\,dr\right\}.$$

In the second integral $(h-r)$ occurs. Now $(h-r) \geqq (h-R)$. Assume that the cylinder has a finite length $h - R$, which exceeds the range of molecular action c. Then $V_2(h-r) = 0$, because $(h-r) \geqq (h-R) > c$, and the second integral is zero. Hence

$$F = -\frac{2\pi\rho^2}{R}\int_0^R V_2(R-r)r\,dr.$$

Put $R - r = s$.

$$F = \frac{2\pi\rho^2}{R}\int_0^R V_2(s)(R-s)\,ds$$

$$= 2\pi\rho^2 \int_0^R V_2(s)\,ds - \frac{2\pi\rho^2}{R}\int_0^R V_2(s)s\,ds,$$

which may be written

$$F = K - \frac{H}{R}. \quad \ldots \quad \ldots \quad (110)$$

In an analogous manner it may be proved that on a similar internal cylinder the force of attraction is

$$F' = K + \frac{H}{R}. \quad \ldots \quad \ldots \quad (111)$$

Comments.—(1) When R is infinite,

$$F = K_{R=\infty} = K_\infty, \text{ say.} \quad . \quad . \quad . \quad . \quad . \quad (112)$$

Hence the expression denoted by K_∞ is the attractive force per unit area exerted by a substance with a plane surface on a cylinder with unit area of cross-section resting on it, outside or inside. Taking a special case, we see that if a plane is drawn through a point in the interior of a large mass of liquid, the attractive force which the liquid on one side of the plane exerts on that on the other side is K_∞ dynes per sq. cm. Since the whole liquid, or any cylinder of it, is in equilibrium, it may be assumed that a repulsive force exists as well as an attraction, and this repulsion also amounts to K_∞ dynes per sq. cm. An externally applied pressure acts in addition to these forces. In this connexion, K_∞ is often called the "intrinsic pressure" of the liquid. K_∞ has also several other meanings. It is approximately equal to the internal latent heat of evaporation per unit volume of liquid. Further, the term a/v^2 in Van der Waals' equation of state, $(p + a/v^2)(v - b) = R_1\theta$, is also equal* to K_∞. K_∞ is also the "tensile strength" of a liquid, i.e. the force per sq. cm. required to pull apart a column of liquid, free from bubbles and dissolved gases. For liquids at ordinary temperatures, K_∞ has a very high value. For water $K_\infty = 1.06 \times 10^{10}$ dynes per sq. cm. approximately.

(2) Except when $R < c$, $K = K_\infty$. Hence when $R > c$ we may regard H/R as the repulsive force introduced by the curvature of the surface, or as the attractive force exerted when the plano-concave lens-shaped portion of space L between the sphere and the tangent plane BB is filled with liquid. In § 23, p. 136, it has been shown that from another point of view, namely, the assumption of the existence of a surface film with a surface tension T, the interior of a sphere of liquid may be supposed to possess an excess pressure with respect to its surroundings, equal to $2T/R$. Comparing the two points of view and the expressions derived from them, we see that $2T/R$ is equivalent to H/R, i.e. $T = \frac{1}{2}H$ or

$$T = \pi\rho^2 \int_0^R V_2(s)s\,ds. \quad . \quad . \quad . \quad . \quad . \quad . \quad (113)$$

(3) If the sphere is composed of a substance of density ρ_2 and the cylinder of density ρ_1, it is clear that the factor ρ^2, in the various expressions, must be replaced by $\rho_1\rho_2$. This applies to the case of a liquid in contact with its own vapour.

Calculation of a Lower Limit for the Range of Molecular Action (Young).—By equation (113), the surface tension T may be written as

$$T = \pi\rho^2 \int_0^R V_2(s)s\,ds, \quad . \quad . \quad . \quad . \quad . \quad . \quad (114)$$

where $s = R - r$, a length.

Although s may have any value between 0 and R, yet if it exceeds c, $V_2(s) = 0$, by an earlier assumption. All the values of s which do not make $V_2(s)$ zero lie between 0 and c, and in this region $c > s$. Hence the expression

$$\pi\rho^2 \int_0^R V_2(s)c\,ds$$

is always greater than

$$\pi\rho^2 \int_0^R V_2(s)s\,ds.$$

* See p. 163. (R_1 is the gas constant.)

Hence T is always less than $\pi\rho^2\displaystyle\int_0^R V_2(s)c\,ds$; that is,

$$T < \pi\rho^2 c\int_0^R V_2(s)\,ds,$$

since c is a constant.

Now $2\pi\rho^2\displaystyle\int_0^\infty V_2(s)\,ds$ is the K_∞ of equation (112). Hence

$$T < \tfrac{1}{2}K_\infty c$$

and

$$c > \frac{2T}{K_\infty}. \quad\ldots\ldots\ldots \quad (115)$$

Hence $2T/K_\infty$ is the lower limit of c, and this may be calculated by substituting numerical values of T and K derived from experiment or theory. For water the lower limit works out at about 6×10^{-9} cm.

(4) From equation (112) we see that on every square centimetre of the surface of a fluid with a plane boundary there is a force directed towards the interior along the normal, of value K_∞, which can be written in the form

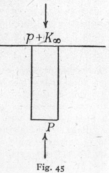

Fig. 45

$a\rho^2$, where $a = 2\pi\displaystyle\int_0^\infty V_2(s)\,ds$. This force is due to the attraction of the rest of the fluid. Now, to an external observer, the fluid is exerting an outward pressure p, say, which is measurable, that is, there must be an externally applied pressure p to keep the fluid in place. This pressure is applied at the boundary. A cylinder of unit area, such as is shown in fig. 45, with one end in the surface and the other in the interior of the fluid, is in equilibrium. On the outer face there is a total force $p + K_\infty$ directed inwards. Hence on the inner face the pressure $P = p + K_\infty$. This accounts for the term a/v^2 in Van der Waals' equation of state of a fluid,

$$\left(p + \frac{a}{v^2}\right)(v - b) = R_1\theta,$$

for the K_∞ of the present section is $a\rho^2$, which can be written as a/v^2, where v is the specific volume.

(II) *Van der Waals' Theory.*—In Laplace's original theory the precise forms of the functions $V_1(x)$ and $V_2(x)$ are not stated. In an extension of the theory by Van der Waals, it is assumed that

$$V_1(x) = -\frac{Ae^{-x/\lambda}}{x}, \quad\ldots\ldots \quad (116)$$

where A and λ are constants; λ is called the radius of the sphere of molecular action. Hence in this case

$$V_2(x) = \int_x^\infty V_1(x)x\,dx \quad\ldots\ldots \quad (117)$$

$$= -A\lambda e^{-x/\lambda}.$$

Also

$$K_\infty = -2\pi\rho^2 A\lambda^2 \quad \text{and} \quad H_\infty = -2\pi\rho^2 A\lambda^3. \qquad (118)$$

Some of the points in the theory from which these expressions are deduced are summarized below.

Laplace's theory and other theories are incomplete in various ways. For example, attractive forces between molecules, particles, or volume elements are not the only forces in operation inside a fluid. There are repulsive forces, for example, (a) those which arise when an attempt is made to superpose one particle on another, and (b) those due to the thermal agitation of the molecules. Further, the equilibrium of a fluid is determined by its " free " or " available " energy, not by the total potential energy of the attractive forces. Finally, the density of a fluid is not constant throughout its whole mass.

Van der Waals takes some of these points into consideration. Instead of assuming that the boundary between a liquid and its vapour is merely a geometrical surface, Van der Waals assumes that a transition layer exists, in which the properties of the substance change continuously but rapidly from those of a liquid to those of a vapour. He divides the transition layer into a large number of extremely thin sheets, each of which possesses a certain density, differing infinitely little from that of its neighbours. By means of this model he calculates the potential energy of unit mass at any point in the transition layer, and hence the total energy per sq. cm. of that layer, its free energy per sq. cm., its thermo-dynamic potentials, its surface tension, and certain critical data. All this leads to the expressions in equations (116), (117) and (118), but the full details cannot be given here.

Bakker, in contrast to Van der Waals, assumes the existence of a transition layer between liquid and vapour, in which the density varies continuously according to the isothermal law obtained by making the temperature constant in Van der Waals' well-known equation of state. He then deduces the total energy in the film, &c., in a similar manner to Van der Waals.

References

Ewald, Pöschl and Prandtl, *The Physics of Solids and Fluids* (Blackie).

Lord Rayleigh, *Scientific Papers*.

Bouasse, *Capillarité* (1924).

Dorsey, *Scientific Papers of the Bureau of Standards*, Vol. 21, p. 563, (1926–27).

Ferguson, *Science Progress*, Vol. 24, p. 120 (1929–30).

Bakker, *Handbuch der Experimentalphysik*, Vol. VI (1928).

CHAPTER VIII

Surface Films

1. Surface Films of Insoluble Substances.

A surface film of a substance A on a liquid B in which it is insoluble is usually obtained by dissolving a small quantity of A in some volatile solvent C, and then dropping a little of the solution from a pipette on to the surface of B. When the whole of C has evaporated, a surface film of A remains on B. For example, A may be a fatty acid, B water, and C benzene. Four types of such films have been found to exist.

In order to describe the properties of the films, N. K. Adam and other authorities use the concept of *surface pressure*, derived by analogy from the kinetic theory of gases. The films are nearly all only one molecule thick, and each molecule of a film, or assemblage of molecules, moves about in a two-dimensional region, colliding with other molecules and with the boundaries of the surface. The momentum imparted to the boundaries per cm. per second may be regarded as a force per cm. length exerted " outwards " by the film. This is the so-called *surface pressure* of the film. This force per cm. may also be regarded as the difference of the surface tensions of the pure solvent and of the solvent covered by the surface film, and is due to the presence of the film. In symbols, the pressure $P = T_1 - T_2$, where T_1 and T_2 are the respective surface tensions of the two liquids. Further, if the solution changes in strength, $dP = -dT_2$, since T_1 is constant. A method of measuring this force is given later (p. 169).

(i) *Gaseous films.*

The first of the four types of film to be discussed is the so-called *gaseous film*, in which single molecules of the substance move about independently. In a perfect gaseous film the lateral attractions of the molecules on one another would be zero and in actual practice they are small. The molecules have properties analogous to those of molecules in a rarefied gas or of molecules of a solute in a dilute solution. They exert a pressure by bombardment of the boundaries. The dimensions of the film pressure are those of force per cm., whereas both the pressure of a gas and the osmotic pressure of a solution have the dimensions of force per sq. cm. The molecules of such a film are prevented from emerging normally from the surface, that is, from evaporation, by the attraction exerted upon them by the molecules of the subjacent liquid; this, however, is not very great, or the film would dissolve. For example, in the case when films of alcohols or fatty acids float on water, this attraction is due to end groups such as OH or COOH, which are termed *hydrophilic*.

It is convenient to exhibit the properties of these films by graphs (fig. 1) in which the abscissa is the pressure in dynes per cm. and the ordinate the product of pressure and area per molecule, the temperature being constant. If the film were perfect, in the sense that a perfect gas is perfect, the product PA would be constant at constant temperature. In practice, e.g. for films of certain esters of the dibasic acids on water, which approach most nearly to the perfect state, the $PA - P$ graph starts, for temperatures near 18° C. and for $P = 0$, at a point where PA is about 400×10^{-16} dynes-cm., which is the value for a perfect gaseous film at that temperature. The graph then descends a little, but soon bends upwards and continues almost as a straight line, like the $PV - P$ graph for real gases.

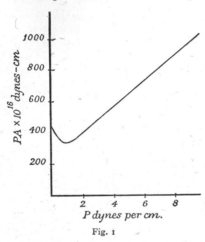

Fig. 1

The value of the product PA for a perfect gaseous film may be calculated as follows. By the theorem of equipartition of energy,* we may assign to every molecule of the film a kinetic energy of $\frac{1}{2}k\theta$ ergs per degree of freedom, where k is Boltzmann's constant, $1\cdot372 \times 10^{-16}$. If we assign two degrees of freedom to each molecule, since it can only move in two directions, the kinetic energy per molecule is $1\cdot372 \times 10^{-16} \times \theta$ ergs. As in the elementary kinetic theory of gases, but replacing PV by PA, we get $PA = 1\cdot372 \times 10^{16} \times \theta$, where A is the area per molecule in sq. cm. At a temperature of 18° C. ($= 291°$ K.), $PA = 399\cdot2 \times 10^{-16}$ ergs.

It is probable that in the gaseous films of long-chain molecules, these molecules lie with their longest dimension more or less parallel to the surface. The characteristic features of a gaseous film are that its surface pressure remains continuous down to very low values at very large areas and that the value of the pressure is still given by $PA = k\theta$, when P is very small.

(ii) *Condensed or " coherent " films.*

This type of film, which is much more common than the last, is composed of groups or " islands " of molecules adhering to one another but separated by relatively large areas. Like the gaseous film, this kind of film is only one molecule thick. Individual molecules leave

---

* See Jeans, *Dynamical Theory of Gases*, sections 99 and 100.

the islands at rare intervals. The surface pressure exerted by the film on the boundaries is due to bombardment by islands, not by individual molecules.

Fig. 2 shows two graphs, in which the abscissa is the area per molecule and the ordinate the surface pressure, for two types of condensed film. Graph I represents the behaviour of a film of a fatty acid on old distilled water. For most of its length it is a steeply-inclined straight line, with a short rounded part at the lower end due to certain experimental errors. The straight part when produced meets the horizontal axis where $A = 20{\cdot}5 \times 10^{-16}$ sq. cm. per molecule. It is probable that in such cases the cross-sections of the end groups of the long-

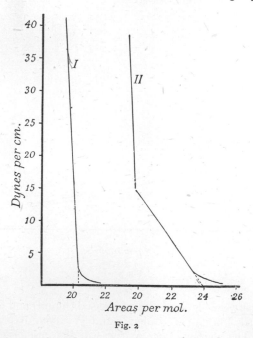

Fig. 2

chain compounds affect the closeness of the packing. If the end groups have large volumes under low pressures, they will prevent the chains from packing tightly together; but if the end groups are compressible or can be " tucked " away into recesses in the chains of neighbouring molecules, increasing pressure will produce changes in area such as are represented by the less steep part of graph II.

Pursuing the analogy between the behaviour of surface films and that of any working substance undergoing pressure and volume changes, we now see that the condensed films are analogous to liquids. The passage of a condensed film into a gaseous one is analogous to the passage of a working substance from the liquid state to the gaseous state. Such changes take place at very low surface pressures, namely, pressures not greater than 0·3 dynes per cm.

For films of fatty acids on water, the graphs connecting pressure and area show just the same features as Andrews' isothermals for carbon dioxide * below the critical point, namely, an almost vertical straight part corresponding to the condensed film, a horizontal part representing the change of state at constant pressure, and a curved part representing the gaseous state. The curves for myristic and tridecylic acids are shown in fig. 3.

(iii) *Expanded films.*

There are two types of film whose properties have no analogy with those of a three-dimensional working substance. Their properties are

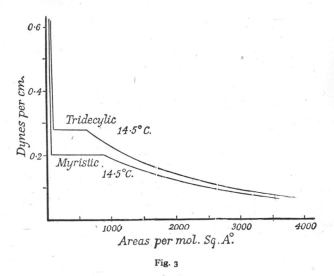

Fig. 3

intermediate between those of the condensed (liquid) and gaseous films. They are called " liquid expanded " and " vapour expanded " films respectively. The characteristic features of the liquid expanded films are that their area per molecule approaches a constant value when the pressure becomes very low, and that they then have a constant surface pressure.

An example of a $P - A$ graph for such a film is shown in fig. 4. LM represents the state at very low pressures. LN represents the film in the liquid expanded state. NOQ represents the gradual change from the liquid expanded to the condensed state. Films of myristic acid on dilute hydrochloric acid show such properties at temperatures near 10° C.

The characteristic feature of vapour expanded films is a gradual expansion, but not to a limiting area or surface pressure. This behaviour

* See Roberts, *Heat and Thermodynamics*, p. 87.

is shown by films of ethyl palmitate on a dilute acid. The precise arrangement of the molecules in these films is still unknown.

The type of graph representing the behaviour of a vapour expanded film is shown in fig. 5.

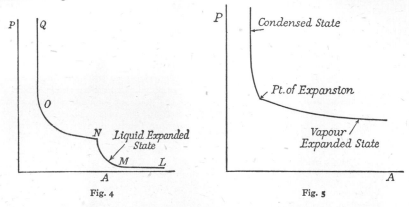

Fig. 4　　　　　　　　　Fig. 5

2. Measurement of Surface Pressures and Areas.

The most sensitive method used is one devised by Langmuir and improved by Adam. The experiments are conducted with films floating on a liquid contained in a shallow rectangular brass trough (fig. 6). In a certain case the trough measured 60 cm. × 14 cm. × 1·8 cm. internally, and the sides were 1 cm. thick and flat on top. The liquid in the trough is cleaned before a film is formed, by

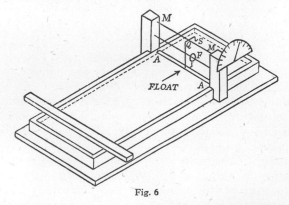

Fig. 6

drawing " barriers ", i.e. strips of plate glass, over the liquid surface to " scrape " it. When the liquid is water, the barriers and tops of the edges of the trough are coated with hard paraffin-wax (a substance which does not contaminate water) to prevent the film creeping past the barriers.

The pressure of the film is exerted on a float, i.e. a vertical plane sheet AA of waxed copper foil, which extends almost the whole width of the trough and dips into the liquid. To block the gaps at each end of the float, thin platinum ribbons about 3 mm. wide, attached to the main framework of the trough but free at the other end, are used. The position of the float is indicated by a kind of optical lever; any movement of the float causes the rotation of a small plane mirror F and hence of a beam of light reflected from it. When a measurement of pressure is made, a force equal to the total thrust of the film on the float is applied to the float in the opposite direction. This force is the forward-acting tension of a fine silver wire attached to the float, and the beam of light is thus kept in the equilibrium position. The tension is applied by twisting a horizontal torsion wire MM of phosphor bronze. A suitable framework supported independently above the trough links this torsion wire to the silver wire which applies the tension to the float. The readings of the torsion head are calibrated by hanging weights on an arm QS of the framework, so that the moment of a weight about the axis of the torsion wire is easily calculated from the dimensions of the framework. To every reading of the torsion head φ there corresponds a definite moment mga. The effective length of the float is taken as its full actual length plus half the width of each gap blocked by the platinum ribbons, and the thrust on it by the film is equal to the " pressure " multiplied by this effective length. Again, this thrust multiplied by the effective length of the " arm " linking the silver tension wire to the torsion wire gives the moment of the thrust about the axis of the torsion wire. When the float is in its equilibrium position under the two forces,

$$mga_1 = Pla_2,$$

where mga_1 is the moment of the forces corresponding to the actual torsion-head deflection φ required to keep the float in its equilibrium position, P is the film pressure to be measured, l is the effective length of the float, and a_2 is the arm or perpendicular from the axis of the torsion wire to the line of action of the resultant thrust of the film. The area of the film is the area of the rectangle between the float and the next barrier.

An apparatus of this kind will measure pressures down to 0·01 dynes per cm. After the area is altered by moving a barrier it is necessary to make quick readings in order to avoid contamination, especially at very low surface pressures.

3. Surface Films of Solutions.

The state of concentration of the surface film of a solution is usually different from that of the general body of the liquid. In fact, the concentration in the film is governed by the general law that a mechanical system free to move will reach a state of equilibrium in which the potential energy has a minimum value. In particular, it is the free surface energy, not the total energy, which has a minimum value. By the reasoning in Chapter VII, section 36 (p. 157), we see that the surface tension is, strictly speaking, equal to the free surface energy.

In a system consisting of two components, e.g. a solvent A and a solute B, the surface film is richer in that component which reduces the free surface energy to a minimum. The general name of *adsorption* is given to the alteration of concentration of a component in the surface film of a liquid, produced by any cause. The terms positive adsorption and negative adsorption are used to indicate the increase and decrease of concentration of a component.

4. Gibbs's Adsorption Formula.

The quantitative relation connecting surface tension and con-centration of solute in the surface film and in the main body of a solution is known as *Gibbs's adsorption formula*. In order to derive it, certain definitions are required.

Consider a system consisting of one solvent and one solute. Let the total volume be v c.c., the absolute temperature θ, the total entropy ϕ c.g.s. units, the surface area A sq. cm., the total internal energy of the solution (including the surface film) U ergs, and the surface tension T dynes/cm, Let the solution have an osmotic pressure of p dynes/sq. cm. Apply the first and second laws of thermodynamics to this system. Let an elementary quantity of heat dH ergs be given to the system and let it be used in increasing the area of the surface by dA sq. cm., and the volume by dv c.c. By the first law of thermo-dynamics,

$$dH = dU + p\,dv - T\,dA, \quad \ldots \ldots \quad (1)$$

since $+p\,dv$ and $-T\,dA$ represent the contributions to the external work done by the working substance. By the second law, if all the energy is used in performing reversible processes only,

$$dH = \theta\,d\phi. \quad \ldots \ldots \ldots \quad (2)$$

Hence

$$dU = \theta\,d\phi - p\,dv + T\,dA. \quad \ldots \ldots \quad (3)$$

We now introduce Φ, the thermodynamic potential at constant temperature and pressure. As is usual in thermodynamics *,

$$\Phi = U - \theta\phi + pv. \quad \ldots \ldots \ldots \quad (4)$$

Differentiation gives

$$d\Phi = dU - \theta\,d\phi - \phi\,d\theta + p\,dv + v\,dp, \quad \ldots \quad (5)$$

and, by (3),

$$d\Phi = -\phi\,d\theta + T\,dA + v\,dp. \quad \ldots \ldots \quad (6)$$

If the system is kept at constant temperature,

$$d\theta = 0 \quad \text{and} \quad d\Phi = T\,dA + v\,dp.$$

Now $d\Phi$ is a perfect or total differential of Φ with respect to any pair of variables such as A and p; hence, by the properties of such differentials,

$$\left(\frac{\partial T}{\partial p}\right)_{A \text{ const.}} = \left(\frac{\partial v}{\partial A}\right)_{p \text{ const.}} \quad \ldots \ldots \quad (7)$$

---

* See Roberts, *Heat and Thermodynamics*, p. 309.

Let the total volume v of solution (represented by $LMNO$ in fig. 7) contain n grammes of solute. Draw an arbitrary horizontal plane XY

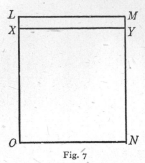

Fig. 7

across the liquid very near the top, so as to cut off a portion $LMYX$ of negligible volume compared with $LMNO$. Call the portion $LMYX$, thus defined, the surface film. Let there be m grammes of solute in $LMYX$. We write this in the form $m = Ax$, where A is the area of the surface film perpendicular to the plane of the diagram. Defined in this way, and reckoned in grammes per sq. cm., the quantity x is called the excess concentration in the surface film, and has the dimensions of mass per unit area. The concentration in grammes per c.c. of the rest of the solution, by the definition of concentration, is

$$\frac{\text{mass}}{\text{volume}} = c, \text{ say,}$$

$$= \frac{n - Ax}{\text{volume } XYNO} = \frac{n - Ax}{v - \text{vol. } LMYX} = \frac{n - Ax}{v},$$

since $LMYX$ is small compared with v. Hence

$$v = \frac{n - Ax}{c}. \quad \cdot \quad \cdot \quad \cdot \quad \cdot \quad \cdot \quad \cdot \quad (8)$$

Substituting from equation (8) in equation (7) and noting that p is constant when c is constant, we find that equation (7) becomes

$$\left(\frac{\partial T}{\partial p}\right)_{A\text{ const.}} = \left(\frac{\partial v}{\partial A}\right)_{p\text{ const.}} = \left(\frac{\partial v}{\partial A}\right)_{c\text{ const.}} = -\left(\frac{x}{c}\right). \quad (9)$$

Assume that the solution is dilute and obeys van't Hoff's law, $p = R_1\theta c$, where

$$R_1 = \frac{\text{universal gas constant } (R)}{\text{molecular wt. of solute}}$$

Then if θ is constant, $dp = R_1\theta\, dc$ and

$$\left(\frac{\partial T}{\partial p}\right)_{A\text{ const.}} = \frac{1}{R_1\theta}\left(\frac{\partial T}{\partial c}\right)_{A\text{ const.}} \quad \cdot \quad \cdot \quad \cdot \quad \cdot \quad (10)$$

Comparing (9) and (10), we get

$$x = -\frac{c}{R_1\theta}\frac{\partial T}{\partial c}. \quad \cdot \quad \cdot \quad \cdot \quad \cdot \quad \cdot \quad (11)$$

This is the so-called Gibbs's equation in a special form. A more general form of it is

$$x = -\frac{a}{R_1\theta}\frac{\partial T}{\partial a}, \quad \ldots \ldots (12)$$

where a is a more general quantity called the " activity " of the solute in the solution (and reduces to c in the special case). The x of equation (12) is the excess concentration in the case of a non-ionized solute.

5. Gibbs's Equation in the case of Ionized Solutes. (Theory of G. N. Lewis.)

In contrast with the last case, we consider a solution in which the solute is ionized. We assume, as is often done, that on the surface of such a solution there is an electric double layer, caused by the positive and negative ions.

In this case the two faces of the surface film are charged with positive and negative electricity respectively, and form, in effect, a charged electrical condenser (fig. 8). The film therefore possesses an additional feature, besides those postulated in the previous section. Let the total charge of each kind of electricity be Q e.s.u., in each case distributed over A sq. cm., and let the potential difference between the faces of the film be V e.s.u. If an elementary quantity of heat dH is given to the film only, an elementary charge $+dQ$ passes across the film from the negative face to the positive. During this process the system has work $+VdQ$ ergs done upon it, that is, it does $-VdQ$ ergs of work. As we are considering phenomena in the film only, the external work done by the osmotic pressure will be ignored in the following equation, which represents the first law of thermodynamics applied to the film:

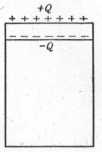

Fig. 8

$$dH = dU - TdA - VdQ. \quad \ldots . (13)$$

If we assume that no heat is used in performing irreversible processes, the second law of thermodynamics gives

$$dH = \theta d\phi. \quad \ldots \ldots (14)$$

Hence

$$dU = \theta d\phi + TdA + VdQ. \quad \ldots . (15)$$

For such a film, the thermodynamic potential at constant electrical potential (instead of pressure) and temperature is

$$\Phi = U - \theta\phi - VQ. \quad \ldots \ldots (16)$$

On differentiating and substituting from (15), we have

$$d\Phi = T\,dA - Q\,dV, \text{ when } \theta \text{ is constant.}$$

Since $d\Phi$ is a perfect differential,

$$\left(\frac{\partial T}{\partial V}\right)_{A \text{ const.}} = -\left(\frac{\partial Q}{\partial A}\right)_{V \text{ const.}} \quad \ldots \ldots \text{ (17)}$$

We now assume that when the charge dQ is carried from one face of the film to the other, it is the net result of the motion of a mass dm_1 grammes of positive ions carrying altogether $+dQ$ e.s.u. in one direction, and of a mass dm_2 grammes of negative ions carrying altogether $-dQ$ e.s.u. in the other. Let the electrochemical equivalents of these ions be ϵ_1 and ϵ_2 respectively. Then, by Faraday's laws of electrolysis,

$$dm_1 = \epsilon_1\,dQ \text{ and } dQ = \frac{dm_1}{\epsilon_1},$$

$$dm_2 = \epsilon_2\,dQ \text{ and } dQ = \frac{dm_2}{\epsilon_2}.$$

Substituting these values of dQ in turn in (17), we have

$$\left(\frac{\partial T}{\partial V}\right)_{A \text{ const.}} = -\frac{1}{\epsilon_1}\left(\frac{\partial m_1}{\partial A}\right)_{V \text{ const.}} \quad \ldots \ldots \text{ (18)}$$

and

$$\left(\frac{\partial T}{\partial V}\right)_{A \text{ const.}} = -\frac{1}{\epsilon_2}\left(\frac{\partial m_2}{\partial A}\right)_{V \text{ const.}} \quad \ldots \ldots \text{ (19)}$$

The expression $\left(\dfrac{\partial m_1}{\partial A}\right)_{V \text{ const.}}$ is interpreted as the increase in the mass of positive ions per unit increase in area of the film at constant V, that is, as the mass of cations which enters every new square centimetre of area produced by stretching the film; in other words, it is the excess concentration of cations in the film. Similarly $\left(\dfrac{\partial m_2}{\partial A}\right)_{V \text{ const.}}$ is the excess concentration of anions in the film. The total excess "electrical" concentration is the sum of these,

$$= \left(\frac{\partial m_1}{\partial A}\right)_{V \text{ const.}} + \left(\frac{\partial m_2}{\partial A}\right)_{V \text{ const.}}$$

$$= -(\epsilon_1 + \epsilon_2)\left(\frac{\partial T}{\partial V}\right)_{A \text{ const.}}, \quad \ldots \ldots \text{ (20)}$$

an equation which also applies to the electrical double layer at an interface. The total excess concentration due to non-ionized and ionized solute in a surface or interfacial film is

$$x = -\frac{c}{R_1\theta}\left(\frac{\partial T}{\partial c}\right)_{A \text{ const.}} - (\epsilon_1 + \epsilon_2)\left(\frac{\partial T}{\partial V}\right)_{A \text{ const.}} \quad . \quad (21)$$

Quantitative experimental tests of this equation have not yet been made.

6. Pressure-Area Relations of Surface Films of Solutions.

(a) *Szyszkowski's relation.*—For certain solutions of those fatty acids which contain from three to six carbon atoms Szyszkowski found an empirical relation, which may be stated thus:

$$P = a \log_{10}\left(1 + \frac{c}{\beta}\right), \quad . \quad . \quad . \quad . \quad (22)$$

where P is the surface pressure, a and β are constants for each acid but are different for different acids, and c is the concentration of the liquid in grammes per c.c.

(b) $PA = k\theta$.—We assume that Gibbs's adsorption equation applies to these solutions, which are not ionized. That is,

$$x = -\frac{c}{R_1\theta}\frac{\partial T}{\partial c},$$

by equation (12), where T is the surface tension. As in section 1, p. 165, $dT = -dP$, where P is the surface pressure. Hence

$$x = +\frac{c}{R\theta}\frac{\partial P}{\partial c}. \quad . \quad . \quad . \quad . \quad (23)$$

Differentiating Szyszkowski's relation gives

$$\frac{\partial P}{\partial c} = \frac{\text{constant}}{(\beta + c)} = \frac{\delta}{\beta + c}, \text{ say.}$$

Substituting in (23), we have

$$x = \frac{\delta}{R_1\theta}\frac{c}{(\beta + c)}. \quad . \quad . \quad . \quad . \quad (24)$$

In dilute solutions $\beta \gg c$ and $c/(\beta + c) = c/\beta$, very nearly. Hence $x = c\delta/R_1\theta\beta$ and x/c is constant when θ, the absolute temperature, is constant. Substituting in (23), we find that $\partial P/\partial c = a$ constant when θ is constant $= K$, say. Hence on integration we have

$$P = Kc,$$

plus a constant which is equal to zero. Now x is the number of grammes per sq. cm. in the surface. Let one gramme contain n molecules. Then nx is the number of molecules per sq. cm. Let A be the area per molecule. Then, since nx molecules occupy 1 sq. cm., $x = 1/An$. Also

$$x = \frac{c}{R_1\theta}\frac{\partial P}{\partial c} = \frac{c}{R_1\theta}\frac{P}{c},$$

since

$$\frac{\partial P}{\partial c} = K = \frac{P}{c}.$$

Equating the two values of x, we get

$$\frac{P}{R_1\theta} = \frac{1}{An},$$

and

$$PA = \frac{R_1\theta}{n} = k\theta, \quad . \quad . \quad . \quad . \quad (25)$$

where $k = \dfrac{R_1}{n} =$ Boltzmann's constant, $1 \cdot 372 \times 10^{-16}$.

This shows that films of solutions of the shorter fatty acids are " gaseous " in the sense of p. 165. As the length of the molecular chain increases, the behaviour of the films diverges more and more from that of the gaseous films. In some cases, in fact, they first become " expanded " and then " condensed ".

REFERENCE

N. K. Adam, *The Physics and Chemistry of Surfaces* (Clarendon Press (1930)).

CHAPTER IX

Kinetic Theory of Matter

1. Introduction.

One of the main aims of theoretical physics in the nineteenth century was the reduction of the various branches of physics to mechanics and the ultimate explanation of physical phenomena in terms of Newton's laws of motion. The kinetic theory of matter, and in particular the kinetic theory of gases, affords one of the best and most successful examples of this method of attack. The application of the kinetic theory to liquids is discussed below (see p. 196). In the case of solids, the results can often be better obtained by quantum and thermodynamical considerations.* On the other hand, the classical kinetic theory of gases has suffered comparatively little modification † and is therefore discussed here at much greater length.

Since all gases obey, at least approximately, very simple gas laws such as those of Boyle and Charles, it is reasonable to suppose that they all possess a common and simple structure. Basically, the kinetic theory rests on a still more fundamental hypothesis, the atomic theory. The latter dates back to the Greek school of philosophy under Lucretius, which maintained that matter is composed of aggregates of hard, indivisible, indestructible similar parts, termed atoms. The physical implications of the atomic theory were emphasized in the seventeenth century by Gassendi, who suggested that mere motion of the atoms might explain diverse physical phenomena without additional hypotheses. A further advance was made by Bernoulli, who deduced Boyle's law on the assumption that the pressure of a gas arises from impact of the molecules on the wall of the containing vessel. Little development occurred in the following century, but the atomic hypothesis received strong support from chemical theory, particularly from Dalton's laws of the combining powers of the elements. It was not, however, until Joule's classical work in 1848 on the strict numerical convertibility of mechanical work and heat was carried out that the kinetic theory could expand and assume its present comprehensive form.

---

* See, for example, J. K. Roberts, *Heat and Thermodynamics*, Chap. XXI (Blackie & Son, Ltd., 1933).

† See, however, Robi, *Review of Scientific Instruments*, Vol. I, No. 9 (Sept., 1935).

The first great advances, due to Clausius in 1857 and succeeding years, were based on the following assumptions, which still form the basis of any elementary treatment of the kinetic theory:

(1) The molecules of a given monatomic gaseous element are regarded as identical solid spheres which move in straight lines until they collide with one another or with the wall of the containing vessel.

(2) The time occupied in collision is negligible and the collision is perfectly elastic.

(3) The molecules are negligible in size compared with the volume of the container.

(4) There are no mutual forces of attraction or repulsion between the molecules.

Clausius also introduced the important conception of the *mean free path* of a gas molecule, which is defined as the average distance traversed by a molecule between successive collisions. The quantities required for a knowledge of the properties and condition of a gas, therefore, are (1) the velocity of the molecules, (2) the value of the mean free path at S.T.P. (standard temperature and pressure), (3) the number of molecules present in unit volume of the gas at S.T.P., (4) the diameter of a gas molecule, regarded as a hard elastic sphere.

The deduction of the gas laws by Clausius and the evaluation of the root mean square velocity of a gas molecule by Joule, some years earlier, were made on the assumption that the velocity of all the molecules in the gas is the same at a given temperature. Maxwell showed later that the velocities were distributed among the molecules according to a probability law. These aspects of the kinetic theory, together with a demonstration of the validity of Avogadro's hypothesis, have already been dealt with in some detail in this series;[*] and it has been shown that

$$p = \tfrac{1}{3}\rho C^2, \qquad . \quad . \quad . \quad . \quad . \quad . \quad (1)$$

where p is the gas pressure, ρ the density, and C^2 the mean square velocity of the gas molecules.

2. Transport Theorems and the Mean Free Path of a Gas Molecule.

Although Clausius did not succeed in evaluating λ, the mean free path of a gas molecule, ν, the number of molecules per unit volume, or σ, the diameter of a gas molecule, he obtained the useful relation [†]

$$\lambda = \frac{1}{\pi\sigma^2\nu}, \qquad . \quad . \quad . \quad . \quad . \quad . \quad (2)$$

connecting the three quantities, so that if two of them are known, the third is easily derived. The result was deduced on the basis of a number of over-simplifying assumptions, but it must be emphasized

---

[*] See Roberts, *Heat and Thermodynamics*, Chap. III.   [†] See Roberts, p. 69.

at this stage that the fundamental rule to be observed in the treatment of problems by the kinetic theory is to make the number of simplifying assumptions a maximum. Any reduction in the number of assumptions almost invariably involves enormous complication in the mathematical treatment. In view of present ideas on the electrical structure and wave-like character of atoms and molecules, such detailed treatment is not warranted; the billiard-ball atom is only a crude approximation to reality. The relation obtained by the more accurate treatment usually differs from that obtained by simpler methods only in the introduction of some numerical factor, which, however, may be essential when *quantitative* comparison is made with experiment.

Assuming that all the molecules are in motion with velocities distributed according to a probability law, Maxwell obtained the relation

$$\lambda = \frac{1}{\sqrt{2}} \frac{1}{\pi\sigma^2\nu}. \qquad \cdots \cdots \cdots (3)$$

Taking into account also the persistence of velocity on collision, Jeans derives the formula

$$\lambda = \frac{1}{\sqrt{2}} \frac{1\cdot319}{\pi\sigma^2\nu}. \qquad \cdots \cdots \cdots (4)$$

Finally, if intramolecular forces are also considered, the formula of Sutherland * may be obtained:

$$\lambda = \frac{1\cdot402}{\sqrt{2}\pi\sigma^2\nu(1 + A/T)}, \qquad \cdots \cdots (5)$$

where A is a constant varying with the nature of the gas and T the absolute temperature.

(i) *Transport theorems: general case.*

Consider a volume of gas, one part of which has some property (such as temperature) whose value differs from the value of that property in another region of the gas. Owing to the kinetic velocities, molecules will be continually passing from one region to the other, and a transport of the particular property will therefore be continually taking place. In order to determine the amount of the property transported across unit area in the gas, the number of molecules passing in any particular direction in unit time is required. The simplest method of averaging this number, known as Joule's classification, is to consider a cube situated in the gas. If the area of a face of the cube is dS and ν is the number of molecules present in unit volume, then, since there are no preferred directions, at any instant one-sixth of the total number of molecules in the volume will be travelling towards any one of the six sides of the cube.

* Sutherland, *Phil. Mag.*, Vol. 36, p. 507 (1893).

If $\bar{c}$ is the mean velocity of the molecules, the number passing in one direction across the area dS in unit time will be

$$n_1 = dS\,\frac{\nu}{6}\,\bar{c}. \qquad \ldots \ldots \ldots \quad (6)$$

Now on the average, the last collision a molecule makes before crossing the area dS (normal to the x-axis) will have occurred at the mean free path λ from dS. Hence if G represents any property which is being transported across the area (fig. 1) and G is its particular value at the plane dS, the molecules which pass in one direction will have, on the average, a value of G given by $\left(G + \dfrac{dG}{dx}\lambda\right)$, and those which pass in the reverse direction will have a value of G given by $\left(G - \dfrac{dG}{dx}\lambda\right)$. The property is assumed to have

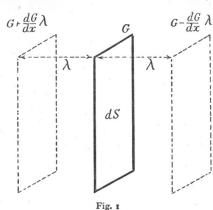

Fig. 1

a uniform gradient over the short distance λ. The net amount of the property transported in unit time is therefore

$$\Delta G = \tfrac{1}{6}\nu\bar{c}\,dS\left(G + \frac{dG}{dx}\lambda - G + \frac{dG}{dx}\lambda\right)$$

$$= \tfrac{1}{3}\nu\bar{c}\,dS\lambda\,\frac{dG}{dx}. \qquad \ldots \ldots \ldots \quad (7)$$

(ii) *Coefficient of viscosity.*

Maxwell applied equation (7) to evaluate the coefficient of viscosity of a gas in terms of the kinetic theory, and was able to deduce a value for λ, the mean free path. Consider a gas flowing over a surface at rest. Denote the drift velocity of any layer parallel to the surface at a distance x by u (fig. 2). Then owing to the presence of viscosity the drift velocity of the gas decreases as the surface at rest is approached and increases in the reverse direction. If an area dS is considered lying in the layer of velocity u, the net transfer of molecules across it will be zero. The molecules from below, however, will transport a drift momentum less than mu, while those from above will transport a drift momentum greater than this value. A change in momentum is therefore continually taking place across the area, and by Newton's second law of motion this gives rise to the viscous force acting along the layer. Here the property G being transported is the momentum mu. Hence, applying equation (7), we have

$$\Delta G = \tfrac{1}{3}v\bar{c}\,dS\lambda m \frac{du}{dx} = F, \quad \ldots \ldots \text{(8)}$$

where F represents the viscous force acting across the area dS. Now Newton's law of viscosity may be written

$$F = \eta\,dS \frac{du}{dx}, \quad \ldots \ldots \ldots \text{(9)}$$

where F is the viscous force across an area dS perpendicular to which there is a velocity gradient du/dx, and η is the coefficient of viscosity. Hence from equations (8) and (9)

$$\eta = \tfrac{1}{3}v\bar{c}m\lambda, \quad \ldots \ldots \ldots \text{(10)}$$

or, since $m\nu = \rho$, the density of the gas,

$$\eta = \tfrac{1}{3}\rho\bar{c}\lambda. \quad \ldots \ldots \ldots \text{(11)}$$

A much more detailed treatment by Chapman* gives the relation $\eta = \dfrac{1}{2\cdot64}\,\rho\bar{c}\lambda$; the treatment by the elementary theory is therefore a very satisfactory approximation.

Experimental determination of η and ρ and the evaluation of $\bar{c}$ in terms of C, the root mean square velocity (see Ex. 4, p. 279), which in turn is given by equation (1), therefore affords a measure of the mean free path λ. In this way Maxwell showed that for hydrogen at N.T.P. $\lambda = 1\cdot85 \times 10^{-5}$ cm.

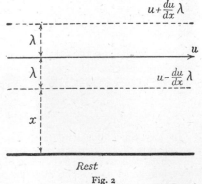

Fig. 2

Examination of equation (11) shows that η should be independent of the density of the gas, since as ρ increases with pressure λ decreases, as is shown by equation (2). This important and unexpected result obtained by Maxwell afforded great support for the kinetic theory of gases. Maxwell demonstrated the independence experimentally with the oscillating disc (see Chapter XII, § 11, p. 256) and showed that over a wide range the rate of damping is independent of the pressure. The relation fails at high and low pressures; the reasons for the failure are discussed later (p. 185). The relation has been retested more recently by Gilchrist, using the concentric cylinder method: the

* Chapman, *Proc. Roy. Soc.*, A, Vol. 93, p. 1 (1916).

effect had actually been noted as early as 1660 by Boyle, who observed that the rate of damping of a pendulum was independent of the gas pressure.

Further examination of equation (11) yields the equally remarkable prediction that, in contrast to liquids, where the viscosity decreases rapidly with rise of temperature, the viscosity of gases increases as the square root of the absolute temperature. Experimentally η is found to be proportional to T^s, where s varies from 0·6 to 1 according to the nature of the gas. The explanation lies in closer consideration of the structure of the molecules and is discussed in § 4 (iii), p. 194.

(iii) *Coefficient of heat conduction of a gas.*

We apply the arguments of the preceding section; here the property being transported is the heat energy of the gas. Hence

$$G = mC_vT, \quad \ldots \ldots \ldots \quad (12)$$

where C_v and T are the specific heat at constant volume and the temperature of the gas respectively. Substitution in the basic equation (7) therefore gives

$$\Delta G = \tfrac{1}{3}v\bar{c}\lambda \, dS \, mC_v \frac{dT}{dx} = \Delta Q, \quad \ldots \quad (13)$$

where ΔQ is the amount of heat transferred across area dS in unit time. Now the equation defining the coefficient of heat conduction is

$$\Delta Q = \kappa \frac{dT}{dx} \, dS, \quad \ldots \ldots \quad (14)$$

where κ is the coefficient of heat conduction and dT/dx is the temperature gradient. Hence from equations (13) and (14) we have

$$\kappa = \tfrac{1}{3}mv\bar{c}\lambda C_v, \quad \ldots \ldots \quad (15)$$

or

$$\kappa = \tfrac{1}{3}\rho\bar{c}\lambda C_v. \quad \ldots \ldots \quad (16)$$

The experimental values for κ are determined either by the parallel plate method, as in the experiments of Hercus and Laby,[*] or by the concentric wire and cylinder method, as in the more recent determinations of Kannaluik and Martin.[†] The values given by the two methods are not in very close agreement, but are sufficiently close to indicate that the experimental value of κ differs from that predicted by equation (16) by a factor of 2.

More detailed treatment introduces a factor of about 1·5, but complete agreement between theory and experiment still appears to be lacking. Probably the explanation is partly that, in contrast to the viscosity problem, the transport is not taking place in equilibrium. Thus, for example, it is assumed that the number of molecules passing across the element of area dS in *both* directions is given by $v\bar{c}/6$, whereas the value of $\bar{c}$, since it represents the temperature of the gas molecules in a layer at a given distance from dS, is different for molecules coming from high- and low-temperature regions.

* Hercus and Laby, *Proc. Roy. Soc.*, A, Vol. 95, p. 190 (1919).
† Kannaluik and Martin, *Proc. Roy. Soc.*, A, Vol. 144, p. 496 (1934).

As with viscosity, the coefficient of thermal conductivity is found to be independent of the pressure, over a moderate range, and to increase approximately as the square root of the absolute temperature, in agreement with equation (16).

(iv) *Coefficient of diffusion.*

An expression for the coefficient of self-diffusion of a gas when different parts of it are at different densities may be obtained from the transport theorem as follows. The property being transported is simply the molecules themselves. Hence if ν represents the number of molecules per unit volume in the immediate neighbourhood of the layer dS, the numbers of molecules per unit volume at a distance equal to the mean free path on either side of dS will be $\left(\nu + \dfrac{d\nu}{dx}\lambda\right)$ and $\left(\nu - \dfrac{d\nu}{dx}\lambda\right)$ respectively. Hence, if we apply Joule's classification (p. 179), the net number Δn of molecules transported across dS in unit time is

$$\Delta n = \tfrac{1}{3}\lambda\bar{c}\frac{d\nu}{dx}\,dS. \quad \cdots \cdots \quad (17)$$

Now the basic law of diffusion, due to Fick, is

$$\Delta n = D\frac{d\nu}{dx}\,dS, \quad \cdots \cdots \quad (18)$$

where D is the coefficient of diffusion and $\dfrac{d\nu}{dx}$ represents the density gradient across dS. Hence from (17) and (18) we have

$$D = \tfrac{1}{3}\lambda\bar{c}. \quad \cdots \cdots \quad (19)$$

Equation (19) may be written generally in the form

$$D_{12} = \frac{1}{3}\frac{(\nu_1\lambda_2\bar{c_2} + \nu_2\lambda_1\bar{c_1})}{\nu_1 + \nu_2}, \quad \cdots \cdots \quad (19a)$$

where D_{12} refers to the coefficient of inter-diffusion of two gases, whose numbers of molecules per unit volume and mean free paths are represented by ν_1, ν_2, λ_1, λ_2 respectively.

The method commonly used to determine the coefficient of diffusion of two gases is that introduced by Loschmidt, in which a long vertical glass cylinder is separated into two parts by a sliding horizontal diaphragm in the centre. The denser gas is placed in the lower half, the lighter gas in the upper half, and the diaphragm is then removed. After a known interval of time the diaphragm is replaced and the mixtures of gases are analysed, either chemically or by means of some physical property (e.g. the refractive index).

An alternative method, introduced by Stefan, is to determine the change in composition of the gas contained in a vertical jar, the top of which is left open to the atmosphere for a stated period. An extension of this method enables the rate of diffusion of a saturated vapour in contact with its liquid to be determined by observation of the rate of evaporation of the liquid when the latter is contained in a narrow vertical tube. The tube and liquid are maintained at a constant temperature, a current of gas is sent across the open top of the tube, and the rate of fall of the level of the liquid in the tube is observed. The method is limited to liquids and is practicable over a small temperature range only.

The experimental results for $H_2 - O_2$, $H_2 - N_2$, $N_2 - O_2$, $H_2 - CO_2$, and $He - A$ show that the variation of D_{12} with the composition of the mixture is very much less than that predicted by equation (19a); various corrections to the simple formula, arising e.g. from consideration of the persistence of molecular velocity after collision, give somewhat better agreement with experiment.

Until recently, it was necessary to use indirect methods* to determine the coefficients of self-diffusion of gases. The discovery that ordinary hydrogen consists of a mixture of two components, ortho-hydrogen and para-hydrogen, made it possible to determine the coefficient of self-diffusion of this gas directly. The two components have the same density and, broadly speaking, the same chemical properties, but they may be distinguished by differences in certain physical characteristics, such as thermal conductivity. In the experiments of Harteck and Schmidt,† para-hydrogen and ordinary hydrogen were contained in two vessels, each about a metre long and separated by a tap. The tap was opened for about ten minutes, and the composition of the mixture was then determined from the value of the thermal conductivity, using an electrically-heated resistance inserted in the gas and the usual Wheatstone bridge arrangement, as in the Pirani gauge (see § 7 (e), p. 212).

According to equation (19), the coefficient of diffusion should be directly proportional to the pressure, a result which is confirmed by experiment. Since ρ is inversely proportional to T and $\bar{c}$ is proportional to $T^{1/2}$, the simple theory indicates that $D \propto T^{3/2}$. Experiment shows that $D \propto T^s$, where s lies between 1·75 and 2·0; a satisfactory explanation has been given by Sutherland on plausible grounds based on the kinetic theory.

It will be observed that by equations (11) and (16) $\kappa = \eta C_v$; also, from equations (11) and (19), $D = \eta/\rho$. More rigorous averaging gives $\kappa = \epsilon \eta C_v$ and $D = f\eta/\rho$, where ϵ and f are constants, each equal to about 1·4. Experiment shows that while the value for f is in approximate agreement with theory, ϵ is nearer 2·5. The value of the kinetic theory, however, lies rather in the general correlation which it establishes between diverse phenomena, such as thermal conductivity, viscosity, and diffusion, than in accurate quantitative predictions.

3. Properties of Gases at Low and Intermediate Pressures.

The application of the kinetic theory to predict the properties of gases at low pressures is of great importance, since the results obtained form the basis for the design and operation of pumps and gauges for the production and measurement of high vacua. (An account of these

---

* See Jeans, *Dynamical Theory of Gases*, Chapter XIII, p. 334 (C.U.P. (1916)).
† *Zeits. f. phys. Chem.*, Vol. 21, B, p. 447 (1933).

is given in §§ 6 and 7, p. 203.) As the gas pressure is reduced, the mean free path increases, until at intermediate pressures it becomes comparable with the linear dimensions d of the containing vessel and at low pressures it becomes much greater than d. At low pressures, therefore, comparatively few collisions occur between the gas molecules themselves, and collisions with the walls of the container become the governing factor.

(i) *Viscous forces at very low pressures.*

Consider two parallel surfaces, of which one is at rest and the other moving in a parallel direction with velocity u_0. All the molecules which strike the moving surface and then move in the direction of the fixed surface ultimately reach it without further collision, since $\lambda \gg d$. It may be shown * that the number of molecules coming from all directions and hitting unit area of a surface in unit time is given by

$$n = \tfrac{1}{4}v\bar{c}. \qquad \ldots \ldots \ldots (20)$$

Now all the molecules will communicate different amounts of sideways momentum to the fixed surface, according to the precise nature of the interaction between the gas molecule and the molecules of the solid. For theoretical purposes, however, it is permissible to define a fraction f, termed the *accommodation coefficient*, such that the fraction is considered to communicate its entire sideways momentum, the remaining fraction $(1 - f)$ being considered to be specularly reflected and to rebound with no transfer of sideways momentum. The sideways momentum transferred per second to the surface at rest is therefore

$$F = \tfrac{1}{4}v\bar{c}fmu_0 = \tfrac{1}{4}\rho\bar{c}u_0 f. \qquad \ldots \ldots (21)$$

Now from Ex. 5, Chap. IX, p. 279,

$$\rho\bar{c} = 4p\left(\frac{M}{2\pi RT}\right)^{\tfrac{1}{2}}, \qquad \ldots \ldots (22)$$

where M is the molecular weight of the gas. Hence

$$F = u_0 pf\left(\frac{M}{2\pi RT}\right)^{\tfrac{1}{2}}. \qquad \ldots \ldots (23)$$

Equation (23) shows that at very low pressures the viscous force is proportional to $M^{\tfrac{1}{2}}$, $T^{-\tfrac{1}{2}}$, and the pressure p. These predictions contrast strongly with the laws for moderate pressures, where the viscous force has been shown to be independent of p and to vary approximately as $T^{\tfrac{1}{2}}$. The value of the accommodation coefficient depends on the nature of the gas and the solid, but is usually about 0·8.

* See Roberts, *Heat and Thermodynamics*, p. 72.

(ii) *Viscous forces at intermediate pressures.*

We again consider two parallel surfaces, one of which is at rest and the other moving with velocity u_0. Referring to fig. 3, we find that at intermediate pressures the gas may be divided as regards its behaviour into two regions. From the fixed surface outwards up to a distance equal to the mean free path, the laws obeyed will be those for a gas at very low pressures, since from anywhere in this region the molecules reach the plate without collision. The effect produced on the plate by molecules with drift velocity in this region is said to give rise to " external " friction. At distances greater than the mean free path from the fixed surface, the laws obeyed will be those deduced for gases at ordinary pressures, since the molecules in this region will collide frequently with one another and will not, in general, reach the fixed plate immediately after a collision. The viscous forces produced in the main bulk of the gas are said to give rise to "internal" friction. "External" friction is again operative for distances up to the mean free path from the moving plate.

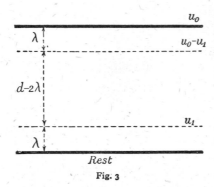

Fig. 3

If the velocity of the layer at a distance λ from the surface at rest is denoted by u_1, "external" friction is operative for velocities from 0 to u_1 and u_0 to $(u_0 - u_1)$. If the distance between the plates is d, the velocity gradient across the interior of the gas is therefore

$$\frac{du}{dx} = \frac{u_0 - 2u_1}{d - 2\lambda}. \qquad \cdots \cdots \quad (24)$$

To evaluate u_1, the internal and external viscosity coefficients may be equated for the layer at a distance λ from the surface at rest. Now

$$F_{\text{int.}} = \tfrac{1}{3}\nu m\bar{c}\lambda \frac{du}{dx}, \qquad \cdots \cdots \quad (25)$$

and if it is assumed that the molecules impinging on the surface at rest have on the average the property of those at a distance λ from it,

$$F_{\text{ext.}} = \tfrac{1}{6}\nu\bar{c}fmu_1, \qquad \cdots \cdots \quad (26)$$

where f is the accommodation coefficient for the molecules colliding with the fixed surface. It should be observed that in equation (26) Joule's classification $\tfrac{1}{6}\nu\bar{c}$ is used instead of the value $\tfrac{1}{4}\nu\bar{c}$. The latter is derived on the basis of all possible mean free paths and hence cannot be used in an elementary discussion in which the molecules are all assumed to possess the property of those at a distance equal to the mean free path. Hence from equations (25) and (26)

$$u_1 = \frac{2\lambda}{f} \frac{du}{dx},$$

or the velocity gradient near the plate is

$$\frac{u_1}{\lambda} = \frac{2}{f} \frac{du}{dx} \quad \cdots \cdots \quad (27)$$

and is approximately twice that in the interior of the gas. The molecules are therefore considered to have, at intermediate pressures, a *velocity of slip* over the fixed surface equal to

$$v_s = \frac{u_1 + 0}{2} = \frac{\lambda}{f} \frac{du}{dx}. \quad \cdots \cdots \quad (28)$$

Now from equations (24) and (27),

$$\frac{du}{dx} = \frac{u_0}{d + 2\lambda(2-f)/f} = \frac{u_0}{d + 2\xi}, \quad \cdots \quad (29)$$

where $\xi = \lambda(2-f)/f$, and is termed the *coefficient of slip*. The effect of lowering the pressure, therefore, has been to increase the distance d at either boundary by an amount approximately equal to the mean free path. The coefficient of viscosity is therefore reduced in the ratio

$$\eta = \frac{\eta_c}{1 + 2\xi/d}, \quad \cdots \cdots \quad (30)$$

where η_c is the constant value of η at moderate pressures. The viscous force per unit area therefore becomes

$$F = \tfrac{1}{3}\rho c\lambda \frac{u_0}{d + 2\lambda(2-f)/f}. \quad \cdots \cdots \quad (31)$$

At moderate pressures, where $d \gg \lambda$, equation (31) reduces to the form already given in equation (11). Conversely, at very low pressures, where $d \ll \lambda$, equation (31) reduces to the form

$$F = \tfrac{1}{6}\rho\bar{c} \frac{u_0 f}{(2-f)}, \quad \cdots \cdots \quad (32)$$

which agrees with equation (21), except for a numerical factor and the way in which f is involved.

(iii) *Effusion of gases through an aperture at low pressures.*

If a partition with a small aperture separates two regions in which the numbers of molecules of the gas per unit volume are ν_1 and ν_2 respectively, there will be a net flow of n molecules per second from one side to the other, where

$$n = \tfrac{1}{4}A(\nu_1 - \nu_2)\bar{c}, \quad \ldots \ldots \quad (33)$$

A being the area of the aperture, and the whole being at a constant and uniform temperature corresponding to a mean velocity $\bar{c}$. By (22),

$$\bar{c} = 4\left(\frac{RT}{2\pi M}\right)^{\frac{1}{2}}.$$

Hence

$$n = A(\nu_1 - \nu_2)\left(\frac{RT}{2\pi M}\right)^{\frac{1}{2}}.$$

Since

$$m\nu = \rho = \frac{Mp}{RT},$$

we have

$$Q = nm = \frac{A}{\sqrt{2\pi}}(p_1 - p_2)\left(\frac{M}{RT}\right)^{\frac{1}{2}}, \quad \ldots \quad (34)$$

where Q is the mass of gas flowing through the aperture per second.

The above formula has been verified by Knudsen,[*] using platinum partitions having small holes 5×10^{-6} sq. mm. and 6×10^{-5} sq. mm. in area and $2 \cdot 5 \times 10^{-3}$ mm. and 5×10^{-3} mm. thick respectively. The work has been extended to high temperatures by Egerton,[†] who used equation (34) to determine the vapour pressures of Zn, Cd, Pb and other metals.

(iv) *Flow of gas through a tube at low pressure.*

If the mean velocity of drift of the molecules is u_0, the momentum transferred to the whole area $2\pi al$ of the tube per second is

$$F = \tfrac{1}{4}\nu\bar{c} \times 2\pi a l m u_0 f. \quad \ldots \ldots \quad (35)$$

When a steady flow is in progress, this force must be equal to the force due to the pressure difference acting over the two ends of the tube. Hence

$$\pi a^2(p_1 - p_2) = \tfrac{1}{2}\pi a l \rho \bar{c} u_0 f,$$

and the mean velocity of drift is given by

$$u_0 = \frac{2a(p_1 - p_2)}{l\rho\bar{c}f}. \quad \ldots \ldots \quad (36)$$

---

[*] Knudsen, *Ann. d. Physik*, Vol. 29, p. 179 (1909).
[†] Egerton, *Proc. Roy. Soc.*, A, Vol. 103, p. 469 (1923).

The mass of gas Q flowing through the tube per second is therefore

$$Q = \pi a^2 u_0 \rho = \frac{2\pi a^3}{lf} \frac{(p_1 - p_2)}{\bar{c}}$$

$$= \frac{\pi}{2} \frac{a^3}{l} \frac{(p_1 - p_2)}{f} \sqrt{\frac{2\pi M}{RT}}. \quad \cdots \quad (37)$$

The flow of gas through a tube at low pressures therefore differs considerably from that at high pressures, being dependent upon a^3 and the pressure difference $(p_1 - p_2)$ instead of a^4 and the difference in the squares of the pressures $(p_1^2 - p_2^2)$ (see Chapter XII, § 11, p. 254).

From more detailed considerations,* for a uniform tube of any circumference O and area of cross-section A, the mass of gas streaming through per second is given by

$$Q = \frac{(p_1 - p_2)}{\frac{3}{8}\sqrt{\frac{\pi}{2}} \frac{O}{A^2} lf} \sqrt{\frac{M}{RT}}, \quad \cdots \quad (38)$$

which for a tube of circular cross-section differs from that in equation (37) only by a small numerical factor.

Equation (38) has been tested experimentally by Knudsen, using tubes ranging from 10^{-2} to 10^{-3} cm. in radius and from 2 to 12 cm. long. The results are in good agreement with the theory.

At intermediate pressures conditions are more complicated, the general relation for the mass of gas Q flowing through the tube per second being given by †

$$Q = \frac{\pi a^4}{8l\eta} (p_1 - p_2) \frac{M}{RT} p\left(1 + \frac{4\eta}{\xi a}\right), \quad \cdots \quad (39)$$

where p is the mean pressure and ξ the coefficient of slip defined in equation (29), p. 187.

(v) Conduction of heat at low pressures.

It has been observed in § 2, p. 182, that the treatment of heat conduction on the simple kinetic theory is not so satisfactory as that of viscosity, partly because the quantity transported is a function of the gas-kinetic velocity and partly because Maxwell's distribution law is strictly true only for a gas in equilibrium. We consider the conduction of heat between two plates at temperatures T_1 and T_2; since $\lambda \gg d$, we note that the molecules which leave either plate arrive at the

---

* See Roberts, *Heat and Thermodynamics*, p. 75.
† Loeb, *Kinetic Theory of Gases*, p. 253 (McGraw-Hill, 1927).

opposite plate without disturbance by collision with other molecules. The net heat transferred per unit area per second is therefore

$$\Delta Q = \tfrac{1}{4}\bar{v}\bar{c}mC_v(T_2 - T_1)f$$
$$= \tfrac{1}{4}\rho\bar{c}C_v(T_2 - T_1)f. \quad \ldots \ldots \quad (40)$$

Equation (40) has been tested by Knudsen for a large number of gases, and the linear relation between conductivity and pressure extends up to 5×10^{-2} mm. for hydrogen. The quantity of heat transferred depends directly upon the pressure, in contrast to the conductivity at ordinary pressures, which is independent of the pressure. This property is made the basis of the Pirani pressure gauge described on p. 212.

It will be observed that the temperature gradient vanishes; Q is therefore no longer dependent on the temperature gradient but depends solely on the temperature difference between the two surfaces.

This may be demonstrated by stretching a tungsten wire down the centre of a tube in the middle of which a large bulb is blown. The wire is sealed in at the ends of the tube and heated electrically to yellow heat. A small side tube leads to a vacuum pump. At atmospheric pressure the quantity of heat lost by the wire in conduction across the gas to the glass container depends directly on the temperature gradient. The wire in the centre of the bulb therefore glows much more brightly than that in the narrow tubes. As the pressure is reduced, however, the conductivity depends progressively less on the temperature gradient, and at low pressures the wire glows practically uniformly along its entire length.

(vi) *Conduction of heat at intermediate pressures.*

Proceeding as on p. 186, we divide the gas into two regions, that up to a distance λ from the plates obeying the low pressure law and the main bulk of the gas obeying the ordinary pressure law. Evaluating the expressions for the heat conducted in the two regions and equating the expressions at the boundary at a distance λ from one of the plates, we find that the temperature gradient at intermediate pressures is

$$\frac{dT}{dx} = \frac{T_1 - T_2}{d + 2\lambda(2 - f)/f}. \quad \ldots \ldots \quad (41)$$

Substitution of this formula in equation (14), p. 182, gives, for unit area,

$$\Delta Q = \tfrac{1}{3}\rho\bar{c}\lambda C_v \frac{T_1 - T_2}{d + 2\lambda(2 - f)/f}. \quad \ldots \quad (42)$$

If $d \gg \lambda$, that is, at moderate pressures, equation (42) reduces to the formula for conduction at moderate pressures, as required, whereas at low pressures, where $d \ll \lambda$, equation (42) reduces to equation (40), except for a numerical factor and the way in which f is involved.

(vii) *Thermal effusion at low pressures.*

If a vessel containing a gas at low pressure is separated into two regions by a partition containing a small hole and the two regions are maintained at different temperatures T_1 and T_2, the condition for equilibrium is no longer that the pressure shall be the same on both sides of the partition. Equilibrium is established when the number of molecules passing in either direction across unit area per second is the same, that is, when

$$\tfrac{1}{4}\nu_1\overline{c_1} = \tfrac{1}{4}\nu_2\overline{c_2},$$

by equation (20). Hence the ratio of the pressures is given by

$$\frac{p_1}{p_2} = \frac{\nu_1 C_1^{\ 2}}{\nu_2 C_2^{\ 2}} = \frac{\overline{c_1}}{\overline{c_2}} = \sqrt{\frac{T_1}{T_2}}. \quad \text{. . . .} \quad (43)$$

The extra speed of the molecules on the high-temperature side therefore balances their lower number, so that as many arrive at the aperture per second as from the cooler side. The same relation holds if the aperture is replaced by a tube, because in the steady state $\nu\overline{c}$ is constant for all sections of the tube.

(viii) *Thermal transpiration at intermediate and higher pressures.*

At higher pressures equilibrium at an aperture in a plate occurs only when the pressure on the two sides is the same. Hence

$$\tfrac{1}{3}\nu_1 C_1^{\ 2} = \tfrac{1}{3}\nu_2 C_2^{\ 2},$$

which simply shows that the densities are inversely proportional to the absolute temperatures. If, however, a tube separates the two regions, conditions are more complicated. Consider any cross-section perpendicular to the axis of the tube, the latter being the x-axis, where the mean gas-kinetic velocity of the molecules is $\overline{c}$. On the average, the molecules crossing the layer per second will be those at a distance originally equal to the mean free path. The net number of molecules crossing unit area per second will, if we use Joule's classification, be

$$n = \left[\frac{\nu\overline{c}}{6} + \frac{\partial}{\partial x}\left(\frac{\nu\overline{c}}{6}\right)\lambda\right] - \left[\frac{\nu\overline{c}}{6} - \frac{\partial}{\partial x}\left(\frac{\nu\overline{c}}{6}\right)\lambda\right]$$

$$= \frac{\nu\lambda\overline{c}}{3}\left(\frac{1}{\nu}\frac{\partial\nu}{\partial x} + \frac{1}{\overline{c}}\frac{\partial\overline{c}}{\partial x}\right). \quad \text{. . . . .} \quad (44)$$

Now

$$p = \frac{\pi}{8}m\nu\overline{c}^2. \quad \text{. . . . .} \quad (45)$$

Therefore

$$\frac{\partial p}{\partial x} = \frac{\pi}{8} m\bar{c}^2 \frac{\partial \nu}{\partial x} + \frac{\pi}{4} \nu m\bar{c} \frac{\partial \bar{c}}{\partial x}$$

$$= p\left(\frac{1}{\nu}\frac{\partial \nu}{\partial x} + \frac{2}{\bar{c}}\frac{\partial \bar{c}}{\partial x}\right). \quad \ldots \ldots \quad (46)$$

Since $\eta = \frac{1}{3}\nu m\lambda\bar{c}$ approximately, if we substitute for $\frac{1}{\nu}\frac{\partial \nu}{\partial x}$ from equation (46) in equation (44), we find that the mass of gas Q flowing per second through the tube is

$$Q = \pi a^2 n m = \pi a^2 \eta \left(\frac{1}{p}\frac{\partial p}{\partial x} - \frac{1}{\bar{c}}\frac{\partial \bar{c}}{\partial x}\right).$$

Further, since $\bar{c} \propto T^{\frac{1}{2}}$,

$$Q = \pi a^2 \eta \left(\frac{1}{p}\frac{\partial p}{\partial x} - \frac{1}{2T}\frac{\partial T}{\partial x}\right). \quad \ldots \ldots \quad (47)$$

Now if the pressure difference between the ends of the tube is small, the application of Poiseuille's equation for the flow of gas through a tube (p. 253) gives

$$Q = -\frac{\pi a^4}{8\eta}\frac{\partial p}{\partial x}\frac{Mp}{RT}, \quad \ldots \ldots \quad (48)$$

where M is the molecular weight of the gas. Hence, for the steady state, by equating (47) and (48), we have

$$\pi a^2 \eta \left(\frac{1}{p}\frac{\partial p}{\partial x} - \frac{1}{2T}\frac{\partial T}{\partial x}\right) = -\frac{\pi a^4}{8\eta}\frac{\partial p}{\partial x}\frac{Mp}{RT},$$

that is

$$\frac{\partial p}{\partial T}\left(\frac{2\eta^2 T}{p} + \frac{Mpa^2}{4R}\right) = \eta^2,$$

or

$$\frac{\partial p}{\partial T} = \frac{\eta^2}{2\eta^2 T/p + Mpa^2/4R}. \quad \ldots \ldots \quad (49)$$

At low pressures equation (49) reduces to

$$\frac{\partial p}{\partial T} = \frac{p}{2T}.$$

Hence p is independent of the nature of the gas and varies as $T^{\frac{1}{2}}$, as has already been shown by equation (43), p. 191. At higher pressures $\partial p/\partial T$ is observed to be inversely proportional to the pressure and the molecular weight of the gas.

4. Properties of Gases at High Pressures; the Size of the Molecules.

The failure of the gas laws deduced for ordinary pressures when applied to gases at low pressures is due to the mean free path becoming comparable with or greater than the size of the container. At high pressures, the disagreement between simple theory and experiment is due to the failure of the second, third and fourth basic assumptions of Clausius, enumerated in § 1, p. 178. As the density of the gas increases, it is no longer possible to ignore the volume occupied by the molecules themselves or the mutual forces of attraction or repulsion that exist between them. The simple equation $pV = RT$ for a perfect gas has to be replaced at higher pressures by a more general equation of state; one such equation is that given by Van der Waals:

$$\left(p + \frac{a}{V^2}\right)(V - b) = RT. \qquad \ldots \quad (50)$$

This equation will now be deduced from the kinetic theory and the significance of the constants a and b will be determined.

(i) *Finite size of the molecules and the significance of b.*

If we represent the molecular diameter and radius by σ and r, it is shown in the solution of Ex. 9, p. 286, that the mean free path is reduced in the ratio

$$\frac{\lambda_\sigma}{\lambda} = \frac{V - 4(4\pi r^3 n/3)}{V} = \frac{V - b}{V}. \qquad \ldots \quad (51)$$

Since the volume of the n molecules themselves is $c = 4\pi r^3 n/3$, we have $b = 4c$.

(ii) *Forces of attraction and repulsion between the molecules and finite time of collision.*

If the forces of attraction and repulsion between the molecules extend over a finite distance from each molecule, the collision will occupy a finite interval of time. Hence the number of collisions against the wall of the containing vessel in unit time will be reduced according to the equation

$$p = \frac{1}{3} \frac{C^2}{(V - b)} \frac{1}{(1 + n\tau)}, \qquad \ldots \quad (52)$$

where τ is the time occupied in one collision and n is the number of collisions per second. Equation (52) may be written in the form

$$p(1 + n\tau) = \frac{1}{3} \frac{C^2}{(V - b)}.$$

Now n is approximately equal to $\pi\sigma^2\bar{c}\nu$, since this represents the number of encounters made by a molecule of effective diameter σ in one second if the other molecules are treated as points. Hence, since $p = \frac{1}{3}\rho C^2$ approximately, we have

$$p + \tfrac{1}{3}\rho C^2 \pi\sigma^2\bar{c}\nu\tau = \frac{1}{3}\frac{C^2}{(V - b)},$$

or

$$p + \frac{\pi^2}{8}\rho^2\frac{\sigma^2\bar{c}^3\tau}{n} = \frac{1}{3}\frac{C^2}{(V - b)}, \quad \cdot \quad \cdot \quad (52a)$$

and since $\rho \propto 1/V$,

$$\left(p + \frac{a}{V^2}\right)(V - b) = \frac{1}{3}C^2, \quad \cdot \quad \cdot \quad \cdot \quad (53)$$

where a is proportional to the coefficient of ρ^2 in the second term on the left-hand side of equation (52a).

A more powerful method of attack for such problems was developed by Clausius and is known as the *Virial Theorem*. The subject is discussed in Roberts, *Heat and Thermodynamics*, Chapter XXII

(iii) *Dependence of η on the size of the molecules.*

By the method of dimensions it is possible to deduce the law of force between the molecules if the variation of the coefficient of viscosity with temperature is determined experimentally. Let the molecules repel one another at small distances apart with a force F given by

$$F = \mu r^{-s}, \quad \cdot \quad \cdot \quad \cdot \quad \cdot \quad \cdot \quad (54)$$

where r is the distance between the molecules, s is the required power, and μ is defined by equation (54). The coefficient of viscosity may be assumed to depend upon m, $\bar{c}$, μ and s, hence

$$\eta = f(m, \bar{c}, \mu, s) = \text{const. } m^\alpha \bar{c}^\beta \mu^\gamma. \quad \cdot \quad \cdot \quad (55)$$

Since s is dimensionless, if we write equation (55) in dimensional form we have

$$ML^{-1}T^{-1} = M^\alpha L^\beta T^{-\beta} M^\gamma L^{(1+s)\gamma} T^{-2\gamma}.$$

Equating indices and solving in terms of s, we have $\alpha = (s + 1)/(s - 1)$, $\beta = (s + 3)/(s - 1)$ and $\gamma = -2/(s - 1)$. Hence

$$\eta \propto (m^{(s+1)}\bar{c}^{(s+3)}\mu^{-2})^{1/(s-1)}. \quad \cdot \quad \cdot \quad \cdot \quad (56)$$

If it is observed experimentally that $\eta \propto T^n$, since $T \propto \bar{c}^2$ we have

$$2n = (s + 3)/(s - 1). \quad \cdot \quad \cdot \quad \cdot \quad \cdot \quad (57)$$

Now for helium $n = 0.68$, hence $s \sim 12$, which indicates an extremely rapid rate of fall in the force as the distance from the molecule is increased, such as we might expect for a small, compact unit like the helium molecule. For carbon dioxide, however, which has a comparatively loose and open structure, $n = 0.98$ and hence $s \sim 5.2$, showing that the force extends over a comparatively large region.

From some aspects the behaviour of the molecules indicates that they may be regarded as having a hard core of radius proportional to a quantity denoted by σ_∞, since at T_∞ the molecules will interpenetrate at each collision until the cores come into contact. Sutherland suggests that the value of σ at any other temperature T will be given by

$$\sigma^2 = \sigma_\infty^2(1 + A/T), \qquad \ldots \ldots \quad (58)$$

where A is a constant. By equation (2), p. 178, therefore, the mean free path changes in the ratio

$$\frac{\lambda_T}{\lambda_0} = \frac{\sigma_{273}^2}{\sigma_T^2} = \frac{(1 + A/273)}{(1 + A/T)}, \qquad \ldots \ldots \quad (59)$$

where λ_0 is the mean free path at $0°$ C. Hence the ratio of the viscosity at any temperature T and the viscosity at $0°$ C. will be

$$\frac{\eta}{\eta_0} = \frac{(\bar{c}\lambda)_T}{(\bar{c}\lambda)_0} = \left(\frac{T}{273}\right)^{3/2} \frac{A + 273}{A + T}. \qquad \ldots \ldots \quad (60)$$

Formula (60) has been tested for nitrogen by Bestelmeyer and is in satisfactory agreement with experiment for temperatures between $90°$ C. and $300°$ C. It is, however, by no means rigorously obeyed by all gases, and fails completely at low temperatures.

5. Determination of Loschmidt's Number and the Molecular Diameter.

(i) *Loschmidt's deduction.*

Since the mean free path is known from Maxwell's work on the viscosity of the gas, a determination of either ν or σ and the use of equation (2), p. 178, enables us to evaluate both quantities. The value of ν was first deduced in 1865 by Loschmidt by considering that in the liquid state all the molecules are as tightly packed as hard spheres can possibly be. The volume occupied by ν such molecules is $\nu\sigma^3/\sqrt{2}$, for the packing will be tetrahedral. Hence if the densities of gas and liquefied gas are δ and Δ respectively, we have

$$\frac{\delta}{\Delta} = \frac{\nu\sigma^3}{\sqrt{2}}. \qquad \ldots \ldots \ldots \quad (61)$$

From equations (2) and (61), therefore,

$$\nu = \frac{1}{2\pi^3\lambda^3}\left(\frac{\Delta}{\delta}\right)^2. \qquad \ldots \ldots \ldots \quad (62)$$

The value obtained was $\nu = 10^{18}$ mols./c.c., a result which is now known to be about twenty times too low. The value of σ deduced, about 10^{-7} cm., was therefore about 5 times too great, but the deductions were of great value in fixing the order of the quantities involved.

(ii) *The Brownian movement and the kinetic theory of liquids.*

The kinetic theory of matter receives quite independent and most spectacular support from the discovery made by Brown in 1827. Using the then new achromatic objective, Brown observed that small particles about 10^{-3} mm. in diameter, such as pollen grains, when held in suspension in a liquid, exhibit unceasing irregular motion in all directions. Initially the phenomenon was ascribed to vital forces, but subsequent work showed that it was also exhibited by small particles held in suspension in the liquid inclusions in granite and other rocks of great age. Not until nearly fifty years after its discovery was it suggested by Wiener and later more convincingly by Delsaulx that the Brownian movement is a visible demonstration of the validity of the kinetic theory of liquids. In any small interval of time a particle will receive more impacts from molecular bombardment on one side than another. If the particle is sufficiently small, it will therefore execute a small motion under the resultant force until its path is altered by further impacts. The observed motion under the microscope is merely the resultant path of a large number of zigzag paths which are each too small to be resolved by the microscope and the eye. The experiments on the Brownian movement are of several types; of those described below, the first has been applied to liquids and the second to liquids and gases.

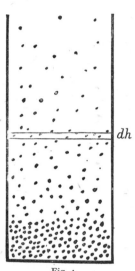

Fig. 4

(a) *Sedimentation equilibrium.*

Sedimentation equilibrium is established when a suspension, emulsion, or colloidal solution is contained in a vertical vessel. Under the opposing influences of osmotic pressure, which on the kinetic theory arises from the bombardment of the molecules, and gravity, a definite vertical concentration gradient is established in the steady state. Referring to fig. 4, we see that if ν represents the number of suspended particles per unit volume at a height h above the bottom of the container, the increase in osmotic pressure dp due to the increase in the number of particles at a height $(h - dh)$ must be sufficient to balance the weight of the particles. Hence

$$dp = \nu m g\, dh, \quad \cdots \cdots \quad (63)$$

where m is the mass of each particle* (all the particles being assumed identical) and g is the acceleration due to gravity. Further,

$$p = \nu k T, \quad \cdots \cdots \quad (64)$$

where k is Boltzmann's constant (p. 166) and T is the absolute temperature. Hence

$$dp = kT\, d\nu, \quad \cdots \cdots \quad (65)$$

and from equations (63) and (65) we have

$$\frac{d\nu}{\nu} = \frac{mg}{kT}\, dh. \quad \cdots \cdots \quad (66)$$

Integrating between heights h_2 and h_1, where the numbers of particles per unit volume are ν_2 and ν_1 respectively, we obtain

$$\log_e \frac{\nu_2}{\nu_1} = \frac{mgN}{RT} (h_2 - h_1), \quad \cdots \cdots \quad (67)$$

where N is Avogadro's number, $6 \cdot 06 \times 10^{23}$ molecules per gramme-molecule, and R is the gas constant referred to one gramme-molecule.

The classical series of experiments on equation (67) was carried out by Perrin between 1900 and 1912. Emulsions of gamboge or mastic were subjected to continuous centrifuging for a month at the rate of 3000 revs./min., the spherical particles being in this way separated into layers containing particles of the same size. A drop of the emulsion was then placed on a microscope slide so as to form a column about 1/10 mm. high, which was then observed with a powerful objective from above. With visual observations it was necessary to limit the field by the use of a plate with a fine hole, otherwise at any instant more particles filled the field than could be counted at a single glance. Great care had to be taken to filter out the heat rays (by using water cells) from the beam of light, which was incident in a horizontal direction. Any inequality of temperature in different parts of the emulsion produced convection currents in the liquid, which were much greater than the Brownian movement. These precautions are even more necessary in the determination of N by the dynamical method discussed later.

On the average about five particles were visible at any instant and a large number of readings were required to eliminate statistical errors. It was found possible, however, to reduce the labour by a factor of 200 by using a powerful light-source to illuminate the suspension and taking a microphotograph of a much larger field. The number of grains present could then be counted at leisure. Owing to the high power of the microscope, the thickness of the layer in focus was about that of the diameter of the particles; consequently only the number present in a very thin layer was observed for one position of the microscope. After sufficient readings had been taken the microscope was racked up a distance d measured

---

* m is, of course, the reduced mass where allowance has been made for the buoyancy.

on an accurately graduated vernier and another set of readings was taken, the distance $(h_2 - h_1)$ being determined from the expression μd, where μ was the refractive index of the emulsion.

To determine the remaining quantity m of equation (67), the volume and density of the grains were obtained by the following methods.

(1) *Density of the grains.*

(a) Specific gravity bottle.

(b) Surrounding the grains by potassium bromide of increasing concentration until the grains neither floated nor sank, when the density of grains and solution was the same.

(c) Adding potassium bromide solution until the grains did not separate on centrifuging.

(2) *Volume of the grains.*

(a) Direct determination of the radius by allowing the emulsion almost to dry on a glass plate. The grains were then pulled into rows by surface tension and the length of a row and the number of grains contained in it were determined with a travelling microscope.

(b) Application of Stokes's law (see Chap. XII, § 10, p. 252),

$$6\pi\eta rv = \tfrac{4}{3}\pi r^3(D - d)g,$$

where r is the radius of the grains, D and d the density of the grains and liquid respectively, η the coefficient of viscosity of the emulsion, and v the terminal velocity, that is, the velocity with which the " edge " of the cloud of grains formed by stirring the emulsion descends under the influence of gravity. The terminal velocity was a few mm. per day, and the application of the uncorrected form of Stokes's law was considered valid, since the radius of the particles was much greater than the mean free path of the molecules in the liquid.

As a check on the results, the weight of the grains was determined in a number of cases by directly weighing a known number of grains which had been made to adhere to a glass plate immersed in the solution when the latter was made slightly acid.

From observations on many thousands of grains the final value $N = 6 \cdot 8 \times 10^{23}$ mols./gram. mol. was obtained, a value some ten per cent greater than that accepted at present. Using the same method, but with colloidal particles of gold and silver, Westgren in 1915 obtained the value $N = 6 \cdot 04 \times 10^{23}$, which is within one-half per cent of the accepted value.

(b) *Einstein and Smoluchowski's equation.*

In 1905, Einstein and Smoluchowski succeeded in deducing a relation between the mean square displacement of a particle undergoing Brownian movement and the time interval between two successive observations. Referring to fig. 5, let a uniform density gradient, increasing in the direction of the negative x-axis, be set up as a result of the fortuitous accumulation of a large number of particles in that region owing to the Brownian movement. We consider only motion parallel to the x-axis and divide the fluid into three shallow layers B, A, C at distances $-x$, 0, and $+x$ from the origin. The number of particles present per unit volume at C is $\nu = \nu_0 - x(\partial \nu/\partial x)$ if the number present in unit volume at A is ν_0. In a given time t a number of particles $d\nu$ will experience a fortuitous variation of their co-ordinates by an amount lying between a and $a + da$. Then

$$d\nu = \nu f(a)\,da, \quad \ldots \ldots \ldots \quad (68)$$

where it is required to find the nature of the function $f(a)$. Quite generally $f(a)$ must satisfy the two relations

$$f(-a) = f(a) \quad \ldots \ldots \ldots \quad (69)$$

and

$$\int_{-\infty}^{+\infty} f(a)\,da = 1, \quad \ldots \ldots \ldots \quad (70)$$

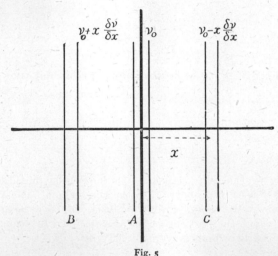

Fig. 5

since there are no preferred directions and the particle must be present somewhere.

Applying equation (68) to the slices B and C, subtracting, and integrating, we obtain the number of particles crossing unit area of the plane at A if the integration is carried out (i) over all values of a from 0 to ∞, since only particles passing towards A can be considered; (ii) over values of x less than a, since for a greater value of x the particle will not reach the plane at A on displacement. Hence, if the number of particles crossing unit area of A in time t is represented by nt, we have

$$nt = 2\frac{\partial \nu}{\partial x}\int_0^{\infty} f(a)\,da\int_0^{a} x\,dx \quad \ldots \ldots \quad (71)$$

or, changing the limits,

$$nt = \frac{1}{2}\frac{\partial \nu}{\partial x}\int_{-\infty}^{+\infty} a^2 f(a)\,da. \quad \ldots \ldots \quad (72)$$

If $\overline{a^2}$ represents the mean square displacement of the particles, since $\int_{-\infty}^{+\infty} f(a)\,da = 1$, we have

$$nt = \tfrac{1}{2}\overline{a^2}\frac{\partial \nu}{\partial x}. \qquad \cdots \cdots \quad (73)$$

Equation (73) may be put into a more convenient form. Since

$$p = \nu kT$$

and the force on unit volume is equal to the gradient of the pressure, the force on each particle in unit volume is

$$F = \frac{1}{\nu}\frac{\partial p}{\partial x} = \frac{kT}{\nu}\frac{\partial \nu}{\partial x}. \qquad \cdots \cdots \quad (74)$$

Now by Stokes's law

$$F = 6\pi\eta rv, \qquad \cdots \cdots \cdots \quad (75)$$

and the number of particles crossing unit area in unit time is

$$n = \nu v. \qquad \cdots \cdots \cdots \quad (76)$$

Hence from equations (73), (74), (75), and (76) we have

$$\overline{a^2} = \frac{RT}{3\pi\eta rN}\,t. \qquad \cdots \cdots \quad (77)$$

According to Einstein's equation, therefore, the mean square displacement increases in proportion to the time which has elapsed since the last observation. By a similar analysis, the *mean square angular displacement* which the particles suffer as a result of rotational motions arising from the Brownian movement may be shown to be

$$\overline{A^2} = \frac{RT}{4\pi r^3 \eta N}\,t. \qquad \cdots \cdots \quad (78)$$

Equations (77) and (78) have been tested by Perrin by observing the motion of particles with a microscope fitted with a transparent squared grating in the eyepiece. The rotational motion is followed by means of observations on an air inclusion in a particle: urea is a particularly useful substance for this experiment. Besides showing that $\overline{a^2}$ is proportional to t, Perrin observed that the lengths of the paths are distributed according to a Maxwellian distribution law. Later experiments by Seddig confirmed those of Perrin and extended the range over a mass variation of $1 : 15,000$.

The validity of Einstein's equation for particles suspended in gases was first investigated by Ehrenhaft and later by de Broglie. The most celebrated experiments are those of Millikan, in which an oil-drop is allowed to fall through a gas between the plates of a parallel plate condenser. With no electric field present, if the drop is small enough, it may readily be shown by observation with a microscope that $\overline{a^2} \propto t$. To avoid determining r, the drop is allowed to fall under gravity, whence, applying Stokes's law, we have

$$6\pi\eta rv = \tfrac{4}{3}\pi r^3(\rho - \sigma)g, \qquad \cdots \cdots \quad (79)$$

where ρ and σ are the densities of the oil and air respectively. The coefficient of viscosity of air has to be determined by a separate experiment (see Chapter XII, § 11, p. 253). If the drop is charged and an electric field is applied just before the drop reaches the lower condenser plate, the drop may be returned to its original position and the reading repeated. Fletcher took over 6000 readings with the same drop.

The method has the following advantages over that with liquid emulsions:

(i) a single particle may be observed for hours;
(ii) identity of a large number of particles is not required;
(iii) the kinetic theory of gases is better established for gases than for liquids;
(iv) the displacement is about ten times as great in gases as in liquids, and by reducing the pressure it may be made 200 times as great.

It may also be observed, as is shown by Ising,* that the sensitiveness of galvanometers reaches its limit when the suspension is so fine that the suspended system has no definite zero, owing to the Brownian movement imparted by the surrounding gas molecules. With a sufficiently thin fibre Gerlach obtained a Brownian movement of over a metre for the spot from a suspended mirror illuminated with a lamp at a distance of a metre from the scale. Continuing Gerlach's work, Kappler has deduced the value of Avogadro's number from a photographic record of the Brownian movement of the spot of light. Since the system has one degree of freedom, by the theorem of the equipartition of energy we have

$$\tfrac{1}{2}c\overline{\theta^2} = \tfrac{1}{2}kT, \qquad \ldots \ldots \ldots \quad (80)$$

where $\overline{\theta^2}$ is the mean square deflection and c the restoring couple in the fibre for unit angle of twist. The value obtained for N is $6 \cdot 06 \times 10^{23}$ and is correct to within 1 per cent. Care had to be taken to reduce the effect of mechanical vibrations and convection currents; the reality of the effect was strikingly shown by the gradual decrease in the motion as the gas pressure was reduced. According to Tinbergen, currents less than 10^{-12} amperes cannot be measured directly even with a sensitive instrument such as the Einthoven string galvanometer, owing to the Brownian movement. For comparison it may be mentioned that the limit of weighing with a chemical balance set by the Brownian movement is 10^{-9} gm.; actually the most sensitive instruments are still far from this limit, weighing to only 10^{-5} gm.

(c) Brillouin's diffusion experiments.

If ν_1 and ν_2 represent the numbers of particles per unit volume in an emulsion, situated a distance apart equal to the root mean square displacement $\bar{a}$, in time t the net interchange of particles between the two regions is approximately

$$n = \tfrac{1}{2}\bar{a}(\nu_1 - \nu_2). \qquad \ldots \ldots \quad (81)$$

By the definition of the coefficient of diffusion D

$$n = D\frac{(\nu_1 - \nu_2)}{\bar{a}}t. \qquad \ldots \ldots \quad (82)$$

Hence

$$\overline{a^2} = 2Dt, \qquad \ldots \ldots \ldots \quad (83)$$

* Ann. d. Physik, Vol. 14 (7), p. 755 (1932).

or, from equations (77) and (83),

$$N = \frac{RT}{D} \frac{1}{6\pi\eta r}. \quad \cdots \cdots \quad (84)$$

To test these relations, Brillouin used a suspension of gamboge in glycerine, in which was immersed a glass plate which acted as a perfect absorber for all grains coming into contact with it. If ν represents the average number of grains per unit volume of the emulsion, the number of particles absorbed per unit area of the plate in time t will be

$$n = \tfrac{1}{2}\nu\bar{\alpha}, \quad \cdots \cdots \cdots \quad (85)$$

since the probability that the particles will be displaced *towards* the plate is equal to $\tfrac{1}{2}$. From equations (83) and (85), therefore, we have

$$n^2 = \tfrac{1}{2}D\nu^2 t, \quad \cdots \cdots \cdots \quad (86)$$

i.e. the square of the number of grains collected should be proportional to the time. Examination of photographs of the glass plate, taken at regular intervals of time, showed agreement with (86) and gave the value $6 \cdot 9 \times 10^{23}$ for N.

(d) Fluctuations in fluids.

If the actual number of particles present in a given volume is n and the average number taken over a long time is $\bar{n}$, the average relative fluctuation is defined by

$$\epsilon = \frac{\overline{n - \bar{n}}}{\bar{n}}. \quad \cdots \cdots \quad (87)$$

From the probability calculus, Smoluchowski[*] showed that

$$\epsilon = \sqrt{\frac{2}{\pi\bar{n}}}, \quad \cdots \cdots \quad (88)$$

and hence, since the fluctuation in a volume containing 10,000 particles is about 1 per cent, the effect should be observable in fluids near the critical point. The effect manifests itself experimentally as *critical opalescence*.

The opalescence, which, as we see, is constant with time, is explained on the molecular view by the fortuitous gathering of a large number of molecules in various places in the fluid, as a result of thermal agitation. The groups of molecules are large enough to scatter light appreciably, and since they are continually breaking up and forming fresh groups, a shimmering opalescence is produced.

Combining Rayleigh's formula for the scattering of light by small obstacles with Smoluchowski's investigations on critical opalescence, Keesom[†] has derived the equation

$$i = \frac{\pi^2}{18} \frac{1}{\lambda^4} \frac{RT}{N} (\mu_0{}^2 - 1)^2 (\mu_0{}^2 + 2)^2 \left(\frac{1}{-v_0(\partial p/\partial v_0)} \right), \quad \cdots \quad (89)$$

[*] See Fürth, *Schwankungserscheinungen in der Physik* (Sammlung Vieweg, Part 48; Brunswick, 1920).   [†] J. Perrin, *Atoms* (Constable & Co. Ltd., 1923)

where i is the fraction of the intensity of the light scattered per c.c. in a direction perpendicular to the incident beam, μ_0 is the refractive index of the fluid for light of wave-length λ in free space, v_0 is the specific volume of the liquid, and $\partial p/\partial v_0$ its isothermal compressibility. Experiments by Keesom and Kamerlingh Onnes on ethylene at $11.18°$ abs. gave a value for N equal to 7.5×10^{23} mols./gramme-molecule.

(e) Size of molecules from Van der Waals' equation.

The size of the molecules of a gas may be determined directly in two ways from Van der Waals' equation, provided the value of N is known. Thus, if the critical volume V_c is measured directly, since $V_c = 3b$, by Van der Waals' equation,* and $b = \frac{2}{3}\pi\sigma^3 n$, σ is obtained. The method is not accurate, for V_c is difficult to measure experimentally; further, the relation $V_c = 4b$ is shown to be in better agreement with the experimental results.

According to Van der Waals, however,

$$\left(p + \frac{a}{V^2}\right)(V - b) = RT \quad \cdots \quad (90)$$

under any conditions. Hence, if $\dfrac{1}{p_0}\left(\dfrac{\partial p}{\partial T}\right)_v$ represents the coefficient of pressure increase of the gas at constant volume,

$$\frac{1}{p_0}\left(\frac{\partial p}{\partial T}\right)_v = \frac{1}{T_0}\left(1 + \frac{a}{p_0 V^2}\right), \quad \cdots \quad (91)$$

from which the value of a is obtained. Further, if $\dfrac{1}{V_0}\left(\dfrac{\partial V}{\partial T}\right)_p$ represents the coefficient of volume increase at constant pressure, from equation (90) we have approximately

$$\frac{1}{V_0}\left(\frac{\partial V}{\partial T}\right)_p = \frac{1}{T_0}\left[1 + \frac{a}{p V_0}\left(\frac{1}{V_0} + \frac{1}{V}\right) - \frac{b}{V_0}\right]. \quad \cdot \quad (92)$$

The value of a having been obtained from equation (91), the value of b is finally given by equation (92).

6. Production of High Vacua.

The maintenance of a high vacuum depends on the freedom of the system from leaks; the whole apparatus must therefore be free from joins and, in general, consist of glass throughout, or of metal and glass directly sealed together where necessary. The speed with which the vacuum is obtained, apart from the nature of the pump, also depends on the breadth and length of the connecting tubes. Examination of equation (37), p. 189, shows that at low pressures the rate of flow of gas is inversely proportional to the length and directly proportional to the

---

* See Roberts, *Heat and Thermodynamics*, p. 91 *et seq.*

cube of the radius of the tube. Finally, the degree of vacuum obtainable and its measured value will depend on the vapour pressures of the materials in the pump (e.g. oil) and pressure gauge (e.g. mercury) respectively.

The pumps used for the production of low pressures may be broadly divided into two groups, according as their action is purely mechanical or depends on the molecular and kinetic properties of the gas. It is now possible to obtain mechanical pumps, such as the Geryk " R.L." type, which by almost complete elimination of oil vapour will produce a vacuum of 10^{-5} mm. of mercury; * again, a mercury pump of the Sprengel or Töpler type, although tedious to use, will produce a vacuum of the same order if a liquid-air trap is inserted between the mercury and the vessel which is being exhausted, to prevent access of mercury

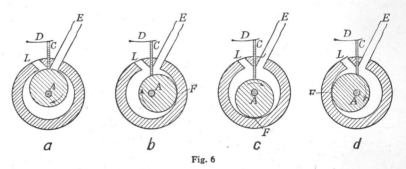

Fig. 6

vapour to the evacuated system. In general, however, mechanical pumps produce vacua only of the order of 5×10^{-3} mm., but their use is essential to provide a fore-vacuum or " backing " for the molecular pumps.

(a) Cenco-Hyvac pump.

As an example of a convenient mechanical pump, the Cenco-Hyvac pump (figs. 6(a) to (d)) will now be described. The rotor A is mounted eccentrically in the cylinder, and four successive positions are shown. In the side of the outer cylinder a vane C slides; it is kept pressed in contact with A by means of a spring arm D. The vessel to be exhausted is connected to E and the exhaust is through the valve at L. The pump is immersed in oil, which is the operative medium in the pumping process, as well as a seal against leakage. In the first position in fig. 6(a), gas has just been admitted via E to the crescent-shaped space. In the second position, the gas is in process of being compressed as the eccentric rotor revolves, while fresh gas is being admitted behind the rotor. Further compression follows in stage (c), and finally at stage (d) the valve L opens and the gas is expelled. The pump is constructed so as to act in two stages, the first pump being operated directly from atmospheric pressure and the second using the vacuum produced by the first as its fore-vacuum. The speed of pumping is about 6 litres a minute and the vacuum attainable about 10^{-3} mm.

---

* In future, mm. will refer to mm. of mercury.

(b) Gaede molecular pump.

It has been shown in § 3, p. 184, that when the mean free path λ of the molecules is greater than the linear dimensions of the apparatus, the molecules acquire the properties of the walls of the apparatus and do not dissipate those properties rapidly by subsequent intramolecular collisions. If, therefore, the gas molecules in a fore-vacuum are allowed to come into contact with a rapidly moving surface, they will to some extent acquire the drift velocity of that surface. If the distance between two parallel boundary planes is d, one of the planes being fixed and the other moving, it may be shown that at low pressures the ratio of the gas pressures at two points a distance l apart measured in the direction of motion is

$$\frac{p_2}{p_1} = \frac{cl}{d}, \qquad \ldots \ldots \ldots \quad (93)$$

where c is a constant. For a given velocity it is the *ratio* of the initial and final pressures which is constant; the fore-vacuum should therefore be as high as possible.

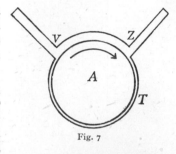

Fig. 7

The principle of the apparatus is shown in fig. 7, where the evacuated system and the exhaust are connected to V and Z respectively. The cylinder A rotates in the outer cylinder T, evacuation resulting from molecules being projected along the groove VZ after impact with the revolving cylinder A. At a speed of 12,000 revs./min. the vacuum attainable is less than 10^{-6} mm. with a fore-vacuum of 1–2 mm.

(c) Mercury vapour pumps.

As is well known, the passage of a steam or mercury vapour jet up the tube AB (fig. 8) gives rise to a vacuum in the system on the right. The pumping process depends on the relative rates of diffusion of the vapour of the jet and the gas through the porous plug. A large increase in efficiency is obtained by the introduction of the vapour trap cooled by water or liquid air. The principle was first applied by Gaede, who called the apparatus a *diffusion pump*. The porous plug was replaced by an adjustable slit, since it was found that the apparatus has maximum efficiency when the width of the slit is approximately equal to λ, the mean free path of the gas molecules. Further, the maximum effect is obtained when the pressure of the mercury vapour is just greater than that of the fore-vacuum. Vacua of less than 10^{-6} mm. may be obtained, but while theoretically there is no limit to the vacuum attainable, in practice two disadvantages arise: (*a*) the exhaust speed is slow, (*b*) careful regulation of the temperature of the mercury vapour is required.

By a modification of the Gaede diffusion pump, by which it became
a *condensation pump*, Langmuir eliminated both these disadvantages.
The main advance consists in cooling the mercury vapour thoroughly
at the jet, so that condensation occurs, back diffusion of the mercury
vapour thereby being completely eliminated.   The apparatus has the
advantage of requiring no critical conditions and the size of the orifice
may vary over a wide range.

A convenient form is shown in fig. 9; mercury is heated in the pyrex glass
bulb *A*, the vapour rising in the curved tube *B*.   Condensation of the vapour
is prevented by the asbestos lagging *H* until the vapour issues from the orifice *P*.
The tube *L* is enclosed in another tube *C*, which is surrounded by a water jacket
J fed by the tubes *K*.   The gas is discharged through *N*.   The mercury vapour
condenses almost instantaneously, very little rising above a point such as *E*.

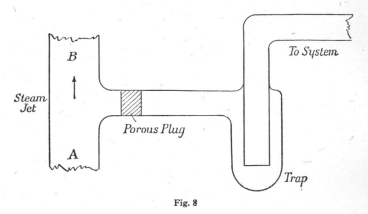

Fig. 8

The system to be evacuated is connected by the tube *R* to the liquid-air trap *G*
and thence by the cross-tube *F* to the tube *C*.   The mercury collects in liquid
form at *D* and is returned to the bulb *A* by the fine tube *M*.   The pump is very
efficient, reducing a pressure of 1 mm. to 10^{-5} mm. in 80 sec. with a speed of working of nearly 4 litres/sec.

(d) Other processes.

To push the vacuum below 10^{-6} mm., methods other than pumping
must be used.   The commonest of these is a *sorption process*, in which
the system is connected to a tube surrounded by liquid air and containing coconut charcoal which has been recently heated.   The gas
is absorbed by the charcoal and a pressure of 10^{-7} mm. may be obtained
in this way.   The rate of absorption is monomolecular.   Gases such as
nitrogen, carbon dioxide, ammonia and hydrogen may be readily
removed.   Hydrogen may also be eliminated by its affinity for palladium
or platinum black.

Traces of oxygen and some other gases may be removed by the
chemical process of "flashing", that is, vaporizing a metal such as

magnesium or calcium in a vessel connected to the system; a compound of negligible vapour pressure is formed. Again, *thermal processes* may be employed; thus nitrogen is slowly removed in the presence of an incandescent tungsten filament. Finally, *electrical processes* are available either in the form of the glow discharge or of impacts of electrons obtained thermionically. The action is generally considered to consist in ionization of the gas atoms or molecules, after which the ions adhere to the walls of the container, particularly if the latter is suitably cooled.

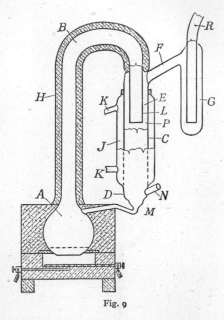

Fig. 9

7. Measurement of Low Pressures.

Of the manometers described below, those under (*a*) and (*b*) are not directly dependent on molecular and kinetic properties of the gas, but are merely refined extensions of methods for measuring ordinary gas pressures. The remaining pressure gauges are all based on known theoretical laws connecting the measured property of the gas with its pressure.

(*a*) *Mercury manometers.*

A direct extension of the ordinary mercury manometer to the measurement of low pressures may be obtained by the use of the optical lever.

Fig. 10 shows an apparatus due to Carver; the mercury cut-off at *A* is initially open, and a tap (not shown) at the top of the gas tube cuts off the system whose pressure is required. The gauge is then exhausted as highly as possible and the zero reading is observed. The reading is provided by a beam of light reflected from the mirror *C*, which is pivoted in the holder *E* on two knife-edges; the movable portion rests on a steel float *D*, which rises and falls as the mercury level changes with a given change of pressure. The apparatus will measure pressures down to 10^{-4} mm. and may also be used at ordinary pressures to determine small differences of pressure. The pressure may be calculated directly from the dimensions of the apparatus, or a McLeod gauge may be used for calibration. The main disadvantage is the unsteadiness of the zero, due to vibration ripples on the surface of the mercury.

The standard instrument against which almost all manometers are in practice calibrated is the *McLeod gauge*, which depends for its action on the validity of Boyle's law at low gas pressures.

Fig. 11 illustrates Gaede's modification of the McLeod gauge; gas from the system whose pressure is required enters the gauge through B and fills the gauge down to the level of the mercury reservoir. The reservoir G is then raised, cutting off the gas present in the bulb H and compressing it into the capillary extension which lies along the scale KK_1. The mercury rises faster in the left-hand arm, and may be made to stand at any arbitrary height in the tube A, above that in the closed tube. Then if the gas pressure in the system is p, the volume of bulb and capillary V, the final pressure $(p + H)$ and the final volume V_1, we have

$$pV = (p + H)V_1,$$

or, since $p \ll H$,

$$p = \frac{HV_1}{V}. \qquad . \quad . \quad . \quad (94)$$

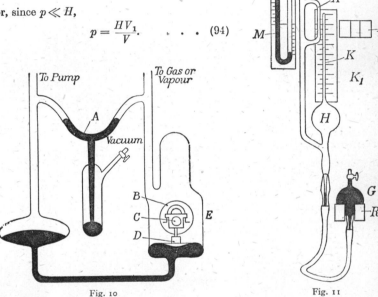

Fig. 10

Fig. 11

An alternative method of using the gauge is to raise the reservoir between fixed positions (R and R_2 in the figure). When the reservoir is at R_2, the bulb and capillary are open to the system; when the reservoir is raised to R, the mercury always rises to the level in A corresponding to the top of the closed capillary and forming the zero of the scale KK_1. (The tube A and the closed capillary are of the same diameter, to avoid differences in pressure arising from the capillary depression of mercury in a narrow tube.) Then applying Boyle's law before and after compression, if p and H are measured in mm. and V_0 is the volume of 1 mm. length of the capillary tube, we have

$$pV = (p + H)HV_0,$$

or, since $p \ll H$,

$$p = \frac{V_0H^2}{V}. \qquad . \quad . \quad . \quad . \quad . \quad . \quad . \quad . \quad (95)$$

The scale KK_1 is graduated directly according to this parabolic law; a large range of pressures is thus obtained on a relatively short scale. Pressures from 100 mm. to 1 mm. can be read directly on the manometer M and from 1 to 10^{-4} mm. on the scale KK_1.

The McLeod gauge measures pressures down to 10^{-5} mm., but of course the pressures include those of mercury vapour and other vapours, unless the latter are removed by suitable condensing traps.

(b) Mechanical manometers.

The common Bourdon brass spiral gauge has been applied to the measurement of low pressures by Ladenburg and others in the form of a spiral of thin glass tubing. The movement of the end of the spiral is registered by an attached mirror which allows the use of an optical lever. A null method is often used, external pressure being applied to bring the mirror back to its zero position: this external pressure is recorded by a McLeod gauge placed at a distance. The pressure of corrosive gases which attack mercury may be found in this way.

Alternatively, a type of aneroid barometer may be used in the form of a brass box containing a thin dividing membrane of copper. One side of the membrane is connected to a very high vacuum and the other side to the system whose pressure is required. The membrane presses against a glass plate, the system is illuminated, and the interference fringes are observed with a microscope. The apparatus is calibrated against the McLeod gauge.

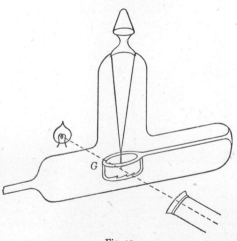

Fig. 12

(c) Viscosity manometers.

Reference to equation (23), p. 185, shows that at low pressures the viscous force existing between two surfaces in relative motion is directly proportional to the pressure of the gas and to the square root of its molecular weight. Manometers based on this relation are of two types, which depend on (a) the rate of damping of a vibrating system suspended in the gas, or (b) the steady torque communicated to a suspended surface placed opposite a surface in motion.

In Coolidge's *quartz fibre manometer* (fig. 12) two fine quartz fibres are arranged in semi-bifilar suspension and end in a common tip, the vibratory motion of which is observed by a microscope with a scale in the eyepiece. If we denote the logarithmic decrement, which is a measure of the total damping, by λ, the general relation will be

$$\lambda = a + bpM^{\frac{1}{2}}, \qquad \dots \dots \dots \quad (96)$$

where a represents the damping due to friction of the support and b is constant at constant temperature. The quantity a is determined from the residual damping when the system is completely exhausted. The apparatus is calibrated against the McLeod gauge; the linear relation is valid over the range 10^{-2} mm. to 10^{-5} mm.

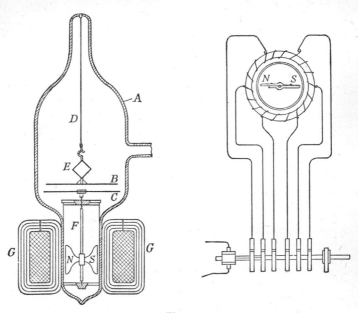

Fig. 13

In *Dushman's molecular gauge*, the viscous drag exerted when a disc C (fig. 13) is rotated rapidly at uniform speed close to a similar plate B suspended by a quartz fibre D is observed by means of a mirror E. The whole system is contained in the glass vessel A, and to ensure absence of leaks from the air the disc C is rotated by the effect of a rotating magnetic field in the Gramme ring GG on the magnet NS, fixed to the vertical axle F. If r_0 is the radius of the upper disc, and we consider a circular strip of radii r and $r + dr$, the total torque exerted by the lower disc, by equation 23, is

$$\tau\theta = \int_0^{r_0} rK\omega rp \left(\frac{M}{RT}\right)^{\frac{1}{2}} 2\pi r\, dr$$

$$= \frac{\pi K p \omega r_0^4}{2} \left(\frac{M}{RT}\right)^{\frac{1}{2}}, \qquad \dots \dots \dots \quad (97)$$

where K is a constant, θ the deflection produced, τ the restoring couple for unit angle of twist, and ω the angular velocity of rotation of the lower disc.

A more correct formula given by Dushman * is

$$\theta = \left(\frac{kt^2D^2}{32\pi\delta}\right)p\omega\left(\frac{M}{RT}\right)^{\frac{1}{2}}, \quad \ldots \ldots \quad (98)$$

where D is the diameter of the rotating disc C, δ and t are the moment of inertia and the period of natural oscillation of the disc B, and k is a constant involving the accommodation coefficient. Pressures down to 10^{-7} mm. may be measured with this apparatus, the usual range extending from 10^{-3} mm. By equation (98), the instrument may be used to measure pressure absolutely, but k is not usually known accurately, so the McLeod gauge is generally used for calibration.

(d) Radiometer gauges.

The common *Crookes radiometer* may be used to measure low gas pressures, but its operation is complicated and still doubtfully under-

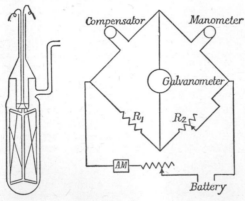

Fig. 14

stood. Its use is therefore restricted to qualitative investigation. On the other hand, *Knudsen's absolute manometer* rivals the McLeod gauge for the absolute determination of low pressures. It has the further advantage of measuring the pressures of vapours, but it is much less convenient to use.

The instrument consists of two fixed mica strips heated electrically and placed on either side of a third strip suspended by a torsion wire. The radiometer forces exert a torque on the suspended strip, measurement being carried out with mirror, lamp and scale.

The torque is proportional to the gas pressure, and the theory of the instrument has already been discussed fully in this series.† The final relation obtained is

* *Phys. Rev.*, Vol. 5, p. 212 (1915).
† Roberts, *Heat and Thermodynamics*, p. 78 *et seq.*

$$p = \frac{8\pi^2\delta\, d_1}{Dat^2 d_2} \frac{T_2}{T_1 - T_2} \text{ dynes/sq. cm.,}$$

where d_1 is the scale deflection, d_2 the distance of the scale from the mirror, and a, t, δ and D are the area of one side, period of oscillation, moment of inertia, and mean diameter of the suspended strip respectively.* The range is from 10^{-2} mm. downwards, and the scale is linear except near the higher limit of pressure.

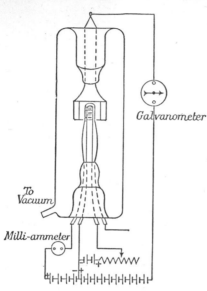

To Vacuum

Galvanometer

Milli-ammeter

Fig. 15

(e) Pirani-Hall gauge.

Since from equation (40), p. 190, the quantity of heat ΔQ conducted through a gas at low pressure is proportional to the pressure, a convenient gauge may be based on the change in electrical resistance of a heated tungsten wire immersed in the gas.

The general arrangement is shown in fig. 14, which shows a modification due to Hall and is self-explanatory. The gauge may be used in three ways: (1) the voltage may be maintained constant and the variation of the current i with the pressure p may be observed, (2) the resistance may be maintained constant and the variation of energy input with p observed, or (3) the current may be maintained constant and the variation of r with p observed (Pirani-Hall method). Linear relations are obtained with different gases over a range 10^{-1} mm. to 10^{-5} mm.; the apparatus is usually calibrated against the McLeod gauge.

(f) Ionization gauges.

These gauges are based on the dependence of ionization on gas pressure. The existence of a linear relation depends on the arrangement of the apparatus, a satisfactory form being that of Dushman and Found, shown in fig. 15.

The plate, which is in the form of a grid and occupies the position normally held by the latter in a triode, has a potential of about $+250$ volts relative to the filament. The collector of the positive ions, which consists of an outer cylinder of molybdenum, has a potential of about -20 volts relative to the cathode. The positive ion current is registered by a sensitive galvanometer and is found to be linearly related to the gas pressure over a wide range. Experiments with argon, the pressure of which was determined simultaneously with a McLeod

* G. W. Todd, *Phil. Mag.*, Vol. 38, p. 381 (1919).

gauge, showed that the greater the electron current, the higher the pressure at which the linear relation remains valid. The range is from 10^{-2} mm. to the lowest pressures attainable.

(g) Effusion gauges.

The use of effusion gauges is normally restricted to the measurement of vapour pressures of metals, an adequate account of which will be found in Roberts' *Heat and Thermodynamics*, p. 168 *et seq.*

REFERENCES

J. H. Jeans, *The Dynamical Theory of Gases* (Cambridge University Press).
L. B. Loeb, *Kinetic Theory of Gases* (McGraw-Hill Book Co., 1927).
L. Dunoyer, *La Technique du Vide* (Presses Universitaires de Paris, 1924).
F. H. Newman, *Production and Measurement of Low Pressures* (Benn).

CHAPTER X

Osmotic Pressure

1. Osmotic Pressure of Solutions.

Various experiments lead to the view that in some way a substance in solution exerts a mechanical pressure on the walls of the containing vessel. To demonstrate this it is convenient to use a so-called semi-permeable membrane. This is a natural or artificial membrane, possessing the property of allowing the molecules of a solvent to pass through freely, but completely obstructing the molecules of a solute. For example, a gelatinous layer of cupric ferrocyanide, deposited in a porous pot, acts in this way with respect to a solution of cane sugar in water. It prevents the passage of the sugar, but freely transmits the water. A porous pot cylinder, with a semi-permeable membrane of cupric ferrocyanide deposited in its walls, is filled with a solution of cane sugar in water. A long glass tube is then fixed through the top of the cylinder, the joint is made watertight, and the cylinder is made to stand in a beaker of pure water. As time goes on, it is found that the liquid inside the glass tube rises to a considerable height and comes to rest.

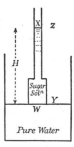

Fig. 1

Fig. 1 represents the situation after equilibrium has been reached. The cylinder has been adjusted so that the semi-permeable base just touches the pure water. Water has entered the cylinder and tube until the difference of the two levels has become H cm. A hydrostatic pressure of $g\rho H$ dynes per sq. cm., plus the pressure at X, now acts on the inner surface of the semi-permeable membrane in the base of the cylinder, where ρ is the density of the solution in its final state. A pressure $g\sigma H$, plus the pressure at X or Z, acts on the solvent at Y, where σ is the vapour density. The same pressure acts upwards on the lower side of the membrane. It may be said that a pressure $gH(\rho - \sigma)$, applied to the inner surface of the membrane or to the solution, prevents more water from entering. This quantity is called the *osmotic pressure* of the solution in its final state:

$$P = gH(\rho - \sigma). \quad \ldots \ldots \ldots \quad (1)$$

Semi-permeable membranes and the phenomenon of osmotic pressure play a great part in connexion with the properties of cells in plants and animals. Solutions with equal osmotic pressures, though not necessarily with the same solute or solvent, are said to be *isotonic*. In giving medical injections, swelling of the red blood corpuscles is avoided by using solutions isotonic with the contents of the corpuscles.

The osmotic pressure of a solution is often regarded as being produced in the same way as the pressure of a gas, that is, it is supposed that the molecules or ions of a solute are endowed with motion, that they bombard the walls of the containing vessel, and that the osmotic pressure is the normal momentum imparted to the walls per sq. cm. per sec. In dilute solutions it is supposed that the molecules or ions of the solute move about, unimpeded by the presence of the molecules of the solvent, and without exerting forces on one another; in fact, the solute behaves as a perfect gas would behave if it occupied the same total volume as the solution. Other views of osmotic pressure have been put forward from time to time, but these will not be considered here.

Experiment shows that the value of the osmotic pressure of a very dilute solution of a solute which does not dissociate when placed in the solvent is, in fact, that which it would have if the solute were a perfect gas occupying the same total volume as the solution. This result is known as *van't Hoff's law*, the classical law of osmotic pressure. In symbols, it may be written

$$\frac{PV}{M\theta} = \frac{R}{W}, \qquad \cdots \cdots \quad (2)$$

where P is the osmotic pressure of the solution, V its volume, θ the absolute temperature, M the mass of solute, W the molecular weight of the solute, and R a constant. If P is in dynes per sq. cm., V in c.c., M in gm., and W the molecular weight, $R = 8 \cdot 315 \times 10^7$. Its dimensions are those of work/temperature or $ML^2T^{-2}\theta^{-1}$. Equation (2) may also be written in the form

$$P = kn\theta, \qquad \cdots \cdots \quad (3)$$

where k is Boltzmann's constant, equal to $1 \cdot 372 \times 10^{-16}$, and n is the concentration of solute molecules in molecules per c.c. In the case of solutes where each molecule completely dissociates into ν ions, van't Hoff's law becomes

$$\frac{PV}{M\theta} = \frac{\nu R}{W}, \qquad \cdots \cdots \quad (4)$$

which reduces to

$$P = \nu kn\theta. \qquad \cdots \cdots \quad (5)$$

Whatever the nature of solutions may be, thermodynamics enables us to deduce various laws connected with their osmotic pressure, vapour pressure, &c. Some of these laws will be discussed before we consider modern views of the nature of solutions.

2. The Osmotic Pressure of a Dilute Solution is Proportional to the Absolute Temperature.

Consider a quantity of a dilute solution enclosed in a cylindrical vessel $ABCD$ (fig. 2). Let the latter be provided with a frictionless piston, the head of which is semi-permcable in the sense used above. Let the volume of solution be V c.c., its osmotic pressure P dynes per sq. cm., and its absolute temperature θ. Let there be pure solvent above the piston head. During any motion of the piston the solute

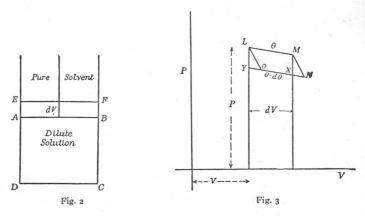

Fig. 2   Fig. 3

is kept in the lower part of $ABCD$, but pure solvent passes freely through the piston head. Let the system be taken through the cycle $LMNO$, which is represented on a PV diagram in fig. 3. (1) Let the initial state P, V, θ be represented by the point L, when the piston is at AB. Let the piston move up very slowly at constant temperature θ, so as to sweep out a volume dV, that is, admitting dV c.c. of solvent. The point M represents the new state of the solute. (2) Let the piston move up a little farther, so that the temperature drops adiabatically to $\theta - d\theta$, that is, take the solute along the path MN to N. (3) Let the piston be pushed down at constant temperature $\theta - d\theta$ until the volume is represented by the point O. (4) Finally, let the piston be pushed down a little farther, so that the enclosed solution has its temperature adiabatically raised by $d\theta$, and the point L is again reached.

Thus $LMNO$ is a Carnot cycle, in the thermodynamic sense. Its efficiency, by a property * of such cycles, is $\{\theta - (\theta - d\theta)\}/\theta = d\theta/\theta$.

---

* See Roberts, *Heat and Thermodynamics*, p. 250.

From another point of view, its efficiency is equal to the area of the cycle divided by the heat taken in by the substance along LM. The area of $LMNO$ = the area of $LMXY = LY\,dV$. The quantity LY may be written in the form $(\partial P/\partial\theta)_v\,d\theta$, for it is the change in osmotic pressure at constant volume corresponding to a change of temperature $d\theta$. Hence the area is $(\partial P/\partial\theta)_v\,d\theta\,dV$. The solution is so dilute that along LM there is no heat of " further " dilution to allow for, and the only heat absorbed along LM by the solution is that required to make up for the work $P\,dV$ done by the solution and so keep the temperature constant. The second expression for the efficiency becomes $\{(\partial P/\partial\theta)_v\,d\theta\,dV\}/P\,dV$. Equating the two expressions and clearing fractions, we have $(\partial P/\partial\theta)_v = P/\theta$. By integration,

$$\log P = \log\theta + \text{a constant,}$$

and

$$P = a\theta, \quad \ldots \ldots \ldots \quad (6)$$

where a is a constant as far as temperature is concerned, but may depend on the volume. This result, of course, is part of van't Hoff's law.

3. Difference between the Vapour Pressure of a Pure Solvent and that of a Dilute Solution.

Consider the simple arrangement shown in fig. 1 and described on p. 214. Let the vapour pressures at points X and Y, just above the surfaces of solution and solvent, be p' and p respectively. Let the densities of the vapour and solution be σ and ρ. Neglect changes in vapour density with height. To get from X to Y, it is possible to proceed in two ways, (1) via the solution and solvent, along the route XWY, (2) via the vapour only, along the route XZY. The pressure change in going from X to Y must be the same along both paths. Along XWY, $p = p' + g\rho H - P$, since the pressure is p' at X, rises by $g\rho H$ in going from X to the bottom of the column of solution, and then falls by P as the semi-permeable membrane is crossed. Along XZY, $p = p' + g\sigma H$, since the drop in level in the vapour is the only cause of change in pressure. Hence $g\rho H - P = p - p' = g\sigma H$, $P = gH(\rho - \sigma)$, and $gH = P/(\rho - \sigma)$. Thus

$$p - p' = g\sigma H = \frac{P\sigma}{\rho - \sigma}. \quad \ldots \ldots \quad (7)$$

Since $\sigma \ll \rho$, the approximation

$$p - p' = \frac{P\sigma}{\rho} \quad \ldots \ldots \ldots \quad (8)$$

is often used.

4. Difference between the Boiling Point of a Pure Solvent and that of a Dilute Solution.

A liquid boils when its saturation vapour pressure is equal to the pressure of the atmosphere above its surface. Fig. 4 shows the curves connecting the saturation vapour pressure and the absolute temperature of a pure liquid and of a dilute solution with the same liquid as solvent. Let A represent the boiling point of the pure solvent at temperature θ. At this temperature the vapour pressure of the solution

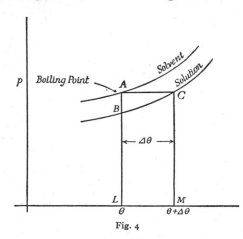

Fig. 4

is lower than that of the solvent, represented by the point B. To make the solution boil, its vapour pressure must be brought up to atmospheric pressure. This is done if the temperature is raised by an amount $\Delta\theta$, say, so that the vapour pressure p of the solution is represented by the point C, where $AL = CM = p$. Let $BL = p'$. The curve BC connects p' and θ. To a change in temperature $d\theta$, there corresponds a change of pressure dp'. Hence to a change in temperature $\Delta\theta$, there corresponds a change of pressure $(dp'/d\theta)\Delta\theta$, which must be equal to $p - p'$. Thus

$$\Delta\theta = \frac{p - p'}{dp'/d\theta}. \qquad \cdots \cdots \quad (9)$$

Assume that the slopes of the two curves near A and B are equal, that is, that $dp/d\theta = dp'/d\theta$, an assumption borne out by experiment. By a relation known as the first latent heat equation, or Clapeyron's equation,*

$$\frac{dp}{d\theta} = \frac{L}{\theta(v_2 - v_1)} \qquad \cdots \cdots \quad (10)$$

during a change of state, where L is the latent heat in ergs per gramme, and v_2 and v_1 are the specific volumes of the vapour and liquid solvent respectively at temperature θ. Hence

$$\Delta\theta = \frac{p - p'}{L/\theta(v_2 - v_1)}. \qquad \cdots \cdots \quad (11)$$

* See Roberts, *Heat and Thermodynamics*, p. 314.

By equation (8),

$$p - p' = \frac{P\sigma}{\rho},$$

where σ is the vapour density of solvent vapour ($=1/v_2$), ρ the density of the dilute solution, and P its osmotic pressure. As the solution is dilute, assume that ρ is the density of the pure solvent. Then $\rho = 1/v_1$. In equation (11) substitute for $p - p'$ from equation (8), neglect v_1 in comparison with v_2, since the specific volume of a liquid is so much less than that of its vapour, and replace v_2 by $1/\sigma$. Then

$$\Delta\theta = \frac{P\sigma/\rho}{L\sigma/\theta}$$

or

$$\Delta\theta = \frac{P\theta}{L\rho}. \quad \cdots \cdots \quad (12)$$

In numerical substitutions, P is in dynes per sq. cm., L in *ergs per gramme*, and ρ in grammes per c.c. $\Delta\theta$ is numerically positive, so that the solution has a higher boiling point than the solvent. Since $P = vkn\theta$, by equation (5),

$$\Delta\theta = \frac{vkn\theta^2}{L\rho}. \quad \cdots \cdots \quad (13)$$

5. Difference between the Freezing Point of a Pure Solvent and that of a Dilute Solution.

The freezing point of a pure solvent is that temperature at which the liquid phase of the substance is in equilibrium with the solid phase and their vapour pressures are equal. If no substance other than the vapour occupies the space above the liquid and solid phases, all three phases, solid, liquid and vapour, can be in equilibrium, and the freezing point is also the triple point. If the vessel is open to the atmosphere, the freezing point is not quite the same as the triple point. For example, the ordinary melting point of ice is 0° C., but the triple point is $+0\cdot0074°$ C.

When a solution freezes, only the pure solvent crystallizes out. The freezing point is lower than that of the pure solvent, and is the temperature at which the solid phase of the solvent is in equilibrium with the liquid solution, that is, at which the vapour pressure of the solution is the same as that of the solid solvent. Consider fig. 5, in which AB represents the $p\theta$ curve of the vapour of the liquid solvent, DB represents that of the vapour of the solid solvent, and DC the $p'\theta$ curve of the vapour of the solution. B represents the freezing point and triple point of the pure solvent, D the freezing point of the solution.

Draw vertical straight lines ADH and BCK through D and B

respectively, and horizontal straight lines DE, AF. Let $OK = \theta$, $OH = \theta - \Delta\theta$. Experiment shows that AB and DC have the same slope. Hence $AD = BC = p - p'$. Hence $AD = P\sigma/\rho$, approximately, by equation (8), p. 217, where σ is the vapour density, ρ the density of the dilute solution (which is nearly equal to the density of the solvent), and P is the osmotic pressure of the solution at θ. Also $AD = BC = BE - CE$. DE represents the lowering of the freezing point $\Delta\theta$ produced by the presence of the solute. $BE = DE \tan BDE = \Delta\theta(\partial p/\partial\theta)$, where $\partial p/\partial\theta$ relates to the vapour pressure of the solid solvent. $CE = DE \tan CDE = DE \tan BAF$, since AB and DC are parallel, $= \Delta\theta(\partial p/\partial\theta)$ where $\partial p/\partial\theta$ relates to the vapour pressure of the liquid

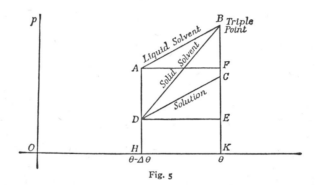

Fig. 5

solvent. Hence $AD = BE - CE = \Delta\theta\left\{(\partial p/\partial\theta)_{\text{solid}} - (\partial p/\partial\theta)_{\text{liquid}}\right\}$.

Clapeyron's equation (10) applied to the transition solid-vapour gives $\partial p/\partial\theta_{\text{solid}} = L_{13}/\theta(v_3 - v_1)$, where L_{13} is the latent heat of transition from solid to vapour, and v_3 and v_1 the specific volumes of vapour and solid respectively. Now $v_3 \gg v_1$, and $v_3 = 1/\sigma$, where σ is the vapour density. Hence $(\partial p/\partial\theta)_{\text{solid}} = L_{13}\sigma/\theta$. Similarly $(\partial p/\partial\theta)_{\text{liquid}} = L_{23}\sigma/\theta$, where L_{23} is the latent heat of transition from liquid to vapour. Hence $AD = \Delta\theta\{L_{13}\sigma/\theta - L_{23}\sigma/\theta\} = \Delta\theta \cdot L_{12}\sigma/\theta$, where L_{12} is the latent heat of transition from solid to liquid, since $L_{13} = L_{12} + L_{23}$ near the triple point. Equating the two values of AD, we have

$$\Delta\theta = \frac{P\theta}{L_{12}\rho}. \qquad \ldots \ldots \ldots (14)$$

An accurate (but indirect) method for measuring osmotic pressure is based on this formula.

6. Measurement of Osmotic Pressure.

Osmotic pressure may be measured directly e.g. by the method of Berkeley and Hartley.*

* Phil. Trans. Roy. Soc., A., Vol. 206, p. 481 (1906).

A horizontal porcelain tube A (fig. 6) has a semi-permeable membrane of $CuFe(CN)_6$ deposited near the outer wall. The gun-metal case B enclosing A is filled with the solution under test by the side-tube C. The brass end-tubes D and E lead respectively to a vertical open graduated glass capillary tube and to a tap. The solvent (water) is placed in the porcelain, brass and glass tubes. Solvent tends to pass through the membrane, but is prevented by a hydrostatic pressure applied through C. When the applied hydrostatic pressure is just equal to the sum of the required osmotic pressure and the small hydrostatic pressure on the solvent in A, the meniscus in F remains stationary. The membrane was strong enough to allow osmotic pressures of 130 atmospheres to be measured.

7. Raoult's Law.

Raoult's law asserts that when a solute is added to a solvent to form a dilute solution, the fractional drop in vapour pressure $(p - p')/p$

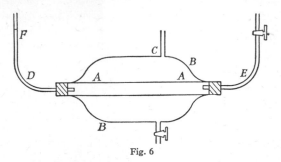

Fig. 6

is equal to N_1/N_2, where N_1 and N_2, respectively, are the total numbers of solute and solvent molecules present (solute undissociated).

To prove this, replace $p - p'$ by $P\sigma/\rho = kn\theta\sigma/\rho$ by equations (8) and (3), where k is Boltzmann's constant, n the number of solute molecules per c.c., σ the vapour density, ρ the density of the solution (and of the solvent, approximately). Further, p, the saturation vapour pressure of the solvent, is given by the equation of state of a perfect gas, since the saturated state may be regarded as the last state to which the equation of state applies as the substance approaches condensation. Hence $p/\sigma = R\theta/W$, where W is the molecular weight of the solvent, and $p = R\theta\sigma/W$. We thus have $(p - p')/p = knW/R\rho$. Write $n = N_1/V$, where V is the volume of solution or solvent. Now ρ/W is the number of gramme-molecules of solvent per c.c., if ρ is regarded as the density of the solvent, $V\rho/W$ the total number of gramme-molecules of solvent present, and R/k the number of molecules in a gramme-molecule. Hence $V\rho R/Wk = N_2$, the number of actual molecules of solvent present. Then we have approximately

$$\frac{p - p'}{p} = \frac{N_1}{N_2}, \quad \cdots \cdots \cdots (15)$$

and $N_1/N_2 = n_1/n_2$, the ratio of the concentrations in molecules per c.c.

8. Two Classes of Electrolytes.

As far as aqueous solutions are concerned, there are two classes of electrolytes. The class of *weak electrolytes* includes those substances which when dissolved in water give solutions in which the process of dissociation into ions is far from complete. This statement holds even when the solutions are very dilute. In this class are many organic acids and bases, carbon dioxide, sulphuretted hydrogen, and ammonia. The class of *strong electrolytes* includes those substances which are now believed to be completely dissociated into ions in dilute and even in moderately strong solutions. To this class belong most neutral salts and those acids and alkalies which have long been called " strong ", for example, HCl, HNO_3, H_2SO_4, $NaOH$, KOH. The properties of solutions of weak electrolytes are well represented by the classical theory outlined on pp. 215–221, but this theory fails to explain the properties of solutions of strong electrolytes. Contributions to the theory of such solutions have been made by Sutherland, Bjerrum, Hertz, Milner, Ghosh and others, and especially by Debye and Hückel (1923 and onwards). As the theory of the last two authors is now generally accepted, an outline of the elementary part of it will be given here.

9. Modern Views of Osmotic Pressure.

The classical theory of the osmotic pressure of dilute solutions regards it as an effect of the same type as the pressure of gases, that is, the value of the osmotic pressure is calculated as the normal momentum imparted to the boundary surfaces per sq. cm. per sec. by the impact of the molecules or ions of the solute. It is assumed that no forces exist between the molecules or ions. Debye and Hückel's theory represents an advance somewhat analogous to that made by Van der Waals in the kinetic theory of gases. Their theory takes into account the forces exerted by ions on one another, due to their electric charges. These forces are given by Coulomb's law of inverse squares, and the solvent enters into the calculation because it fills the spaces between the ions and the value of its dielectric constant affects the value of the forces. Any given ion is more likely to be approached by ions of the opposite kind than by ions of the same kind. This affects the kinetic energy of the ions and reduces the osmotic pressure. In solutions of weak electrolytes the charged ions also exert forces on one another, but as they are relatively few in number compared with the total number of undissociated molecules present, the effect of the forces is relatively small, and weak electrolytes behave according to the classical theory.

10. Debye and Hückel's Theory of Strong Electrolytes.*

It is convenient to describe first the experimental results obtained with solutions of strong electrolytes. Suppose that the actual osmotic pressure of a solution is P, and that the osmotic pressure which the solution would have if it were completely dissociated into ions is P_a. Write $P/P_a = \beta$; β is called the *osmotic coefficient* of the solution, and is determined by experiments on the depression of the freezing point, &c. According to the classical theory of solutions,

$$1 - \beta = (\nu - 1)n^{\nu-1}/\nu K, \quad \ldots \quad (16)$$

where n is the concentration of the electrolyte in molecules per c.c., ν the number of ions into which each molecule dissociates, and K the constant of equilibrium supposed to exist between molecules and ions, as given by the law of mass action (see Ex. 1, p. 280).

In the case of binary electrolytes like NaCl, $\nu = 2$ and $1 - \beta = n/2K$. A graph connecting $1 - \beta$ and n for such substances ought to be a straight line, beginning at the origin and making a finite angle θ with the axis of n, where $\tan \theta = 1/2K$. In other cases, when $\nu > 2$, the graph connecting $(1 - \beta)$ as ordinate and n as abscissa ought to be a curve starting at the origin with the axis of n as its tangent. The actual experimental results are in sharp contrast with these. Inspection of fig. 7 shows that in all cases the graph connecting $(1 - \beta)$

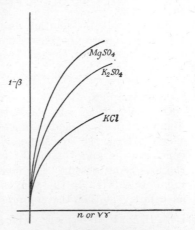

Fig. 7

(γ is the concentration in gramme-molecules per litre of solution.)

and the concentration n is a curve leaving the origin in such a way that the axis of $(1 - \beta)$ is a tangent to it. Thus the classical theory of osmotic pressure fails as regards strong electrolytes. It appears on closer examination that the states of such solutions are not governed by the classical law of mass action. Fig. 7 also shows that for a given concentration the value of $(1 - \beta)$ depends on the valency of the ions of the electrolyte concerned, that is, on the electric charges upon the ions. The classical theory fails in that it does not take into account the forces due to these electric charges. In the present exposition of Debye and Hückel's theory it is initially assumed that (1) the solutions under discussion have fairly low or low concentrations, (2) the electrolyte is completely dissociated into ions.

* Debye and Hückel, *Physikalische Zeits.*, Vol. 24, pp. 185, 305 (1923).

The classical value of the osmotic pressure P_a of a solution is $P_a = vnk\theta$, by equation (5). Let the actual osmotic pressure be P. It is required to express P in terms of P_a. Consider a volume V_0 of a solution, enclosed in a cylindrical vessel provided with a piston of which the head is semi-permeable, that is, permeable to molecules of the solvent but impermeable to molecules of the solute. Let there be pure solvent behind the piston head. Consider the work which must be done by an external agent, who may be called the operator, to obtain V c.c. of solution, starting with pure solvent, working at constant temperature and by purely reversible processes. Two convenient ways of effecting this change offer themselves, and, by a property of the quantity known as the available energy of a system, or otherwise, it may be shown that the work done by the operator is the same in each case.

First of all, the solution may be compressed infinitely slowly from the state of zero concentration (infinite dilution) and volume V_0 to the final volume V. The total work done by the operator in this process is $-\int_{V_0}^{V} P\,dV$ ergs $= W_1$, say. Note that in the usual notation of thermodynamics, $\partial W_1/\partial V = -P$. Secondly, the operator may start with a solution of zero concentration, regarding it as containing ions infinitely far apart, and take away the charges from the ions infinitely slowly. Then the solution may be compressed from a state of zero concentration and volume V_0 to the final volume V, the charges on the ions being absent. The charges may then be restored to the ions infinitely slowly. In this way the solution reaches the same final state as before. During the compression, the work done by the operator is $-\int_{V_0}^{V} P_a\,dV = W_2$, say, where P_a represents the osmotic pressure calculated by classical reasoning, since electric charges are absent. Hence $\partial W_2/\partial V = -P_a$. Let the work done by the operator in removing and restoring the electric charges be W_E. Then since the total work done by the operator is the same in the two processes,

$$W_1 = W_2 + W_E. \qquad \ldots \ldots \quad (17)$$

Differentiate with respect to V, keeping the temperature constant. This gives

$$\frac{\partial W_1}{\partial V} = \frac{\partial W_2}{\partial V} + \frac{\partial W_E}{\partial V},$$

or

$$-P = -P_a + \frac{\partial W_E}{\partial V}.$$

Hence

$$P = P_a - \frac{\partial W_E}{\partial V}. \qquad \ldots \ldots \quad (18)$$

Thus the question of finding P in terms of P_a is reduced to the problem of finding $\partial W_E/\partial V$. The quantity W_E consists of two parts, (a) the work w_1 done by the operator in removing the charges from the ions when the ions are infinitely far apart, (b) the work w_2 done by the operator in restoring the charges after the final concentration has been reached. If we regard the ions as spheres, each of radius b cm., charge e e.s.u., infinitely far apart, and immersed in a solvent of dielectric constant D e.s.u., the energy of each ion, regarded as a charged condenser of capacity Db e.s.u., is $e^2/2Db$ ergs. It is this energy which is allowed to return to infinity when the ions are discharged. Thus the work done by the operator per ion is $-e^2/2Db$ ergs. If in V c.c. of solution there are N ions of each kind, the total work is

$$w_1 = -\frac{Ne^2}{Db} \text{ ergs.} \qquad \ldots \ldots \quad (19a)$$

In calculating w_2, the work of restoring the charges to the ions at finite concentration, we must take account of the work done in bringing up a charge to each ion against the mean potential due to other ions, as well as against its own potential. Thus w_2 consists of two parts, which we shall call w_3 and w_4 respectively. The work done against an ion's own potential, by a similar calculation to that just carried out, is equal to $+e^2/2D'b$ ergs per ion, where D' represents the effective dielectric constant of the medium around an ion.

For the N ions of each kind in V c.c. of solution, the total work

$$w_4 = \frac{Ne^2}{D'b}. \qquad \ldots \ldots \quad (19b)$$

In strong solutions $D' \neq D$, on account of the proximity of other ions, although in dilute solutions D and D' may be assumed to be equal.

The work w_3 done against the mean potential due to other ions is much greater than either of the quantities of work just calculated, and requires detailed consideration. Assume that the aqueous solution under discussion contains a single binary monovalent electrolyte such as NaCl or KCl, whose ions carry charges $+e$ and $-e$ respectively, where e is $4{\cdot}774 \times 10^{-10}$ e.s.u. We now calculate the mean electrostatic potential which the neighbouring ions produce at a point which is about to be occupied by the centre of a given ion. Let there be n ions of each kind per c.c. The number of negative ions surrounding a given positive ion, when averaged over a certain time, exceeds the number of positive ions, because of the attraction of unlike charges. The excess is affected by temperature changes. Let ϕ be the as yet uncalculated resultant potential at a point at a definite distance from the centre of a selected positive ion and outside it, due to that selected ion and to the rest of the ions. To bring a charge $+e$ there, work $e\phi$

ergs must be done by the operator, and $-e\phi$ ergs are required to bring a charge $-e$ there. We now apply the Maxwell-Boltzmann theorem* to calculate the average concentration (in time) of ions of each sort in an element of volume dV near the point in question. According to that theorem, the number of positive ions in this element is $A\epsilon^{-e\phi/k\theta}\,dV$, where k is Boltzmann's constant, and ϵ is the base of Napierian logarithms. A is a constant which is equal to n, since the expression must hold when $\theta = \infty$, a temperature at which we may assume that the ions are uniformly distributed, with a concentration n of each kind per c.c., and $A\epsilon^0\,dV = A\,dV = n\,dV$. Similarly, the number of negative ions in the element dV is $n\epsilon^{+e\phi/k\theta}\,dV$. Since the ionic charges are $+e$ and $-e$ respectively, the net amount of positive charge in the element dV is $ne\{\epsilon^{-e\phi/k\theta} - \epsilon^{+e\phi/k\theta}\}dV$, that is,

$$ne\{\epsilon^{-e\phi/k\theta} - \epsilon^{+e\phi/k\theta}\} \text{ e.s.u. per c.c.} = \rho, \text{ say.}   . . . \quad (20)$$

As this is a problem in electrostatics, Gauss's theorem holds. Apply it to the element dV, which may be regarded as a rectangular parallelepiped. This gives Poisson's equation,

$$\frac{\partial^2\phi}{\partial x^2} + \frac{\partial^2\phi}{\partial y^2} + \frac{\partial^2\phi}{\partial z^2} = -\frac{4\pi\rho}{D}, ... \quad (21)$$

which may be written in the shorter form

$$\Delta\phi = -\frac{4\pi\rho}{D}.   . . . . . \quad (22)$$

In this equation substitute the value of ρ from equation (20). Then

$$\Delta\phi = \frac{4\pi ne}{D}(\epsilon^{e\phi/k\theta} - \epsilon^{-e\phi/k\theta}).   . . . . \quad (23)$$

Assume that the electrical energy $e\phi$ is small compared with the mean kinetic energy $k\theta$ due to thermal agitation. The exponentials can then be expanded in series of terms in $e\phi/k\theta$, so that, neglecting terms in ϕ of degree higher than the first, we get

$$\Delta\phi = \frac{8\pi ne^2\phi}{Dk\theta}, \text{ approximately.}   . . . . \quad (24)$$

This may be written in the form $\Delta\phi = x^2\phi$, where $x^2 = 8\pi ne^2/Dk\theta$. Debye and Hückel call $1/x$, which has the dimensions of a length, the *characteristic length* of the solution.

When Poisson's equation is expressed in polar co-ordinates, and

* Jeans, *Dynamical Theory of Gases*, 3rd ed., equation (936) (Cambridge University Press, 1921).

when the element of volume dV has the form of a spherical shell contained between spheres of radii r and $r + dr$, the equation becomes

$$\frac{1}{r^2}\left(\frac{d(r^2\,d\phi/dr)}{dr}\right) = \frac{8\pi ne^2\phi}{Dk\theta} \quad \cdots \quad (25)$$

$$= x^2\phi. \quad \cdots \quad (26)$$

This type of element has the advantage of spherical symmetry. One general solution of equation (26) is

$$\phi = \frac{A\epsilon^{-xr}}{r} + \frac{B\epsilon^{+xr}}{r}. \quad \cdots \quad (27)$$

Since $\phi = 0$ when $r = \infty$, this reduces to

$$\phi = \frac{A\epsilon^{-xr}}{r}. \quad \cdots \quad (28)$$

This is the potential at a point outside the selected ion. Now in aqueous solutions it may be shown that each ion carries with it a layer of surrounding water molecules, which increases its effective size. Assume that each such ion is effectively a sphere of radius a cm.,* of which the interior is a medium of dielectric constant D, with a point charge $+e$ or $-e$ at the centre. Assume that the potential at any point inside this sphere is

$$\phi' = \frac{e}{Dr} + B, \quad \cdots \quad (29)$$

where B is a constant to be determined. At the boundary of the sphere of radius a, two conditions must be fulfilled. For $r = a$, $\phi = \phi'$, and also for $r = a$, $\partial\phi/\partial r = \partial\phi'/\partial r$. From the first condition,

$$\frac{A\epsilon^{-xa}}{a} = \frac{e}{Da} + B. \quad \cdots \quad (30)$$

From the second,

$$A\epsilon^{-xa}\frac{(1 + xa)}{a^2} = \frac{e}{Da^2}. \quad \cdots \quad (31)$$

From equations (30) and (31),

$$A = \frac{e\epsilon^{xa}}{D(1 + xa)} \quad \cdots \quad (32)$$

and

$$B = -\frac{ex}{D(1 + xa)}. \quad \cdots \quad (33)$$

The value of B represents the potential which the surrounding ions produce at the centre of the given ion. e/Dr is the potential at any

---

* The quantity a represents the average value of the shortest distance between the centres of the selected ion and other ions of both kinds. The quantity b of p. 225 is the radius of the actual ion, and $b \ll a$.

internal point due to the ion's own charge. When xa is small compared with unity, that is, when x is small and the concentration is small, the value of B, namely, $-ex/D(1 + xa)$, reduces to

$$B = -\frac{ex}{D}. \qquad \ldots \ldots \quad (34)$$

The further discussion is limited to this case.

It is now necessary to find the work required to bring up a charge $+e$, in elements each of value de, from infinity to a point where there is a potential due to other charges of value $B = -ex/D$. (This process is a purely mathematical device, since actually the charge can exist only as a multiple of the electronic charge.) The element of work done in bringing a charge $+de$ to the point is

$$B\,de = -\frac{ex\,de}{D}. \qquad \ldots \ldots \quad (35)$$

Substitute the value of x given by equation (24) in (35). This gives

$$B\,de = -\left(\frac{8\pi n}{Dk\theta}\right)^{\frac{1}{2}}\frac{e^2\,de}{D},$$

and by integration the total work done in bringing up $+e$ is $-(8\pi n/Dk\theta)^{\frac{1}{2}}e^3/3D$ ergs, that is, $-e^2x/3D$ ergs per ion, since $x = (8\pi ne^2/Dk\theta)^{\frac{1}{2}}$ by equation (24). If in the solution of volume V c.c. there are N ions of each kind, the total work done in bringing up their charges against the potentials of the surrounding ions is

$$w_3 = -\frac{2Ne^2x}{3D} \text{ ergs.} \qquad \ldots \ldots \quad (36)$$

This is a negative quantity. It is far greater numerically than w_1 or w_4, where $w_1 = -Ne^2/Db$ and $w_4 = Ne^2/D'b$ as given by equations (19a) and (19b), respectively, for dilute solutions, since D and D' are nearly equal. Hence the quantity W_E of equation (17) $= w_1 + w_2 = w_1 + w_3 + w_4 = w_3$ approximately. That is,

$$W_E = -\frac{2Ne^2x}{3D} \text{ ergs,} \qquad \ldots \ldots \quad (37)$$

and, on substituting $x = (8\pi ne^2/Dk\theta)^{\frac{1}{2}}$ and $n = N/V$, we have

$$W_E = -2Ne^2\frac{(8\pi Ne^2/VDk\theta)^{\frac{1}{2}}}{3D}. \qquad \ldots \quad (38)$$

Hence

$$\frac{\partial W_E}{\partial V} = Ne^2\frac{(8\pi Ne^2/Dk\theta)^{\frac{1}{2}}}{3DV^{\frac{3}{2}}},$$

if we keep N constant during the differentiation, or

$$\frac{\partial W_x}{\partial V} = \frac{e^2 x N}{3DV}.$$

Equation (18) becomes

$$P = P_a - \frac{e^2 x N}{3DV}. \quad \cdot \quad \cdot \quad \cdot \quad \cdot \quad (39)$$

For an aqueous solution of a binary salt of the type considered, the classical value of the osmotic pressure is $P_a = \nu n k\theta = 2nk\theta$. Hence

$$P = 2nk\theta \left(1 - \frac{e^2 x}{6Dk\theta}\right). \quad \cdot \quad \cdot \quad \cdot \quad \cdot \quad (40)$$

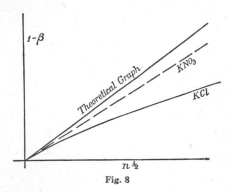

Fig. 8

Now the osmotic coefficient

$$\beta = \frac{P}{P_a} = 1 - \frac{e^2 x}{6Dk\theta}, \quad \cdot \quad \cdot \quad \cdot \quad \cdot \quad (41)$$

and

$$1 - \beta = \left(\frac{P_a - P}{P_a}\right) = \frac{e^2 x}{6Dk\theta}. \quad \cdot \quad \cdot \quad \cdot \quad \cdot \quad (42)$$

Since

$$x \propto n^{\frac{1}{2}}, \ 1 - \beta \propto n^{\frac{1}{2}}. \quad \cdot \quad \cdot \quad \cdot \quad \cdot \quad (43)$$

This relation agrees well with experiment for solutions of low concentration (see fig. 8).

11. Solutions of Strong Electrolytes of any Type.

Consider an aqueous solution of a single strong electrolyte, each of whose molecules splits up into $\nu_1, \nu_2, \ldots, \nu_i$ ions of types $1, 2, \ldots, i$ respectively, with valencies $z_1, z_2, \ldots, z_i$ respectively. Let n be the concentration of molecules per c.c. Then the concentrations of the ions are $n\nu_1, n\nu_2, \ldots, n\nu_i$ respectively. In this case, when Boltzmann's theorem is applied as on p. 226, the number of ions of class i in an element of volume dV is found to be $n\nu_i\epsilon^{-z_ie\phi/k\theta}dV$, and their contribution to the total charge per c.c. is $z_ien\nu_i\epsilon^{-z_ie\phi/k\theta}$. If, as before, we assume that the index is small and expand the exponential to two terms, this charge becomes $+nz_i\nu_ie(1-z_ie\phi/k\theta)$ approximately, and the total charge per c.c. due to all classes of ions is

$$\rho = \Sigma nz_i\nu_ie\left(1 - \frac{z_ie\phi}{k\theta}\right) \text{ approximately.} \quad . \quad . \quad (44)$$

Now an undissociated molecule is electrically uncharged. Hence $\Sigma z_i\nu_i = 0$, for it is the sum of the charges on the ions arising out of a single molecule. Hence, expanding the expression for ρ, we find that $\rho = \Sigma nz_i\nu_ie - ne^2\phi\Sigma\nu_iz_i^2/k\theta$ is given by the second term only, that is,

$$\rho = -\frac{ne^2\phi\Sigma\nu_iz_i^2}{k\theta}. \quad . \quad . \quad . \quad . \quad (45)$$

Poisson's equation $\Delta\phi = -4\pi\rho/D$ becomes

$$\Delta\phi = \frac{4\pi ne^2\phi\Sigma\nu_iz_i^2}{Dk\theta} \quad . \quad . \quad . \quad . \quad . \quad (46)$$

or

$$\Delta\phi = x^2\phi, \quad . \quad . \quad . \quad . \quad . \quad . \quad (47)$$

where

$$x^2 = \frac{4\pi ne^2\Sigma\nu_iz_i^2}{Dk\theta}. \quad . \quad . \quad . \quad . \quad (48)$$

The further steps in the theory are the same as for solutions of binary salts. As before, the solution of equation (47), expressed in polar co-ordinates, is

$$\phi = \frac{Ae^{-xr}}{r} \quad . \quad . \quad . \quad . \quad . \quad . \quad (49)$$

outside the ion. If an ion is supposed to be a sphere of radius a_i cm., with a charge z_ie at the centre, the sphere being composed of a medium of dielectric constant D, then the internal potential at any point may be supposed to be

$$\phi' = \frac{z_1e}{Dr} + B. \quad . \quad . \quad . \quad . \quad (50)$$

B is that part of the internal potential contributed by external ions, and z_1e/Dr is that part of the internal potential contributed by the ion itself. At the surface of the sphere there must be continuity of field and potential, that is, when $r = a_i$, $\phi = \phi'$ and $\partial\phi/\partial r = \partial\phi'/\partial r$.

After substituting the values of ϕ and ϕ' derived from equations (49) and (50), in these boundary equations, we find that

$$A = \frac{z_i e \epsilon^{xa_i}}{D(1 + xa_i)} \quad \cdots \cdots \quad (51)$$

and

$$B = - \frac{z_i ex}{D(1 + xa_i)}. \quad \cdots \cdots \quad (52)$$

For dilute solutions,

$$xa_i \ll 1 \quad \text{and} \quad B = - \frac{z_i ex}{D}. \quad \cdots \cdots \quad (53)$$

As in the case of solutions of binary salts, the work required to bring a charge up to a point against the potential of surrounding ions is the most important part of W_E (see p. 228), and the other quantities of work done in discharging the ions at zero concentration and in charging the ions against their own potential are neglected in comparison with this. To bring up a charge $z_i e$ in elements, each of value $z_i de$, from infinity to a point where the potential is B, the work required is $\int_0^e B z_i \, de$, that is, by equation (53), $- \int_0^e z_i^2 ex \, de / D$. The quantity x can be written in the form $x = Ce$, where C does not contain e, by equation (48). After substituting and integrating, we find that the work required is $- Cz_i^2 e^3 / 3D$ ergs $= - z_i^2 e^2 x / 3D$. There are ν_i ions of this kind per molecule, so that the work required to bring up all their charges is $- \nu_i z_i^2 e^2 x / 3D$ ergs. Hence W_E, the total work for all the ions of all kinds in N molecules, is given by

$$W_E = - \frac{Ne^2 x (\Sigma \nu_i z_i^2)}{3D} \text{ ergs.} \quad \cdots \cdots \quad (54)$$

As before, by equation (18), $P = P_a - \partial W_E / \partial V$, where V is the total volume of solution. V enters into the expression for W_E in the factor $x = \{4\pi ne^2 (\Sigma \nu_i z_i^2) / Dk\theta\}^{\frac{1}{2}}$ by equation (48). In fact, $n = N/V$ and $W_E = -Fn^{\frac{1}{2}} = -FN^{\frac{1}{2}}/V^{\frac{1}{2}}$, where F is a factor which does not contain n or V. Hence $\partial W_E / \partial V = FN^{\frac{1}{2}} / 2V^{\frac{3}{2}} = - W_E / 2V$. If in this we substitute the full expression for x, equation (18) can be written in the form

$$P = P_a - Ne^2 \left\{ 4\pi ne^2 \frac{\Sigma \nu_i z_i^2}{Dk\theta} \right\}^{\frac{1}{2}} \frac{\Sigma \nu_i z_i^2}{6DV}. \quad \cdots \quad (55)$$

Write $P_a = (n\Sigma \nu_i)k\theta$, for $n\Sigma \nu_i$ is the number of ions per c.c. Then

$$P = (n\Sigma \nu_i)k\theta \left[1 - Ne^2 \left\{ 4\pi ne^2 \frac{\Sigma \nu_i z_i^2}{Dk\theta} \right\}^{\frac{1}{2}} \frac{\Sigma \nu_i z_i^2}{6DVk\theta n\Sigma \nu_i} \right].$$

Now the osmotic coefficient $\beta = P/P_a$ and $N = Vn$. Hence

$$1 - \beta = \frac{P_a - P}{P_a} = e^2 \left\{ 4\pi n e^2 \frac{\Sigma \nu_i z_i^2}{Dk\theta} \right\}^{\frac{1}{2}} \frac{\Sigma \nu_i z_i^2}{6Dk\theta \Sigma \nu_i}.$$

Write $\Sigma \nu_i = \nu$ and $n = \gamma \times 6 \cdot 06 \times 10^{23}/1000 = \gamma N_A/1000$, where γ is the concentration in gramme-molecules per litre, and N_A is the number of actual molecules in a gramme-molecule. Then $(1 - \beta)$ may be written in the form given by Debye and Hückel, namely,

$$1 - \beta = e^2 \left\{ \frac{4\pi N_A e^2}{1000 Dk\theta} \right\}^{\frac{1}{2}} \left\{ \frac{\Sigma \nu_i z_i^2}{\nu} \right\}^{\frac{3}{2}} \frac{(\gamma \nu)^{\frac{1}{2}}}{6Dk\theta}. \quad \cdot \quad \cdot \quad (56)$$

Comments.—(1) This expression shows that $(1 - \beta)$, with small concentrations, depends on the number and valency of the ions, as represented by $\Sigma \nu_i z_i^2$, on the nature of the solvent, as represented by D, and on the temperature θ.

(2) $(1 - \beta)$ is proportional to $(\gamma \nu)^{\frac{1}{2}}$.

(3) The expression $\{\Sigma \nu_i z_i^2 / \nu\}^{\frac{3}{2}}$ is called the *valency factor* and may be denoted by v.

(4) For dilute aqueous solutions at ordinary temperatures, $D = 88 \cdot 23$ and $(1 - \beta) = 0 \cdot 263 v (\gamma \nu)^{\frac{1}{2}}$.

(5) For KCl, $v = 1$; for K_2SO_4, $v = 2\sqrt{2}$; for $La(NO_3)_3$, $v = 3\sqrt{3}$; and for $MgSO_4$, $v = 4\sqrt{4} = 8$.

(6) Fig. 9 shows graphs connecting $(1 - \beta)$ and $(\gamma \nu)^{\frac{1}{2}}$. Curves derived from experiment and from the above theory agree well at low concentrations, but an increasing divergence appears as the concentration is increased. The experimental values of β were obtained by determining the depression of the freezing point in each case.

(7) Equation (18), which is derived from thermodynamics, is true no matter what detailed theory of osmotic pressure may be adopted.

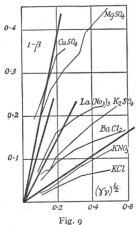

Fig. 9

12. More Exact Theory.

If in the equation $B = -z_i ex/D(1 + xa_i)$ on p. 231, xa_i is not very small compared with unity, that is, if the solution is not assumed to be very dilute, the theoretical results and the graph agree well with those derived from experiment up to much higher concentrations. Space will not permit a full account of the theory.* It will suffice to quote the result for aqueous solutions, namely,

$$1 - \beta = 0 \cdot 263 v (\gamma \nu)^{\frac{1}{2}} f(xa), \quad \cdots \cdots \cdots (57)$$

where a is the mean value of all the quantities a_i; $f(xa)$ is a function of xa, namely

$$f(xa) = 1 - \frac{3xa}{2} + \frac{9x^2 a^2}{5} - 2x^3 a^3 + \cdots \quad \cdots \quad (58)$$

The other symbols have the same meaning as in section 11.

To apply equation (57), Debye and Hückel take as the mean ionic radius a that value of a which makes the theoretical value of $1 - \beta$ for the highest con-

* See Debye and Hückel, *Physikalische Zeits.*, Vol. 24, pp. 185, 305 (1923).

centrations coincide with the experimental value. It is then found that there is very good agreement at lower concentrations (fig. 10). The value of the mean radius a for KCl solutions is $3\cdot76 \times 10^{-8}$ cm.

Even with the more general theory just given, various discrepancies between experiment and theory still persist. When the mean ionic radii of the alkali chlorides, calculated from the above theory, are examined, it appears that LiCl has the greatest diameter, NaCl the next, and so on to CsCl, which has the least.   From the X-ray examination of crystals, however, it appears that LiCl has the smallest diameter, in contradiction to the above. At very high concentrations, moreover, the value of $1 - \beta$ for LiCl decreases as $\gamma\nu$ is increased. Finally $1 - \beta$ changes sign, so that β becomes greater than unity, and the osmotic pressure P exceeds the classical value P_a. To explain these and other points it is necessary to take into account the deformability of the ions in strong fields and the presence of dipoles in the molecules of the solvent.

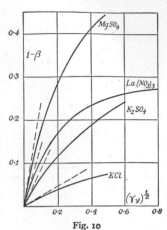

Fig. 10

CHAPTER XI

Diffusion

1. Diffusion in Liquids.

The diffusion or wandering of the molecules or ions of a solute in a solution * from a region of high concentration to one of low concentration is a process resembling the conduction of heat in a metal from a point of high temperature to one of low temperature. Regarded from the macroscopic point of view, i.e. when attention is directed not to the behaviour of one particular ion but to the general effect, it is irreversible. A portion of a pure solvent, having once become impregnated with a solute, never again rids itself of the solute, unless aided by some external agent. Although in the case of strong electrolytes the molecules are completely dissociated and the ions move about separately, yet from the macroscopic point of view it is usual to consider the diffusion of the solute as if its molecules remained undissociated. For example, chemical analysis of a portion of a liquid taken from a particular region gives the concentration of the solute there.

The quantitative treatment of the phenomenon is based upon Fick's law of diffusion, which is analogous to Fourier's law of conduction of heat and to Ohm's law of conduction of electricity, all governing processes which in a certain sense are irreversible. Fick's law may be stated thus:

$$Q = -KA\frac{dn}{dx}, \qquad \ldots \ldots \ldots \quad (1)$$

where Q is the mass of a solute in grammes carried across an area A sq. cm. of a surface normal to the direction of diffusion in one second, n is the concentration of solute in grammes per c.c. at a point x cm. distant from some arbitrary origin, and $-dn/dx$ is the gradient or rate of decrease of concentration per cm. in the direction of diffusion. K is a quantity called the *coefficient of diffusion* or the *diffusivity* of the solute in a solution of concentration n. It is found that the value of K depends on that of n, so that the diffusivity of a given solute in a given solvent is not constant, but a function of n. As an example of a recent accurate determination of K, an account of Clack's method will be given.

* For a brief discussion of diffusion of gases see Chap. IX, p. 183.

2. Measurement of Diffusivity. Clack's Method.*

The object of this series of experiments is to measure K for aqueous solutions of KCl, NaCl, and KNO$_3$, of various strengths. The method is based on Fick's law. Consider the upward diffusion of a solute in a uniform vertical tube FG (fig. 1). At the base there is a saturated solution, kept saturated by the presence of crystals of solute. At the top a slow uniform stream of pure water flows across the end of the tube, and, by carrying off the solute as it arrives there, becomes a very dilute solution. Let n be the concentration in grammes per c.c. at P, a level x cm. from F and l cm. from the top G. Let ρ be the density of solution at the level P. Let i be the net decrease in mass of the system in grammes per sec., due to departure of solute at the top and arrival of solvent, when the steady state has been reached. Let δ be the ratio of w, the mass of solvent entering the tube per second at G, and c, the mass of salt leaving the tube per second at G; that is, let $\delta = w/c$. We may rewrite Fick's law in the form

$$K = -\frac{Q}{A}\frac{dx}{dn}. \qquad \qquad (2)$$

Clack rearranges this in a form in which direct substitution from experimental results can be made.

(1) Since $x = L - l$, where L is the constant full length of the tube, $dx = -dl$ and $-dx/dn = dl/dn$.

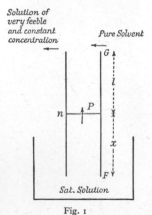

Solution of very feeble and constant concentration

Pure Solvent

Sat. Solution

Fig. 1

(2) dl/dn may be split up into two factors $(dl/d\mu)(d\mu/dn)$, where μ is the optical refractive index of the solution at the level P. Both these factors can be found by experiment.

(3) The upward diffusion of solute in the tube is not the only effect taking place in which motion of the solute is involved. There is a downward flow of liquid in bulk, with constant velocity v cm. per sec., say. This has the same value at all levels. At level P, where the concentration is n gm. of solute per c.c., a mass Avn gm. of solute per sec. flows downwards, on account of this mass motion. Further, since the concentration of solvent at this level is $\rho - n$ gm. per c.c., $Av(\rho - n)$ gm. of solvent flow downwards per sec. At the top of the tube, the mass of solute leaving the tube per second, expressed in two ways, gives

$$c = Q - Avn. \qquad \qquad (3)$$

Hence

$$Q = c + Avn. \qquad \qquad (4)$$

Again, the mass of solvent entering the tube per second, expressed in two ways, gives

$$w = Av(\rho - n).$$

Hence

$$Av = \frac{w}{(\rho - n)}. \qquad \qquad (5)$$

* Clack, *Proc. Phys. Soc.*, Vol. 36, p. 4 (1924).

Substituting for Av in equation (4), we obtain

$$Q = c + \frac{nw}{(\rho - n)}.$$

Now $\delta = w/c$ by definition; hence $w = c\delta$ and

$$Q = c + \frac{nc\delta}{(\rho - n)}$$

$$= \frac{c(\rho - n + n\delta)}{(\rho - n)}. \quad \cdots \cdots \cdots \quad (6)$$

The net loss in mass of the system per second (i) is equal to the loss in mass of solute per second minus the gain in mass of solvent, that is,

$$i = c - w = c - c\delta = c(1 - \delta).$$

Hence

$$c = \frac{i}{(1 - \delta)}, \quad \cdots \cdots \cdots \quad (7)$$

and if we substitute this in equation (6) it becomes

$$Q = \frac{i(\rho - n + n\delta)}{(1 - \delta)(\rho - n)}. \quad \cdots \cdots \cdots \quad (8)$$

Thus equation (2) can now be transformed, on inserting this value of Q, into

$$K = \left\{ \frac{i}{(1 - \delta)A} \right\} \left\{ \frac{\rho - n + n\delta}{\rho - n} \right\} \left(\frac{dl}{d\mu} \right) \left(\frac{d\mu}{dn} \right). \quad \cdots \cdots \quad (9)$$

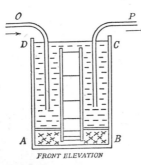

FRONT ELEVATION

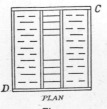

PLAN

Fig. 2

This is the equation used by Clack.

We have now to describe the experimental arrangements used in obtaining the various quantities in this equation. The cell, of which a front elevation and a plan are shown in fig. 2, consists of a rectangular tube of height about 5 cm., of width about 1 cm., and of depth in the other perpendicular horizontal direction about 4 cm. It is made of glass plates, and fits at the bottom into a glass box containing air-free saturated solution and crystals of the solute under investigation. Above the box, but outside the tube, are compartments containing distilled water, and the level is 5 mm. above that of the central tube. An inlet tube for distilled water and an exit tube to carry off very dilute solution are added. It takes about 12 days for the system to reach a steady state fulfilling the above theoretical conditions. A special device is used to keep the flow of water steady at a rate of about 50 c.c. per day. A thermostat keeps the temperature of the whole system constant at about 18·5° C.

In a preliminary series of experiments the cell was suspended from a balance in a large tank of distilled water, all the conditions being as described above, and the change in weight per second i_0 was directly determined. It is left to the student to prove that the quantity i, defined on p. 236, is equal to $i_0(N - N_0)/N$, where N_0 and N are the concentrations of solute at the top and bottom of the tube. N_0 is very small, but the neglect of N_0 introduces an error of about 2 per cent in i and K, in the case of a solution of KCl in water. The quantity δ is equal to $(D - N)/(Z - N)$, where D is the density of saturated salt solution in grammes per c.c., N is the concentration at the bottom of the tube, and Z is the density of salt crystals. To prove this, note that $\delta = $ gain of water/loss of salt, in any time (p. 236). Let V_1, v_1 be the volumes of solution and salt not in solution, respectively, in the cell at any instant, and V_2, v_2 the corresponding volumes at a later instant. The loss of salt in the interval $=$ amount of salt at the beginning less amount of salt at the end $= V_1N + v_1Z - V_2N - v_2Z$. The gain of water $=$ amount of water at the end less amount

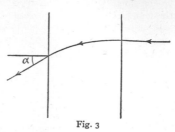

Fig. 3

of water at the beginning $= V_2(D - N) - V_1(D - N)$. The quotient $\delta = $ gain of water/loss of salt reduces to $(D - N)/(Z - N)$, since $V_1 + v_1 = V_2 + v_2 =$ total volume of the cell $=$ a constant.

Further, $d\mu/dl$ is the rate of increase of the refractive index of the liquid with depth. To measure it, a narrow beam of monochromatic light incident horizontally is made to traverse the cell (which is 4·2 cm. in thickness) in a direction

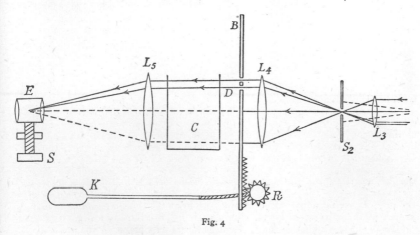

Fig. 4

perpendicular to the plane of fig. 2 (see fig. 3). The beam is refracted in a vertical plane and pursues a curved path, whose form is that of a catenary. It finally emerges in a downward direction, making an angle α with the horizontal. It can be shown that

$$\frac{d\mu}{dl} = \frac{\sin\alpha}{t}, \qquad \dots \dots \dots (10)$$

where t is the horizontal thickness of the cell.

The quantity $\sin\alpha$ is determined by a special optical arrangement (fig. 4). Monochromatic green light from a mercury arc ($\lambda = 5461$ A.U.), emerging from a horizontal slit S_2, is rendered parallel and horizontal by a lens L_4, and then passes through two horizontal slits, each 0·25 mm. wide and 1·3 mm. apart, in a vertical screen B. It next passes through the experimental cell C and falls on a lens L_5, which causes the light to converge to the focal plane of an eyepiece E. An observer looking into this eyepiece sees nine sharp horizontal interference fringes, for the two narrow slits act as sources, and the rest of the optical system is akin to that used in the well-known biprism experiment. The central fringe, which can always be identified, is used as a fiducial mark. The observer can control the height of the slits in B by turning a knob K. Observations are commenced with B as high as possible. It is then gradually lowered, and the fringes suddenly become visible in the eyepiece. The eyepiece is adjusted until the central fringe is on the cross-wire, and the scale verniers fixing the heights of the eyepiece E and slits D are read. The slits are lowered until three fringes cross the cross-wire, moving upwards, and then E is raised until the central fringe is once more on the cross-wire, when scale readings are again taken. In this manner, by movements corresponding to a shift of three fringes, the bottom of the cell is finally reached. A similar series of readings is taken with the cell full of distilled water, to eliminate the effect of

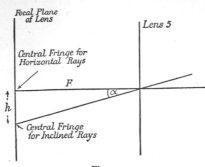

Fig. 5

imperfections in the cell. The difference of corresponding readings of the eyepiece in the two cases gives a quantity h, and from fig. 5 we see that $\tan \alpha = h/F$, where F is the focal length of the lens L_5. Since α is very small, $\tan \alpha = \sin \alpha = h/F$ and

$$\frac{d\mu}{dl} = \frac{h}{Ft}, \qquad \qquad \cdots \cdots \cdots \quad (11)$$

for a particular known value of l.

The quantity $d\mu/dn$ is obtained by means of a Rayleigh interferometer for solutions with the various values of n; n, the concentration at any point of the tube, is obtained as follows. The values of $d\mu/dl$, obtained as above, are plotted as ordinates of a graph, with values of l as abscissæ. First, as a check, the total area under the graph between the straight lines $l = 0$ and $l = L$, where L is

the full length of the tube, is measured. This area is $\int_0^L \left(\frac{d\mu}{dl}\right) dl = \mu_N - \mu_{N_0}$,

where μ_N is the refractive index at the bottom of the tube, where $l = L$, and μ_{N_0} is that at the top, where $l = 0$. As μ_N and μ_{N_0} are already known with great precision, the agreement of the two values serves as a check on the method.

If this is satisfactory, the area under the graph between the straight lines

$l = 0$ and $l = l$ is measured. This area is $\int_0^l \left(\frac{d\mu}{dl}\right) dl = \mu_n - \mu_0$. From the

result the value of the refractive index μ_n at any level l is easily obtained. A table of values is constructed. In a similar manner μ_n is obtained in terms of n by means of a graph in which values of $d\mu/dn$ are ordinates and values of n are abscissæ. The area under the graph between vertical lines $n = 0$ and $n = n$

gives $\int_0^n \left(\frac{d\mu}{dn}\right) dn = \mu_n - \mu_0$, where μ_n is the refractive index of solution of

concentration n and μ_0 is the refractive index of pure water. As μ_0 is accurately known, μ_n is easily obtained for various values of n. When the tables of (a) μ_n

and l and (b) μ_n and n are compared, interpolation enables a table of corresponding values of n and l to be obtained. From the various quantities obtained as above, values of K, the diffusivity, are obtained at various concentrations n. Results are shown in fig. 6.

Note.—The trend of the results for aqueous solutions of KCl is similar to that for NaCl. Starting at a certain finite value for the lowest concentrations measured, K soon decreases to a minimum value, and then undergoes a slow steady rise. In the case of KNO_3 there is a slow decrease of K to a minimum, which is scarcely passed at the highest concentrations.

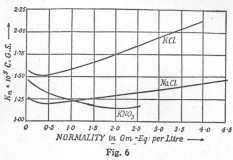

Fig. 6

3. Osmotic Pressure and Diffusion.

Case I. Solution with undissociated solute only.

The osmotic pressure and the diffusivity of a solute in solution are connected in the following way. When the concentration of solute at one point A is greater than that at another point B, the osmotic pressure is also greater, by van't Hoff's law. The osmotic pressure may be regarded as a force giving the dissolved molecules an acceleration from one point to another point where the concentration is less. Consider the forces due to osmotic pressure, in the direction of increasing x, on an elementary cylinder of solution of unit cross-section (fig. 7). At A the force is P dynes, where P is the osmotic pressure. At B it is $-\{P + (dP/dx)\,dx\}$ dynes, and the net result is $(-dP/dx)\,dx$ dynes. If n is the concentration of molecules in this cylinder, the total number is $n\,dx$, for the volume is

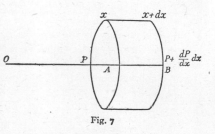

Fig. 7

dx c.c. Hence it appears that $n\,dx$ molecules experience an accelerating and diffusing force to the right, of value $(-dP/dx)\,dx$ dynes, so that the force per molecule is

$$-\frac{1}{n}\frac{dP}{dx} \text{ dynes.} \quad \ldots \ldots \quad (12)$$

Suppose that the motion of the molecules is impeded by retarding forces, such as the viscosity of the solvent, so that they acquire a constant terminal velocity, and that F_1 is the retarding force on each molecule when it is moving with a constant velocity of 1 cm. per sec. F_1 is also the driving force necessary to produce a terminal velocity of 1 cm. per sec. Hence a force of $(-1/n)(dP/dx)$ dynes produces a terminal velocity of $(-1/F_1 n)(dP/dx)$ cm. per sec. The number of molecules crossing unit area near A per second is the number enclosed by a cylinder of length equal to the velocity and of cross-section 1 sq. cm. It is therefore

$$-\frac{1}{F_1}\frac{dP}{dx} \text{ molecules per sec.} \quad \ldots \quad (13)$$

Now by van't Hoff's law $P = nk\theta$, where k is Boltzmann's constant, and this law holds for such solutions. Hence the number of molecules transferred across unit area per second is $(-k\theta/F_1)(dn/dx)$, and their mass is $(-mk\theta/F_1)(dn/dx)$ gm., where m is the mass of a molecule. This mass is also given by Fick's law of diffusion. In the statement of that law on p. 234, the mass per c.c. is represented by n. Here we shall denote it by n_1 to avoid confusion, for we have used n for the number of molecules per c.c. Fick's law becomes $Q = -KA\, dn_1/dx$. Also $n_1 = nm$ and $Q = -KAm\, dn/dx$. The mass transferred per unit area per second is $-Km\, dn/dx$. On equating the two values of this mass just obtained we find that

$$K = \frac{k\theta}{F_1}. \quad \ldots \quad (14)$$

Case II. *Solution with one electrolyte, dissociated into two monovalent ions.*

Let the velocities of the cation $(+)$ and anion $(-)$ in a unit electric field, that is, the mobilities of the ions, be U and V cm. per sec. respectively. Each ion is driven along by the osmotic pressure like a molecule in case I above. As in that case, the force per cation is $(-1/n)(dP/dx)$ dynes, where n is now the concentration per c.c. of each kind of ion, and P is the total osmotic pressure of the solution. Again, the velocity of a cation due to the osmotic pressure is $(-1/F_1 n)(dP/dx)$, that is,

$$-\frac{U}{n}\frac{dP}{dx}, \quad \ldots \quad (15)$$

and that of an anion is

$$-\frac{V}{n}\frac{dP}{dx}. \quad \ldots \quad (16)$$

As a rule $U \neq V$, so that if the osmotic pressure were alone responsible for the driving forces on the ions, the two kinds of ions would become separated. Another force, however, is called into play. For example, if an aqueous solution of HCl were placed at the bottom of a column of water, the hydrogen ions, the cations, would have a mobility U exceeding the mobility V of the chlorine anions. The liquid in such a vessel as is shown in fig. 8 would become positively charged near the top and negatively charged near the bottom, owing to the more rapid movement of the hydrogen ions towards the top. An electric field would thus be set up, which would reduce the velocity of the faster ions and increase that of the slower ions. A final state would be reached when the two kinds of ions travelled at equal rates, without separation.

Assuming this to occur, we may calculate the coefficient of diffusion. Let the electric field at any point in the solution, in the Ox direction, be X e.s.u., $= -dE/dx$ e.s.u., where E is the potential at that point. A monovalent ion at such a point experiences a force $\pm edE/dx$ dynes, according to the sign of its charge. Since the velocity of a cation under unit force is U cm. per sec., a force $-edE/dx$ produces a terminal velocity of $-UedE/dx$ cm. per sec. Similarly, the terminal velocity of an anion is $+VedE/dx$ cm. per sec. The total velocity of a cation due to both osmotic pressure and electric field is $-U(1/n \cdot dP/dx + edE/dx)$ cm. per sec., and of an anion $-V(1/n \cdot dP/dx - edE/dx)$ cm. per sec. We may assume from both experimental and theoretical considerations that the number of ions of each kind crossing unit area per second is the same, dN/dt, say. This quantity is also equal to the velocity of the ions concerned multiplied by their concentration, for it is the number of ions inside a cylinder of unit cross-section and length equal to the velocity. Hence

Fig. 8

$$\frac{dN}{dt} = -U\left(\frac{dP}{dx} + ne\frac{dE}{dx}\right) = -V\left(\frac{dP}{dx} - ne\frac{dE}{dx}\right). \quad (17)$$

Eliminate dE/dx. This gives

$$\frac{dN}{dt} = -\frac{2UV}{(U+V)}\frac{dP}{dx}. \quad \cdots \cdots (18)$$

According to van't Hoff's law, if all the n molecules per c.c. were ionized, each giving one ion of each kind, there would be altogether $2n$ ions per c.c. and the osmotic pressure would be $P_a = 2nk\theta$. But as has been mentioned above on p. 223, the actual osmotic pressure is $P = \beta P_a$, where β is a factor less than unity for dilute solutions. Then

$$\frac{dP}{dx} = 2\beta k\theta\frac{dn}{dx}, \quad \cdots \cdots (19)$$

and from equation (18)

$$\frac{dN}{dt} = -\frac{4\beta k\theta UV}{(U+V)}\frac{dn}{dx}. \quad \cdots \cdots (20)$$

Let the mass of each cation and anion be m_1 and m_2 gm. respectively.

9

Then the total mass crossing unit area per second in one direction is

$$-\frac{4\beta k\theta UV(m_1 + m_2)}{(U + V)}\frac{dn}{dx}$$

$$= -\frac{4\beta k\theta UVm}{(U + V)}\frac{dn}{dx}\text{ gm. per sec.,}\quad \ldots \quad (21)$$

where m is the mass of one molecule of the solute. As in case I, Fick's law gives the mass crossing unit area per second as $-K\,dn_1/dx = -Km\,dn/dx$, since $n_1 = nm$. By comparing the two equal masses we find that

$$K = \frac{4\beta k\theta UV}{(U + V)}.\quad \ldots \ldots \quad (22)$$

4. Interdiffusion of Solids.

Though true solids have a definite crystalline structure, that is, a definite space lattice, it is found that two solids placed in contact diffuse into one another. Further, a solid metal A diffuses into a different solid metal B much more readily than it does into a second portion of A itself. Fick's law, $Q = -KA\,dn/dx$, applies to solids, and the value of the diffusivity K has been obtained in certain cases.

Roberts-Austen investigated the diffusion of solid gold and other metals into lead. The lead was in the form of a cylinder 7 cm. long and 1·4 cm. in diameter. In one case a thin plate of gold was fused on one end of it in such a manner that immediately after the fusion the gold did not penetrate more than a millimetre into the lead. Then the cylinder was kept for about a month in a constant-temperature enclosure, at a temperature below the eutectic point of lead-gold alloys, that is, below their lowest melting point. After this the cylinder was cut up into slices of equal thickness, and the quantity of gold in each was determined by chemical analysis. The balance used weighed to 2×10^{-6} gm. From the masses of gold in the slices, K was calculated by a method which is too long to reproduce here. In recent experiments by Seith and others, the apparatus was similar to that of Roberts-Austen, but the concentration of the diffusing metal in the slices was measured by the method of quantitative spectral analysis.

Groh and Hevesy used a novel method in their determination of the coefficient of diffusion of solid lead in solid lead, that is, the self-diffusivity of lead. To a rod of ordinary pure lead, 1·5 cm. long, was fused a rod, 0·5 cm. long, of Joachimsthal lead, which is a mixture of three isotopes, namely, ordinary lead, uranium lead, and radium D. Of these, radium D alone is radioactive. The electron shells of all three isotopes, and therefore the "sizes" of the atoms, were assumed to be the same. In effect, the conditions as regards diffusion were the same as if ordinary lead were diffusing into ordinary lead. The time allowed for diffusion was about 400 days. Then the rod which was originally ordinary lead was cut into slices, and the α-ray activity of each slice was measured by means of an α-ray electroscope. These α-rays came from the polonium formed by radioactive disintegration of the radium D which had diffused, and hence the mass of the latter in each slice could be calculated. It was assumed that the proportions of the three isotopes diffusing were the same as in Joachimsthal lead; the total mass of diffused lead in each slice was calculated, and hence the diffusivity.

CHAPTER XII

Viscosity

1. Newton's Law of Viscous Flow.

When a liquid flows over a fixed surface such as AB (fig. 1), it is found experimentally that a layer D at a distance $x + dx$ from AB flows with a velocity greater than that of a layer at C, a distance x from AB. If the difference in the velocities of the two layers is dv, the velocity gradient between C and D will be dv/dx. As a result of this relative motion of the layers, *internal friction* or *viscosity* arises. Newton's law of viscous flow for stream-line motion (as opposed to turbulent flow) is

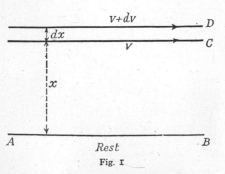

Fig. I

$$F = \eta A \frac{dv}{dx}, \quad \cdots \cdots \cdots \quad (1)$$

where F is the tangential viscous force between two layers of area A a distance dx apart, moving with relative velocity dv. The quantity η is termed the *coefficient of viscosity* of the liquid.

2. Fugitive Elasticity.

There are two theoretical modes of approach to problems involving viscosity. The first is by analogy with the elastic properties of solids, and the second by consideration of the implications of the kinetic theory of matter. The former mode of approach is more applicable to the discussion of the viscosity of liquids and the latter to the viscosity of gases.

Maxwell considered that a liquid possesses a certain amount of rigidity but is continually breaking down under the shearing stress.

243

The analogy is emphasized by the formal similarity between the two equations

$$\text{Rigidity } n = \frac{\text{stress}}{\text{strain (shear)}} = \frac{P}{\theta} = \frac{P}{dy/dx}, \quad . \quad . \quad (2)$$

$$\text{Viscosity } \eta = \frac{\text{stress}}{\text{velocity gradient}} = \frac{P}{dv/dx}. \quad . \quad . \quad (3)$$

A liquid is therefore regarded as exerting and sustaining a certain amount of shearing stress for a short time, after which it breaks down and the shear is reformed. Let the rate at which the shear breaks down be proportional to its value θ, and be given by $\lambda\theta$. If y is the displacement, $\theta = dy/dx$, and the rate of formation of shear $= d\theta/dt = \frac{d}{dt}\left(\frac{dy}{dx}\right) = \frac{d}{dx}\left(\frac{dy}{dt}\right) = \frac{dv}{dx}$. Thus

$$\lambda\theta = \frac{dv}{dx} \quad . \quad . \quad . \quad . \quad . \quad . \quad (4)$$

when the steady state of flow of liquid has been reached. Hence from (2), (3) and (4),

$$\eta = \frac{n}{\lambda}. \quad . \quad . \quad . \quad . \quad . \quad (5)$$

The quantity $1/\lambda$ is termed the *time of relaxation* of the medium and measures the time taken for the shear to disappear when no fresh shear is applied.

3. Methods of Determining η.

All the methods used for determining η require the flow to be streamline. The necessary and sufficient conditions for this criterion to be fulfilled will be considered later (p. 247).

The main methods available for determining the coefficient of viscosity of liquids fall into two groups, the first involving the measurement of the rate of flow of a liquid through a capillary tube, and the second involving observation of the motion of a solid body moving through the liquid.

4. Flow Methods: Poiseuille's Formula.

The following formula for the volume of liquid flowing per second through a cylindrical tube of circular cross-section is due to Poiseuille. Its validity rests on three conditions:

(1) there must be streamline flow;

(2) the pressure must be constant over any cross-section, that is, no radial flow must occur;

(3) the liquid in contact with the walls of the tube must be at rest.

We assume that these conditions are satisfied and that a steady flow of liquid is in progress. Let the velocity of the liquid (fig. 2) at a distance r from the axis be v; then the velocity gradient will be dv/dr and the tangential stress $\eta\, dv/dr$. If a pressure difference p exists between two points in the tube a distance l apart, the force causing motion of the volume of the cylinder of liquid of radius r is $\pi p r^2$.

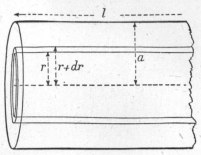

Fig. 2

Hence, equating this accelerating force to the retarding viscous force, we obtain the condition for steady flow, namely

$$p\pi r^2 = -\eta \frac{dv}{dr} 2\pi r l$$

or

$$\frac{dv}{dr} = -r \frac{p}{2\eta l}. \quad \cdots \cdots \quad (6)$$

The velocity gradient is therefore proportional to r, the distance from the axis of the tube, and vanishes on the axis.

At the wall of the tube $r = a$ and $v = 0$: integrating from $r = a$ to $r = r$, we have

$$a^2 - r^2 = \frac{4\eta l v}{p}$$

or

$$v = \frac{p}{4\eta l}(a^2 - r^2). \quad \cdots \cdots \quad (7)$$

The profile of the advancing liquid is therefore a parabola.

The volume of liquid dQ flowing through the tube per second between the radii r and $r + dr$ is given by

$$dQ = 2\pi r v\, dr.$$

Hence the total volume of liquid flowing through the tube per second is

$$Q = \int_0^a \frac{p\pi}{2\eta l}(a^2 - r^2) r\, dr = \frac{\pi p a^4}{8 l \eta}. \quad \cdots \cdots \quad (8)$$

An accurate and convenient method for determining η by Poiseuille's method is shown in the accompanying diagram (fig. 3). A long piece of glass tubing 2 to 3 mm. in diameter is selected and tested for uniform bore by observing the length of a thread of mercury in various positions. When about 50 cm. of tubing which does not vary in bore by more than about 3 per cent has been found, the tube is cut. Two small crosses are then made on the tube about 30 cm. apart, after which, by rotating a pointed file (using turpentine as lubricant), two small holes are bored at these points. They are judged to be large enough when a fine needle will pass freely through them. Two T-pieces are then constructed from tubing about 5 mm. in diameter and these are slipped over the narrower tube. The centres of the T-tubes are adjusted so as to lie over the fine holes in the central

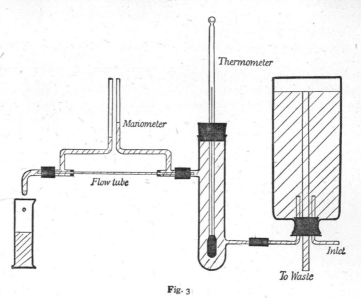

Fig. 3

tube, and the joints between the two tubes are then sealed with wax so as to render the system watertight. The T-tubes are connected to two upright glass tubes forming a manometer, and the pressure difference over the distance l is thus measured directly. The remainder of the apparatus is shown in the diagram, the part on the right being a device to maintain a constant head of water.

5. Corrections to Poiseuille's Formula.

With the apparatus described above Poiseuille's formula requires no corrections if the flow of liquid is slow,* the experimental conditions approaching the ideal as the pressure-holes are diminished in size. In many experimental arrangements, however, the excess pressure is often regarded as that due simply to the head of water at the inlet end. Two sources of error must then be considered:

(1) Accelerations occur near the inlet to the tube, the velocity distribution

* If the flow is fast, a correction for the kinetic energy imparted to the liquid must be made, as is explained in (2) below.

being non-uniform until a short length of the tube has been traversed. To correct for this a quantity na must be added to l, where $n = 1\cdot64$ approximately.

(2) The pressure difference between the two ends is used partly in communicating kinetic energy to the liquid and not wholly in overcoming viscous resistance.

An approximate value of the correction for the latter may be obtained in the following way. The kinetic energy given to the liquid, of density ρ, per second is

$$\tfrac{1}{2}\rho \int_0^a 2\pi r v^3\, dr = \pi\rho\left(\frac{p}{4\eta l}\right)^3 \int_0^a r(a^2 - r^2)^3\, dr$$

$$= \pi\rho\left(\frac{p}{4\eta l}\right)^3 \frac{a^8}{8} = \left(\frac{\pi p a^4}{8 l \eta}\right)^3 \frac{\rho}{\pi^2 a^4}. \quad \cdots \quad (9)$$

The work done in overcoming the viscosity is pQ; the total loss of energy per second is therefore

$$pQ + \frac{Q^3\rho}{\pi^2 a^4}. \quad \cdots \cdots \cdots \quad (10)$$

If the total external pressure is p_1, then

$$p_1 Q = pQ + \frac{Q^3\rho}{\pi^2 a^4}$$

or

$$p = p_1 - \frac{Q^2\rho}{\pi^2 a^4}. \quad \cdots \cdots \quad (11)$$

This correction has been tested experimentally by Hagenbach, by Couette, and by Wilberforce, but it is only approximately true, and according to some authorities (Edser), the correction is twice that given by (9). In the form given here it implies a radial pressure gradient at the end cross-section of the tube. The correction should be $-mQ^2\rho/\pi^2 a^4$, where m is found experimentally to be approximately unity; its value must be obtained by calibration, if accurate results are required.

The complete corrected formula is therefore

$$\eta = \frac{\pi p_1 a^4}{8Q(l + 1\cdot64a)} - \frac{mQ\rho}{8\pi(l + 1\cdot64a)}. \quad \cdots \cdots \quad (12)$$

6. Critical Velocity.

Poiseuille's formula is valid only so long as the flow of liquid in the tube is streamline. This condition is fulfilled at low velocities and for tubes of small radius. It is convenient to remember that for a tube 50 cm. long, of bore about 3 mm., the pressure difference between the ends of the tube must not be greater than about 3 cm. when water is used. The velocity (V_c) at which turbulent flow sets in is termed the *critical velocity*. It can be shown by the method of dimensional analysis that $V_c = k\eta/\rho a$, where η is the coefficient of viscosity of the liquid, ρ its density, and a the radius of the tube. The quantity k is termed *Reynolds' number* and generally has a value about 1000. The relation between the volume of liquid Q and the pressure p is shown in fig. 4.

At low velocities, that is, when the motion is streamline, Q is proportional to p, in agreement with Poiseuille's relation. As the rate of flow is increased beyond the critical velocity, however, the quantity flowing through increases less rapidly and soon becomes independent of the viscosity of the liquid and dependent mainly on the density. When the motion is quite turbulent, the quantity flowing is nearly proportional to the square root of the pressure. The pressure difference is now used up in overcoming the turbulent motion and communicating kinetic energy to the liquid. The fact that the rate of turbulent flow is independent of the viscosity explains the rapid flow of viscous lava from volcanoes. The effect may be demonstrated in the laboratory by introducing a small quantity of coloured liquid along the axis of a tube. While streamline flow is in progress, the coloured liquid is drawn out into a thin filament parallel to the length of the tube. As soon as turbulent flow sets in, the filament becomes wavy and spreads out, the coloured liquid eventually filling the entire tube.

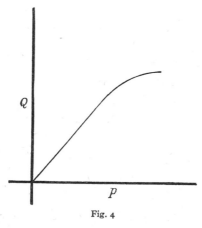

Fig. 4

It may be shown, by a simple extension of the theory leading to Poiseuille's formula, that the presence of an axial wire, of diameter only 1/1000 that of the tube, should reduce the flow by about 15 per cent. Lea and Tadros experimentally found that the reduction was much less than this, except when the radius of the core approached one-half the radius of the tube; then theory and experiment were in good agreement. With a core present, the critical velocities are much lower, and local turbulence at the boundary of the core co-existing with streamline flow in the bulk of the liquid in the tube is found to account adequately for the discrepancy.

7. Accurate Determination of η.

To avoid the use of the uncertain Hagenbach correction, the standard viscometer is made in a form suggested by Couette: the following arrangement is used at the *Reichsanstalt* (fig. 5).

The liquid flows from the reservoir A through the two capillaries K_1, K_2, which are connected in series, to the outlet F, where the volume is measured. When the whole apparatus is immersed in a temperature bath, the liquid may be introduced through G, the air escaping through the tube H. A device supplies a steady flow of compressed air to the reservoir through the tube L and thus keeps the pressure constant as the liquid level sinks. The pressures at the ends of the two capillaries are given directly by the heights h_1, h_2 and h_3 of the liquid in the tubes M_1, M_2 and M_3. The heights are determined with a cathetometer. Since the correction is the same for both tubes, we have

$$\eta = \frac{\pi}{8Q} \frac{a_1^4(p_1 - p_2) - a_2^4(p_2 - p_3)}{l_1 - l_2}.$$

The expression takes a much simpler form if $a_1 = a_2$, but this is difficult to realize experimentally.

Viscometers which are simple to use but which require calibration are available commercially in a variety of forms. The type invented by Ostwald is described here (fig. 6).

The liquid, which is initially introduced through A into the bulb B, is sucked into the bulb C through the capillary K until a mark m_1 is reached. The time t taken for the meniscus to fall vertically under gravity from m_1 to m_2 is then observed. Since with such an arrangement the effective pressure difference is proportional to the density ρ

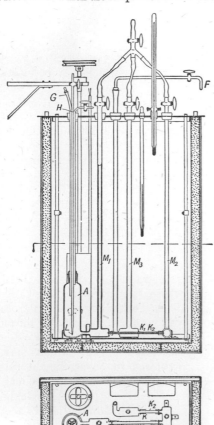

Fig. 5 *

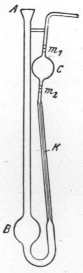

Fig. 6

of the liquid, the Poiseuille formula, together with the Hagenbach correction, may be written

$$\eta = A\rho t - \frac{B\rho}{t}, \qquad \ldots \ldots \ldots \quad (13)$$

* This figure, together with figs. 6, 8, 9, 11, 12, 13, 14 of this chapter, are taken from Wien-Harms, *Handbuch der Experimentalphysik* (Akademische Verlagsgesellschaft, Leipzig).

9*

where A and B are constants which must be determined with two liquids of known viscosity. The instruments are generally so constructed that the correction term may be neglected; a single calibration is then sufficient.

To determine the viscosity of molten metals, an instrument of the Ostwald type is generally used, the flow tube being constructed of quartz or silver. The passage of the meniscus past two fixed points is recorded electrically. For non-conducting liquids, a cylindrical metal reservoir may be connected as a cylindrical condenser in an oscillating circuit. The change in capacity produced by the change in level of the meniscus of the contained liquid serves to indicate a given volume change.

8. Other Methods for Measuring η.

The second general method of measuring viscosity, in which a body moves in a liquid, has many variations, which may be classified as follows.

(1) The rotation viscometer.

(2) Maxwell's oscillating disc.

(3) Stokes's method, by the damping of a pendulum vibrating in the liquid.

(4) Damping of a solid sphere vibrating about a diameter and immersed in the liquid.

(5) Damping of the vibrations of a hollow sphere filled with the liquid.

(6) Stokes's falling-body viscometer.

Methods (1) and (6) will be considered here in detail.

9. The Rotation Viscometer.

Consider two concentric cylinders of radii a, b, the space between them being filled with the liquid whose viscosity is required (fig. 7).

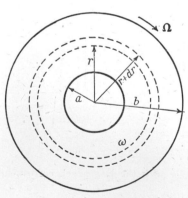

Fig. 7

If the outer cylinder is rotated with uniform velocity, a torque is communicated to the inner cylinder, the magnitude of which may be registered by suspending it from a torsion wire. We consider the motion of any concentric cylinder of liquid of radius r; let its angular velocity of rotation be ω. Then the velocity gradient at this point will be

$$\frac{d}{dr}(r\omega) = \omega + r\frac{d\omega}{dr}. \quad (14)$$

The first term on the right-hand side represents the angular motion which the layer would have if no viscous slip occurred; the second term is responsible for the viscous stress introduced, and if we apply

Newton's law, the viscous torque Γ over unit length of the surface of the cylinder will be

$$\Gamma = 2\pi\eta r^3 \frac{d\omega}{dr}. \quad \ldots \ldots \quad (15)$$

When the steady state is reached, this torque must be equal to that exerted on the inner cylinder. Hence, integrating equation (15) and using the conditions $r = a$, $\omega = 0$, and $r = b$, $\omega = \Omega$, where Ω is the angular velocity of the outer cylinder, we have

$$\Gamma = 4\pi\eta\Omega \frac{a^2 b^2}{(b^2 - a^2)}. \quad \ldots \ldots \quad (16)$$

The torque over the base of the inner cylinder has been neglected in this treatment; in practice the correction is eliminated by measurements with two different lengths of cylinder immersed. Representing the torque on the base by $f(B)$, we have, for depths of immersion l_1 and l_2,

$$\Gamma_1 = 4\pi\eta\Omega \frac{a^2 b^2}{(b^2 - a^2)} l_1 + f(B),$$

$$\Gamma_2 = 4\pi\eta\Omega \frac{a^2 b^2}{(b^2 - a^2)} l_2 + f(B).$$

Hence

$$\Gamma_1 - \Gamma_2 = 4\pi\eta\Omega \frac{a^2 b^2}{(b^2 - a^2)} (l_1 - l_2). \quad \ldots \quad (17)$$

The torque may be measured in two ways: (i) by the twist produced in a suspension of known rigidity; (ii) by using a fixed external cylinder and measuring the angular velocity of rotation of the internal cylinder when a known couple is applied.

As typical of the first method, we shall consider *Hatschek's viscometer* (fig. 8).

A wooden cylinder A is suspended by a torsion wire B from a fixed support C. The outer coaxial cylinder D is rotated by the pulley G, which is coupled to an electric motor. The space E may be used to provide an electrically heated water-bath. The cylinders F and F' are introduced to act as guard rings, and end corrections for the cylinder A are thus avoided.

In *Searle's method*, a diagram of which is given in fig. 9, the inner cylinder a is pivoted about a vertical axis b and rotates under the couple provided by the weights in the scale-pans c. The couple is transferred by cords passing over frictionless pulleys d to a drum e. The outer cylinder f can be raised or lowered by rotating the ring g. The speed of rotation is determined with a stop-watch, by observing the transits of the point i over the circular scale h. The apparatus is stopped or released by raising or lowering the stop k.

As in the case of Poiseuille's formula, the validity of application of the theoretical formulæ to the experiments with the rotation viscometer depend on the condition of streamline flow. The relation between Ω and Γ is shown in fig. 10. When Ω is small the motion is streamline and Γ is proportional to Ω; when turbulent motion first sets in the relation becomes irregular. At higher speeds Γ becomes approximately proportional to Ω^2. The relations are therefore exactly similar to those which exist between the quantity of liquid flowing per second through a right circular cylinder and the pressure difference between the ends.

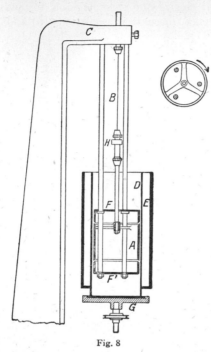

Fig. 8

Taylor * has investigated the transition from streamline to turbulent motion for concentric cylinders. Above the critical velocity, the liquid contains helical vortices situated at regular intervals parallel to the axis of rotation and at a distance apart approximately equal to $(b - a)$, measured in the same direction.

Reynolds's method for investigating turbulent motion has been improved by Andrade and Lewis,† who substitute colloidal particles for the usual colouring matter. The method has two advantages: (i) the velocity distribution may be found by illuminating and photographing with a known exposure, since each particle traverses a distance proportional to its velocity; (ii) since interdiffusion does not occur, the phenomena may be observed for any length of time.

10. Stokes's Falling-body Viscometer.

From hydrodynamical considerations of a perfectly homogeneous continuous fluid of infinite extent, Stokes derived the relation $F = 6\pi\eta av$ for the viscous retarding force F which is exerted on a sphere of radius a moving with uniform velocity v through a fluid with coefficient of viscosity η. For a sphere falling under gravity, the relation will be

$$6\pi\eta av = \tfrac{4}{3}\pi a^3(\rho - \sigma)g, \quad . \quad . \quad . \quad . \quad (18)$$

where ρ is the density of the sphere and σ that of the liquid. Since the

* Taylor, *Phil. Trans.*, A., Vol. 223, p. 289 (1923).

† Andrade and Lewis, *Journ. Sci. Inst.*, Vol. 1, p. 373 (1924).

terminal velocity v may be measured from the time of transit between two fixed marks on the sides of a vertical glass tube, this furnishes a convenient method for finding η.

If the total height of the liquid contained in the tube is divided into three equal parts, the centre division being used for the velocity determination, Ladenburg has shown that in order to correct for the finite extent of the liquid, the equation should be

$$\eta = \frac{2}{9} \frac{(\rho - \sigma)ga^2}{v} \frac{1}{(1 + 2 \cdot 4a/R)(1 + 3 \cdot 3a/h)}, \quad . \quad (19)$$

where R is the radius of the tube and h the total height of the liquid. Consideration of the deviations from Stokes's law which occur during

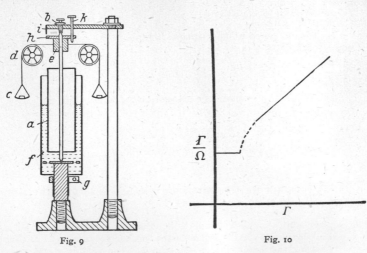

Fig. 9   Fig. 10

the fall of small drops through gases is of great importance, since Millikan's experiment for the determination of the charge on the electron is based on this principle.

11. Viscosity of Gases.

All the methods considered for the determination of the viscosity of liquids are applicable to gases if certain modifications are made in the experimental technique and in the associated formulæ.

(1) *Extension of Poiseuille's Method.*

As a liquid is assumed to be incompressible under the conditions of the experiment, the equation

$$Q = - \frac{\pi a^4}{8\eta} \frac{dp}{dx},$$

which is a differential form of equation (8), p. 245, may be integrated directly. For a gas, however, the density will decrease along the tube, and we have now to express the fact that the mass and not simply the volume traversing any cross-section is constant. If ρ represents the density and Q the volume passing any cross-section per second, $\rho Q =$ constant or $pQ =$ constant, since the density is proportional to the pressure. Then if p_1 is the pressure at the inlet of the tube and Q_1 is the volume entering per second,

$$p_1 Q_1 = pQ = -\frac{\pi a^4}{8\eta} p \frac{dp}{dx}; \qquad \ldots \quad (20)$$

or

$$\int_0^l p_1 Q_1 \, dx = -\frac{\pi a^4}{8\eta} \int_{p_1}^{p_2} p \, dp,$$

where p_2 is the pressure at the outlet. Hence

$$p_1 Q_1 = \frac{(p_1{}^2 - p_2{}^2)}{16 \eta l} \pi a^4. \qquad \ldots \ldots \quad (21)$$

The complete formula, when the Hagenbach correction and also the slipping which occurs at the sides of the tube are taken into account, has been shown by Erk * to be

$$\eta = \frac{\pi a^4}{16 l p_1 Q_1} (p_1{}^2 - p_2{}^2)\left(1 + \frac{4\xi}{a}\right) - \frac{\rho Q_1}{8\pi l}\left(m + \log_e \frac{p_1}{p_2}\right), \quad (22)$$

where ξ is a constant for the particular gas and is termed the *slipping coefficient*.

The experimental arrangement due to Schultze is shown in fig. I1. The gas is contained in the spheres a and b and is passed through the capillary k at constant pressure by raising the mercury c up the scale d. The volume of gas passed is recorded electrically as the mercury passes the points f and g.

(2) Rankine's Method.

There are many experimental methods for determining the viscosity of a gas by means of a pellet of mercury which slides down a vertical tube and forces the gas through a capillary tube during the descent. A convenient arrangement due to Rankine is shown in fig. 12.

A capillary tube K and a wider tube D are joined as shown to form a closed system. A drop of mercury E slides between two fixed marks A and B in the wide tube and thus traverses a volume Q, which is equal to the volume of gas which flows through the capillary tube. The general equation connecting t, the time of fall of the drop, and m, its mass, is

$$t = \frac{\beta}{(m - \alpha)}, \qquad \ldots \ldots \ldots \ldots \quad (23)$$

* Erk, *Zeits. f. techn. Phys.*, Vol. 10, p. 452 (1929).

where α and β are constants, the former depending on the surface tension and being commonly known as the *sticking coefficient*. It may be eliminated by performing experiments with pellets of two different masses. The effective pressure difference is given by $p = \beta g / At$, where A is the area of cross-section of the fall-tube. Hence if we neglect the Hagenbach correction, formula (21) becomes approximately

$$\eta = \frac{\pi a^4 \beta g}{8lQtA} \left(1 + 4 \frac{\xi}{r}\right). \quad . \quad . \quad . \quad . \quad . \quad . \quad (24)$$

Since β is constant, the apparatus is convenient for comparing the viscosities of different gases. Alternatively, steam or liquid at a known temperature may be

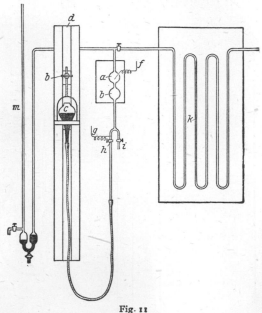

Fig. 11

circulated through PQ and the variation of viscosity with temperature may be investigated.

(3) *Edwards' Constant Volume Method.*

In contrast to the two methods previously described, in which the viscosity is measured at constant pressure, Edwards has devised a method, as shown in fig. 13, for determining η at constant volume.

Gas is contained in the large bulb B at a pressure p_1 which is registered by the mercury in the arms of the manometer ab. The tap T_2 is then closed and T_3 opened to atmosphere for a certain time t. Finally T_3 is closed and the new pressure p_2 is observed. Let the volume of the bulb be Q. Then if Q_1 is the volume of gas entering the capillary tube K per second at time t when the pressure in the apparatus is p, for a slow rate of flow

$$pQ = (p + dp)(Q + Q_1 dt),$$

when p changes to $p + dp$ in time dt. Hence

$$pQ_1 = -Q\frac{dp}{dt} \text{ approximately.}$$

But

$$pQ_1 = \frac{\pi a^4(p^2 - p_0^2)}{16\eta l},$$

where p_0 is the atmospheric pressure. Hence

$$\frac{\pi a^4 t}{16\eta l Q} = -\int_{p_1+p_0}^{p_2+p_0} \frac{dp}{p^2 - p_0^2} = \frac{1}{2p_0} \log \frac{(p_2 + 2p_0)\, p_1}{(p_1 + 2p_0)\, p_2}.$$

If the slipping coefficient is also considered, we have

$$\eta = \frac{\pi a^4 t}{8 l Q} \frac{p_0\left(1 + 4\frac{\xi}{r}\right)}{\log \dfrac{(p_2 + 2p_0)\, p_1}{(p_1 + 2p_0)\, p_2}}. \qquad . \quad . \quad (25)$$

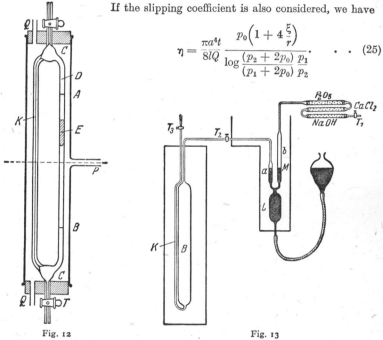

Fig. 12   Fig. 13

(4) Maxwell's Oscillating-disc Viscometer.

The rotation viscometer of Hatschek (pp. 251–2) may be applied directly to the determination of the viscosity of gases.

As typical of the viscometers dependent on damping, Maxwell's oscillating disc will now be described; the rate of damping is approximately proportional to the viscosity of the gas. In instruments of this type the expansion of the gas which is inevitable in the flow methods is avoided, and it was with the oscillating disc that Maxwell's prediction from the kinetic theory, that the viscosity should be independent of the pressure, was verified. The viscosity of gases at very low temperatures has been determined with a recent form of the apparatus due to Vogel * (fig. 14).

A thin glass disc *dd* was attached by a nickel wire to the mirror *s*, the whole being suspended by a fine platinum wire from the hook *k*. A rotation head *e* enabled the zero to be set easily. The fixed plates were clamped by the clamps *FF* to two fixed pieces *MM*. The gas was introduced through *E* and the apparatus was set in operation magnetically by means of the astatic pair of magnets *ff*.

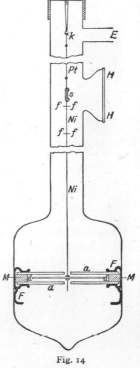

While the lower part of the apparatus could be immersed in any desired temperature bath, the platinum suspension was sufficiently distant for its elastic properties to remain constant.

The theory of the instrument is complicated and involves many uncertain corrections, so that the method is suitable only for comparison and not for absolute measurements. The corrections may be avoided to some extent by the use of a guard ring. The method has useful applications in the determination of the viscosity of molten metals, since the inertia of the liquid is large and the mass movements of the liquid are small; hence the size of the vessel is unimportant and the use of a guard ring becomes unnecessary. The flow methods lead to considerable error unless precautions are taken to avoid oxidation, and the apparent viscosity is often greatly increased by the formation of a skin of impurities on the surface of the flow tube.

12. Variation of the Viscosity of Fluids with Pressure.

(1) *Liquids.*

Little work was done on the variation of the coefficient of viscosity of liquids with pressure before Bridgman (p. 84).

In certain qualitative features the behaviour of all liquids, except water, is similar, although there are large quantitative differences. The viscosity of liquids increases with pressure at a rapidly increasing rate. Refer-

Fig. 14

ence to Chapter V shows this to be unusual, most pressure effects diminishing as the pressure is increased. The behaviour of water is exceptional. Between 0° C. and 10° C. there is a minimum viscosity at about 1000 kg./cm.². At 30° C. and 75° C. experiments showed that the minimum had disappeared, and a regular increase of viscosity with pressure was observed. No really satisfactory theory of the variation of the viscosity of liquids with pressure has yet been proposed.

* H. Vogel, *Ann. d. Physik*, Ser. 4, Vol. 43, p. 1235 (1914).

(2) *Gases*.

It is shown in Chap. IX (p. 181) that according to the kinetic theory of gases the coefficient of viscosity should be independent of the pressure at ordinary pressures. At low pressures, on the other hand, when the mean free path of a gas molecule becomes greater than the linear dimensions of the containing vessel, the kinetic theory shows (p. 185) that η should be proportional to p. Both predictions are in good agreement with experiment. At very high pressures, Bridgman has shown that the coefficient of viscosity of gases increases with increasing pressure. The problem has recently received independent investigation by Boyd, who has shown that the Hagenbach correction becomes increasingly important at higher pressures.

Highly purified nitrogen and hydrogen and mixtures of the two were passed through a steel flow tube at pressures up to nearly 200 atmospheres. The maximum relative increase in the viscosity of nitrogen was 25 per cent, of hydrogen 10 per cent, and of the mixture 20 per cent. Further work by Michels and Gibson, using nitrogen up to a pressure of 1000 atmospheres and over a temperature range 0–100° C., shows agreement with a comprehensive theory of molecular attraction developed by Enskog. The expression η/ρ, where ρ is the density, decreases to a minimum at $\rho = 400 \times 10^{-3}$ gm./c.c. and then increases indefinitely.

13. Variation of Viscosity of Fluids with Temperature.

(1) *Liquids*.

The viscosity of liquids decreases rapidly with rise of temperature. For water, the viscosity at 80° C. is only one-third of its value at 10° C. Although the relationship has been the subject of many investigations, no satisfactory simple formula has been suggested which expresses the connexion with any great degree of accuracy. The empirical formula of Slotte,

$$\eta_t = \frac{\eta_0}{1 + at + \beta t^2}, \qquad \cdots \cdots \cdots (26)$$

where a and β are constants, is only in approximate agreement with experiment, while a modification

$$\eta_t = \frac{A}{(1 + Bt)^C}, \qquad \cdots \cdots \cdots (27)$$

where A, B and C are constants, is cumbersome and does not apply to the important practical case of oils, which are mixtures of chemical compounds not easily separable. Owing to the lack of a satisfactory theory of liquids, no theoretical relation of any value had been derived until the recent work of Andrade.*

On Andrade's theory, a liquid is considered to consist of molecules vibrating under the influence of local forces about equilibrium positions which, instead of being fixed as in a solid, are slowly displaced with

* Andrade, *Phil. Mag.*, Vol. 17, p. 698 (1934).

time. The liquid state is here regarded as being closer to the solid state than to the gaseous state. At extreme libration (compare Lindemann's theory of fusion*) a molecule of one layer may momentarily combine with one of an adjacent parallel layer, supposed to be moving past it with a drift velocity given by the bulk velocity gradient, the combination being of extremely short duration but sufficing to ensure a sharing of momentum parallel to the drift. If the frequency of vibration of a liquid at the melting point is taken as that of the solid form at the same temperature, a coefficient of viscosity can be calculated for simple substances in the liquid state which agrees closely with the experimental value. Communication of momentum takes place only if the mutual potential energy, probably determined by the relative orientation of the approaching molecules, is favourable. Under the influence of local intermolecular forces the molecules tend to be similarly orientated within very small groups, the boundary and molecular population of each group changing continually. The tendency to orientation which is favourable for interchange of momentum is disturbed by the thermal agitation. On this basis the formula

$$\eta v^{\frac{1}{3}} = A^{c/vT} \qquad \ldots \ldots \ldots (28)$$

is derived for the variation of viscosity with temperature, A and c being constants and v the specific volume. This formula agrees closely with experiment for all liquids so far examined, except water and certain tertiary alcohols. It applies to ordinary associated liquids as well as to non-associated liquids, although the meaning to be attributed to the constant c is somewhat different in the two cases.

(2) *Gases.*

The viscosity of all gases increases with rise of temperature. For a discussion of the results reference should be made to Chapter IX, p. 181.

14. Viscosity of Mixtures and Solutions; Variation with Chemical Constitution.

A large number of experiments have been made on the viscosity of mixtures and of solutions, but no general laws have resulted in either case. With some solutions the viscosity is less than that of the pure solvent, while with others it is greater, reaching a maximum for a certain concentration. With mixtures, the viscosity is generally less than the arithmetic mean of the viscosities of the components of the mixture. Again, the dependence on chemical constitution is anything but straightforward; experiments by Pendersen on the ethers show a very general decrease in viscosity with increasing molecular weight, although many exceptions occur.

REFERENCE

G. Barr, *A Monograph of Viscometry* (Oxford University Press, 1931).

* See Roberts, *Heat and Thermodynamics*, p. 445.

CHAPTER XIII

Errors of Measurement; Methods of Determining Planck's Constant

1. Introduction.

In making measurements which are intended to be as accurate as possible, the experimenter attempts to eliminate all the sources of error in his method. All sources of *systematic error* are first removed. If the readings are then taken with the highest possible precision, the uncertainty principle of Heisenberg asserts that uncertainties will still remain even if the observer and the apparatus are "perfect". A full discussion of this principle cannot be given here,* but it may be mentioned that uncertainties still remain in measurements of length, velocity, momentum, &c., even if the apparatus is "perfect". Other *accidental errors*, bigger than those just mentioned, arise in all measurements, because the personal judgment of the observer is employed, for example, to estimate the coincidence of two linear graduations, or of two events in time, or of analogous things, and the estimate made is always faulty to a greater or less degree. It is with these accidental errors that we are particularly concerned in this chapter. To deduce the "most accurate" value of a quantity from a set of experimentally measured values different methods are available, according as the quantity sought (a) is the quantity directly measured, (b) satisfies a linear relation, or (c) satisfies some other relation.

The theory of these methods is in many cases based on the Gaussian theory of errors. Although doubt has recently been thrown on the application of the theory to physical calculations, it is still accepted by most authorities.

2. The Gaussian or Normal Error-distribution Law.

Suppose that a large number n of experimental values of a single quantity, $x_1, x_2, x_3, \ldots, x_n$, have been found, all of which are equally reliable and free from constant or systematic error. It may be shown

---

* See e.g. Born, *Atomic Physics*, p. 86 (Blackie and Son, Ltd., 1935).

on plausible grounds that the most accurate value x is that of the average or arithmetic mean, defined by $(x_1 + x_2 + \ldots + x_n)/n$. Let the quantities $d_1 = x_1 - x$, $d_2 = x_2 - x$, &c., be calculated. The quantities d_1, d_2, &c., are called *residuals, deviations* or *divergences*. The total number of the residuals is equal to n, the total number of observations. Consider the number dn of residuals whose numerical value, independent of sign, lies between two limits z and $z + dz$. The Gaussian error-distribution law asserts that in *all* cases

$$dn = Ane^{-h^2z^2} dz, \quad \ldots \ldots \quad (1)$$

where A and h are constants.

Since the total number of residuals equals n, and their possible range is from $z = 0$ to $z = \infty$,

$$\int_0^n dn = n = An \int_0^\infty e^{-h^2z^2} dz = \frac{An\sqrt{\pi}}{h}.$$

Hence $A = h/\sqrt{\pi}$ and

$$dn = nhe^{-h^2z^2} \frac{dz}{\sqrt{\pi}}. \quad \ldots \ldots \quad (2)$$

The constant h is called the *Gaussian measure of precision.*[*] If h is large, the residuals are crowded more closely towards the value zero; if h is small, the residuals are spread over a large range. Thus h has different values for different sets of results.

Tests of the truth of the Gaussian error-distribution law include (a) one by Bessel, using 470 observations by Bradley, of a certain astronomical angle. There is very good agreement between the actual and Gaussian values of dn, in various ranges z to $z + dz$, except when z is very large. More large residuals are found experimentally than are predicted by theory. (b) Birge (1932) made 500 settings of a cross-wire on the centre of a wide spectrum line. The distribution of the residuals was in good agreement with the Gaussian law, even for large residuals. (c) Astronomical observations by Merriman, 300 in number, gave a strictly Gaussian distribution of residuals.

According to Campbell,[†] on the other hand, the Gaussian theory has for many years been held in such superstitious reverence that no effort has been made to accumulate data by which a decision might be made between Gaussian rules (of which the above is one) and possible alternatives. He agrees, however, that Gaussian rules lead in certain circumstances to permissible results, and that they have long been employed with apparent success.

A graph representing the normal or Gaussian law of error-distribution is shown in fig. 1.

---

[*] It must not be confused with Planck's constant of action, also denoted by h.

[†] *Measurement and Calculation*, pp. 162–163 (Longmans, 1928).

3. Measurement of a Single Quantity. Probable Error.

Suppose that a large number n of experimental determinations of a single quantity have been made. Let these be $x_1, x_2, \ldots, x_n$. It is required to calculate the most accurate value of x given by the experiments.

Method I.—One convenient and permissible procedure is to arrange the n values of x_1, x_2, &c., in ascending order, and if n is odd, simply select the middle quantity as the required " most accurate " value of x. This quantity is known as the *median*. If n is even, select the two middle values of x and find their mean.

Method II.—The usual method is to proceed as on p. 261 and find the average or arithmetic mean $x = (x_1 + x_2 + \ldots + x_n)/n$. This is more laborious than Method I.

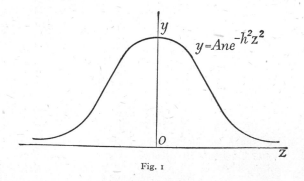

$$y = Ane^{-h^2z^2}$$

Fig. 1

Such a result is often stated thus: the most accurate value of the quantity sought is $x \pm a$. For example, Millikan announced his value of the electronic charge as $(4 \cdot 774 \pm \cdot 004) \times 10^{-10}$ e.s.u. The symbol a usually, though not always, indicates a quantity known as the *probable error* or *dispersion* of the arithmetic mean. It is appended to x in order to give a quantitative estimate of the dispersion, range, or spread of the set of experimental investigations. If the values $x_1, x_2, \ldots, x_n$ are spread over a wide range, the precision of the measurements is not so great as if they are spread over a narrow range. In a large set of results, half of the errors exceed and half fall short of a certain quantity $\sqrt{n}\,a$. The probable error a is defined thus: it is a number such that the arithmetic mean x is just as likely to be in error by a number falling short of a as by a number exceeding a. Or, it is just as likely that the true value of x lies within the range of $x - a$ to $x + a$ as outside that range (sometimes referred to as the *fifty per cent zone*). Or, again, the odds that the true value lies within the range $x - 5a$ to $x + 5a$ are 1000 to 1, which is reckoned as a certainty. The quantity $5a$ is called the *maximum error*. In Millikan's case, the probable error is 0·004, and the maximum error is $5 \times 0·004 = 0·02$, so that the odds are 1000 to 1 that the true value of e lies within the range $(4·754 - 4·794) \times 10^{-10}$ e.s.u. and not outside it.

According to the Gaussian theory of errors, the probable error is calculated as follows. Having obtained the arithmetic mean x, we calculate the residuals $d_1 = x_1 - x$, $d_2 = x_2 - x$, &c., and then the sum $d_1{}^2 + d_2{}^2 + \ldots + d_n{}^2 = \Sigma d^2$, say. Then

$$a = ·6745 \sqrt{\frac{\Sigma d^2}{n(n-1)}}, \quad \ldots \ldots \quad (3)$$

where n is the total number of values.* The approximate value

$$a = \frac{2}{3n} \sqrt{\Sigma d^2} \quad \ldots \ldots \quad (4)$$

is sufficiently accurate for most purposes. The quantity $\pm\sqrt{\Sigma d^2/n}$ is called the *standard deviation* or *mean deviation* from the arithmetic mean. Thus the probable error is $2/3\sqrt{n}$ times the standard deviation. Another expression given by Gaussian theory for the probable error is

$$a = \frac{·8453}{n} \sqrt{\frac{\Sigma d}{n-1}} = \frac{5}{6n} \sqrt{\frac{\Sigma d}{n}}, \text{ approximately.} \quad . \quad (5)$$

It appears that not all authors, when stating a result in the form $x \pm \alpha$, mean thereby that α is the probable error. Some authors intend α to mean the standard deviation.† It is therefore essential to find out exactly what each author means by the statement that his result is $x \pm \alpha$. Engineers dimension their drawings in the form $x \pm \alpha$, meaning by x the nominal dimension and by $\pm\alpha$ the tolerance or allowable margin of error either way.

4. Probable Error or Dispersion of a Single Observation.

After making the n observations $x_1, x_2, \ldots, x_n$, suppose that one more observation is made. Where is it likely to lie? A quantity β, called the *probable error* or *dispersion of a single observation*, exists such that it is equally likely that the new value obtained differs from the true value by a quantity exceeding β as by a quantity falling short of β. Theory gives

$$\beta = a\sqrt{n}. \quad \ldots \ldots \quad (6)$$

It can be shown that the probable error of a itself is $0·4769a/n^{\frac{1}{2}}$, or, as is sometimes stated, the fractional probable error of a itself is $0·4769/n^{\frac{1}{2}}$.

---

* Proofs of formulæ (3), (5), and (6) are given in Whittaker and Robinson, *The Calculus of Observations*, pp. 205, 206 (Blackie and Son, Ltd., 1929).

† See remarks by Baker, *Proc. Phys. Soc.*, Vol. 45, p. 283 (1933).

5. The Weighting of Observations.

When more confidence can be placed in one measured quantity than in another, it is said to have more weight. The question arises, how is this to be taken into consideration quantitatively in calculating the most accurate value of a physical quantity from a set of experimental values?

Consider a case in which a large number of values $x_1, x_2, \ldots, x_n$ of a single quantity have been obtained by experiment, and suppose that if equal confidence could be placed in all the values the arithmetic mean would be chosen as the "most accurate" value of x. What is to be done if equal confidence cannot be placed in all the values? Some authors, e.g. Campbell,* say that observations should *never* be weighted. "The accuracy of a given set of observations, if they are sufficient in number, can never be improved by combining them with less accurate observations. If their number is insufficient it should be increased. . . . It is quite common to see a value for some important constant obtained by the combination of the results of many different workers, some of whose experiments were obviously less valuable than those of others. I can see no justification for this procedure ; if the experiments that criticism shows to be the most trustworthy do not give a trustworthy result, then no trustworthy result is available."

While ideally it may be desirable to increase the number of accurate observations and reject all those of lesser precision, practical considerations of time and expense are by many authors considered to justify the inclusion of the more doubtful results, if they are given suitable weight.

One method, which is sometimes used but seems unsatisfactory, is to assign numerical integers $w_1, w_2, \ldots$, to each quantity $x_1, x_2, \ldots$ respectively, basing the values of $w_1, w_2, \ldots$ on a purely intuitive estimate of the relative confidence to be placed in $x_1, x_2, \ldots$. For example, in a certain case it might be considered that twice as much confidence could be placed in x_1 as in x_2, or in $x_3, \ldots$, and values $w_1 = 2, w_2 = 1, w_3 = 1, \ldots$ might be assigned to $x_1, x_2, x_3, \ldots$ respectively. These numbers $w_1, w_2, \ldots$ are called the *weights* of $x_1, x_2, \ldots$ respectively. In the general case, after the weights are assigned, a quantity

$$x = \frac{w_1 x_1 + w_2 x_2 + \ldots}{w_1 + w_2 + \ldots}, \quad \cdots \cdots (7)$$

called the *weighted mean*, is calculated.

Another procedure is to combine results obtained by different observers as follows. A certain observer announces the result of his

---

* *Measurement and Calculation*, p. 167.

measurements of a certain quantity as $x_1 \pm a_1$; another investigator gives *his* result for the same quantity as $x_2 \pm a_2$, a third as $x_3 \pm a_3$, and so on. Assume that a_1, a_2, ... are the respective probable errors of the arithmetic means. To combine these results, begin by calculating the weights w_1, w_2, ... of the different results, which on Gaussian theory are given by $w_1 = 1/a_1{}^2$, $w_2 = 1/a_2{}^2$, and so on. The final most accurate value of x is taken to be

$$x_m = \frac{w_1 x_1 + w_2 x_2 + \dots}{w_1 + w_2 + \dots} = \frac{x_1/a_1{}^2 + x_2/a_2{}^2 + \dots}{1/a_1{}^2 + 1/a_2{}^2 + \dots}, \quad . \quad (8)$$

which can be written in the form

$$x_m = \frac{\Sigma wx}{\Sigma w}. \quad \dots \dots \quad (9)$$

Before we combine results in such a way, a test ought to be applied to see whether such a combination is permissible. According to Birge,[*] the test is that the quantity $Z = 0{\cdot}6745\{\Sigma w\, \delta^2/(N-1)\}^{\frac{1}{2}}$ ought to be equal to unity, except for statistical fluctuations. Here $\delta_1 = x_1 - x_m$, $\delta_2 = x_2 - x_m$, ..., where x_m is the weighted mean, as in equation (8), w_1, w_2, ... are the weights $1/a_1{}^2$, $1/a_2{}^2$, ... respectively, $\Sigma w\, \delta^2 = w_1 \delta_1{}^2 + w_2 \delta_2{}^2 + \dots$, and N is the number of independent sets of results which are to be combined. Provided that Z does not differ from unity by a quantity exceeding $0{\cdot}4769/N^{\frac{1}{2}}$, the combination of results is permissible. If Z differs from unity by five times $0{\cdot}4769/N^{\frac{1}{2}}$, there is only one chance in a thousand that such a deviation is due to mere statistical fluctuation, that is, the odds are 999 to 1 that constant or systematic errors are present in one or more sets of results, and it is not permissible to combine them.

It may be shown that the value of the weighted mean x_m, given by equation (8), has a probable error

$$a = 0{\cdot}6745\{\Sigma w\, \delta^2/(N-2)\Sigma w\}^{\frac{1}{2}},$$

where the symbols have the meanings just given.

6. Calculation of the Constants in the Linear Law $y = mx + c$.

Suppose that it is known that "exact" values of two quantities, x and y, obey a linear law of the form $y = mx + c$. Suppose also that a large number of pairs of values of x and y have been obtained experimentally. It is required to find the "most accurate" values of m and c, the constants in the equation. If exact values of x and y were available, two pairs of them, x_1, y_1, and x_2, y_2, would be sufficient to determine exact values of m and c. As, however, the values available are only experimental, another procedure must be adopted. Various methods are regarded as permissible.

* Birge, *Phys. Rev.*, Vol. 40, p. 207 (1932).

(i) *Graphical Method.*—A graph connecting x and y is plotted, each point being plotted immediately after each single pair of observations is made. The straight line which lies most evenly among these points is determined by a black thread or a transparent celluloid rule with a central straight line engraved upon it. Immediate plotting reduces the number of observations needed. The most accurate values of m and c are given by the tangent of the angle of slope and the intercept on the y-axis respectively. The accuracy of this method is limited, because there are practical limits to the accuracy with which an angle or a length can be measured. The accuracy is also affected by the scale of the graph, a large scale being better than a small one.

(ii) *Method of Zero Sum* (Mayer's or Campbell's Method).—In making the experiments, one of the two quantities x and y is usually arranged or set at some value, the other being allowed to come as it may. For example, in measuring the coefficient of linear expansion of a rod, the temperature may be set at definite values, and the length allowed to come as it may. The present method of obtaining the most accurate values of m and c is as follows.

Arrange the values of the set quantity, which may be taken as x, in ascending order of magnitude, $x_1, x_2, x_3, \ldots$. Write down equations in the order $y_1 = mx_1 + c$, $y_2 = mx_2 + c$, $\ldots$. Suppose that in all there are n equations. If n is even, add the first $n/2$ equations together, obtaining a single " normal " equation of the form $Y_1 = mX_1 + nc/2$, where $Y_1 = y_1 + y_2 + \ldots + y_{n/2}$ and $X_1 = x_1 + x_2 + \ldots + x_{n/2}$. Add the second group of $n/2$ equations together, obtaining a second normal equation of the form $Y_2 = mX_2 + nc/2$. Then solve this pair of simultaneous normal equations for m and c in the ordinary way. We get

$$m = \frac{Y_1 - Y_2}{X_1 - X_2},$$

$$c = \frac{2(X_1 Y_2 - X_2 Y_1)}{n(X_1 - X_2)}. \quad \ldots \ldots \quad (10)$$

If n is odd, add the first $(n-1)/2$ equations to the next equation (the middle one of the set), multiplied throughout by $1/2$, to get a single normal equation. Add the middle equation multiplied by $1/2$ to the remaining $(n-1)/2$ equations to get a second normal equation. Then solve the two normal equations for m and c in the usual way.

The arithmetic of this method is fairly quick, but it gives different values of m and c according to which of the two experimental quantities we " arrange " or " set ".

(iii) *Gaussian Method of Least Squares.*—The deviation of any two observed values x_1, y_1 from the straight line $y = mx + c$ may be written as $d_1 = c + mx_1 - y_1$. For several pairs of readings, the *method of least squares* states that the best representative values of m and c are those for which the sum of the squares of the deviations is least; to find these values we proceed as follows.

Take the first of the set of n equations, namely, $y_1 = mx_1 + c$. Multiply it by the coefficient of m, i.e. by x_1, which gives $x_1 y_1 = mx_1^2 + cx_1$. Repeat with all the n equations and add; this gives $X_1 Y_1 = mX_1^2 + cX_1$, where $X_1 Y_1 = \Sigma xy$, $X_1^2 = \Sigma x^2$, and $X_1 = \Sigma x$. Next take the first equation and multiply it by the coefficient of c, which happens to be unity; this simply gives $y_1 = mx_1 + c$. As the coefficient of c in every equation is unity, simply add the n equations as they stand; this gives $Y_1 = mX_1 + nc$, where $Y_1 = \Sigma y$. Solve the two normal equations thus obtained for m and c; this gives

$$m = \frac{nX_1 Y_1 - Y_1 . X_1}{nX_1^2 - X_1 . X_1}, \qquad \dots \dots \quad (11)$$

$$c = \frac{X_1^2 . Y_1 - X_1 . X_1 Y_1}{nX_1^2 - X_1 . X_1}. \qquad \dots \dots \quad (12)$$

The probable errors of the values of m and c obtained by the method of least squares, equal weights being assumed for every pair of values of x and y, may be shown to be

$$a_m = 0 \cdot 6745 \left\{ \frac{n\Sigma \delta^2}{(n-2)(nX_1^2 - X_1 . X_1)} \right\}^{\frac{1}{2}}$$

and

$$a_c = 0 \cdot 6745 \left\{ \frac{\Sigma \delta^2 . X_1^2}{(n-2)(nX_1^2 - X_1 . X_1)} \right\}^{\frac{1}{2}}.$$

Here X_1 and X_1^2 have their previous meanings. Each δ is calculated as follows. In the equation $y = mx + c$ we use the calculated values of m and c, derived from equations (11) and (12), and, in turn, insert the set values $x_1, x_2, \dots$, and *calculate* values of y, which may be called $y_1', y_2', \dots$. Then δ_1 is the difference between the calculated value y_1' and the experimental value y_1, or $\delta_1 = y_1' - y_1$, $\delta_2 = y_2' - y_2, \dots$. Hence $\Sigma \delta^2 = (y_1' - y)^2 + (y_2' - y_2)^2 + \dots$.

The arithmetic in this method is usually somewhat laborious, though the use of modern calculating machines reduces the labour considerably. The method has the advantage of giving the same result no matter which quantity is "arranged" or "set" at definite values. It is not now regarded as having any better theoretical justification than other methods, but is classed along with others as *a* possible method.

(iv) *Cauchy's* (or *Awbery's*) *Method.*—This method has the advantage of involving much less arithmetical labour than that of least squares. Suppose that n pairs of observations $y_1, y_2, \dots, y_n, x_1, x_2, \dots, x_n$

have been made. As before, the law is known to be of the form $y = mx + c$. Its graph is a straight line. Find a point X, Y which may be called the centroid of all the points, i.e. find $X = \Sigma x/n$, $Y = \Sigma y/n$. Next, divide the n values into two sets as follows. Let i of them have values of x less than X, the other $n - i$ having values of x greater than X. Find the centroid of the i values such that $x < X$, i.e. find $\Sigma x/i$ and $\Sigma y/i$ for these i values. Let $\Sigma x/i = X_1$ and $\Sigma y/i = Y_1$. Also find the centroid of the remaining $n - i$ values, for which let $\Sigma x/(n - i) = X_2$ and $\Sigma y/(n - i) = Y_2$. Assume that the best value of m is $(Y_2 - Y_1)/(X_2 - X_1)$, which is the slope of the straight line joining the points (X_1, Y_1), (X_2, Y_2) on a graph. Assume that the best value of c is the value of c given by putting $Y = mX + c$, i.e. $c = Y - mX$, where (X, Y) is the centroid of all the points and $m = (Y_2 - Y_1)/(X_2 - X_1)$.

7. Probable Error of a Function of Quantities Measured Experimentally.

The values of many physical quantities are calculated by substituting experimental values of various measurable quantities in a formula; for example, the viscosity of a liquid is calculated from Poiseuille's formula $\eta = \pi p a^4/8Ql$ (p. 245). All the quantities p, a, Q, r, t, and l are measured in some way. The value of each has its own probable error. What is the probable error of the result that is obtained for η?

To put this in more general terms, if a quantity Z is a function of $x, y, z, \ldots$, and if the probable error of x is $\pm a_1$, of y, $\pm a_2$, of z, $\pm a_3$, $\ldots$, what is the probable error a of the value of Z obtained by calculating $f(x, y, z, \ldots)$? Theory indicates that

$$a^2 = \left(\frac{\partial f}{\partial x}\right)^2 a_1{}^2 + \left(\frac{\partial f}{\partial y}\right)^2 a_2{}^2 + \cdots$$

where $\partial f/\partial x$ means the partial derivative of $f(x, y, z, \ldots)$ with respect to x when $y, z, \ldots$ are treated as constants, and so on.

For example, the volume V of a cone is $\pi r^2 H/3$. Let the probable errors of r and H be a_1 and a_2 respectively. Since $V = \pi r^2 H/3$, $\partial V/\partial r = 2\pi r H/3$ and $\partial V/\partial H = \pi r^2/3$. Hence $a^2 = 4\pi^2 r^2 H^2 a_1{}^2/9 + \pi^2 r^4 a_2{}^2/9$. Other exercises for solution are given on p. 281.

8. Determination of Planck's Constant.

The determination of the most reliable value for Planck's constant of action h by Bond and by Birge, which is described later, affords a good example of the application of the method of least squares. The description of Bond's work is preceded by a short account of the other main methods of determining h. It has been found necessary to assume a fair knowledge of sub-atomic physics on the part of the student, since proofs of the various formulæ used would lead us beyond the scope of this book.*

9. Method based on Bohr's Theory of Atomic Structure.

According to Bohr's theory of atomic structure,

$$R_\infty = \frac{2\pi^2 e^5}{h^3 c^2 (e/m)},$$

where R_∞ is the Rydberg constant for infinite mass, and its units are cm.$^{-1}$, e is the electronic charge in absolute e.s.u., and e/m is in absolute e.m.u. Further,

$$R_\infty = R_H \left(1 + \frac{m}{m_H} \right),$$

where R_H is the observed Rydberg constant for hydrogen, m is the rest-mass of an electron, and m_H the mass of the nucleus of a hydrogen atom, that is, of a proton.

This may also be written in the form

$$R_\infty = R_H \left\{ 1 + \frac{F}{(H - m)e/m} \right\},$$

where F is the value of the electric charge associated in electrolysis with one gramme-equivalent of any ion, in absolute e.m.u., that is, the value of the faraday in e.m.u., and H is the mass of a hydrogen atom in grammes. Hence, since

$$h^3 = \frac{2\pi^2 e^5}{R_\infty c^2 (e/m)},$$

we have

$$h = \left[\frac{2\pi^2 e^5}{c^2 (e/m) R_H [1 + F/\{(H - m)(e/m)\}]} \right]^{\frac{1}{3}}. \quad . \quad . \quad (13)$$

The most accurate value of c yet obtained is that of Michelson (1927), namely, $c = 2\cdot99796 \times 10^{10}$ cm. sec.$^{-1}$. In making the numerical calculation, the errors affecting e are far more important than those affecting the other quantities. Millikan's value for e, as corrected by Birge, is used.

10. Ionization Potential Method.

The ionization potential hitherto most accurately determined is that of mercury by Lawrence.† Its value is given as $10\cdot40 \pm 0\cdot02$ international volts ($= V'$, say). To reduce V' to absolute e.s.u. of

---

* See e.g. Wilson, *Modern Physics*; Born, *Atomic Physics* (Blackie & Son, Ltd., 1935).

† *Phys. Rev.*, Vol. 28, p. 947 (1926).

potential difference, it is not permissible simply to divide by 300. Allowance must be made for the fact that the international volt is 1·00046 absolute volts and that c, the velocity of light in vacuo, is $2·99796 \times 10^{10}$ cm. per sec. The relation between h and the ionization potential, measured in absolute e.s.u. of potential difference, is

$$h\nu = eV$$

or

$$h = \frac{eV}{\nu} = \frac{e\lambda V}{c},$$

where λ is the wave-length corresponding to the ionization potential of mercury; e and V are in absolute e.s.u., ν in vibrations per second, and λ in cm. As

$$V = \frac{V' \times 1·00046 \times 10^8}{c},$$

$$h = \frac{e\lambda V' \times 1·00046 \times 10^8}{c^2}. \quad \ldots \ldots \text{(14)}$$

11. X-ray Continuous Spectrum Method.

This method is analogous to the last, but makes use of X-rays. If the intensity wave-length diagram of the continuous X-ray spectrum of any anticathode is examined, it is found that the point where the curve cuts the wave-length axis is constant, no matter what the nature of the anticathode is, provided the applied potential is constant. It is assumed that the corresponding frequency of the X-ray beam is connected with the full applied potential V by the relation

$$h\nu = \frac{hc}{\lambda} = eV, \quad \ldots \ldots \text{(15)}$$

or

$$h = \frac{\lambda eV}{c}. \quad \ldots \ldots \text{(16)}$$

Here V and e are in absolute e.s.u., λ in cm. and c in cm. per sec. In this case λ is measured by regular reflection from a calcite crystal, using Bragg's law, namely, $\lambda = 2d \sin \theta$, where d is the lattice constant of the crystal. The most accurate values for λ available are those by Duane, Palmer and Yeh (1921), and Wagner (1920).

Hence

$$h = \frac{2eVd \sin \theta}{c}$$

or

$$h = \frac{2eV'd \times 10^8 \times \sin \theta \times 1·00046}{c^2}, \quad \ldots \text{(17)}$$

where V' is the potential applied to the X-ray tube in international volts.

12. Photoelectric Method.

In this method use is made of Einstein's law, namely,

$$Ve = h\nu - P, \quad \ldots \ldots \quad (18)$$

which connects P, the work required to extract an electron from a metal, with V, the retarding potential, and ν, the frequency of the incident radiation. On differentiating and rearranging, we have

$$\frac{\partial V}{\partial \nu} = \frac{h}{e}. \quad \ldots \ldots \quad (19)$$

In the accurate work of Lukirsky and Prilezaev (1928), the critical potential V', at which light of frequency ν sets up electron emission from a metal, is measured for a large number of values of ν, and for several metals. A graph connecting V' and ν is plotted. Its slope gives $\partial V'/\partial \nu$.

As before, the potential as measured is V' international volts, and $V = V' \times 1{\cdot}00046 \times 10^8/c$ e.s.u. Then

$$\frac{h}{e} = \frac{\partial V}{\partial \nu} = \frac{1{\cdot}00046 \times 10^8}{c} \frac{\partial V'}{\partial \nu}$$

and

$$h = \frac{1{\cdot}00046 \times 10^8 \times e}{c} \frac{\partial V'}{\partial \nu}. \quad \ldots \quad (20)$$

13. Wien's Displacement Law Method.

It follows from Wien's displacement law concerning full or black-body radiation that [*]

$$\lambda_{\max} \theta = \text{a constant} = \frac{hc}{k\beta}, \quad \ldots \quad (21)$$

where $\lambda_{\max}$ is the wave-length corresponding to the peak of one of Planck's spectral distribution curves, θ is the temperature of the full radiator concerned, k is Boltzmann's constant, and β is the positive root of the equation

$$e^{-\beta} + \frac{\beta}{5} - 1 = 0; \quad \ldots \ldots \quad (22)$$

$\beta = 4{\cdot}9651$ to four places of decimals. Hence

$$h = \beta k \lambda_{\max} \frac{\theta}{c}$$

$$= \beta R \lambda_{\max} \frac{\theta}{Nc}, \quad \ldots \ldots \quad (23)$$

[*] Roberts, *Heat and Thermodynamics*, p. 393.

where R is the universal constant for one gramme-molecule of a perfect gas and N is the number of molecules in a gramme-molecule. Among the quantities present in this equation N is the one whose value is known least accurately, its value being given by the relation $Ne = F$, where F is defined as in equation (13), p. 269.

14. Stefan's Law Method.

Stefan's fourth power law * may be stated as $E = \sigma\theta^4$, where E is the total energy contained in rays of all wave-lengths emerging from an aperture in the walls of a full radiator per sq. cm. per sec., θ is the absolute temperature of the full radiator, and σ is a measurable constant. Further, h is connected with σ by the relation

$$h = \left(\frac{2\pi^5 k^4}{15c^2\sigma}\right)^{\frac{1}{3}}. \qquad \cdots \cdots \quad (24)$$

Perhaps the most accurate value of σ yet obtained is that of Hoare (1928), namely, $\sigma = 5\cdot735 \times 10^{-5}$ erg cm.$^{-2}$ deg.$^{-4}$ sec.$^{-1}$. The quantity e is introduced through Boltzmann's constant $k = R/N = Re/F$.

15. Eddington's Method.

According to a theory of Eddington (1929),

$$\frac{hc}{2\pi e^2} = 137. \qquad \cdots \cdots \quad (25)$$

If this is true,

$$h = 274\pi \frac{e^2}{c}, \qquad \cdots \cdots \quad (26)$$

where e is in absolute electrostatic units. According to Birge (1932), the most accurate value of the numerical constant in equation (25) is not 137, but $137\cdot369 \pm 0\cdot048$.

16. Bond's Method.

Having noticed that the various formulæ connecting h and e can be written generally as a power formula

$$h = A_n e^n, \qquad \cdots \cdots \quad (27)$$

where A_n and n are constants, Bond (1930 and 1931) used the method of least squares in conjunction with 36 sets of independent results to find the most accurate value of A_n, n being given, and thence the most accurate values of h and e. As presented by Birge, the method is as follows.

---

* See Roberts, *Heat and Thermodynamics*, pp. 379, 393.

Write equation (27) in the form

$$A_n = he^{-n}. \qquad \ldots \ldots \ldots \quad (28)$$

This is of the form

$$A_n = f(h, e) = he^{-n}. \qquad \ldots \ldots \quad (29)$$

Let e_0, h_0 be any pair of known values of e and h which are known to be not far from the true values. Write

$$e = e_0 + \Delta e, \qquad \ldots \ldots \ldots \quad (30)$$
$$h = h_0 + \Delta h. \qquad \ldots \ldots \ldots \quad (31)$$

Apply Taylor's theorem, namely,

$$f(h, e) = f(h_0, e_0) + \left(\frac{\partial f}{\partial h}\right)_{h = h_0} \Delta h + \left(\frac{\partial f}{\partial e}\right)_{e = e_0} \Delta e + \text{negligible terms.}$$

Now

$$\left(\frac{\partial f}{\partial h}\right)_{h = h_0} = e_0^{-n}, \quad \left(\frac{\partial f}{\partial e}\right)_{e = e_0} = -nh_0 e_0^{-(n+1)}, \quad f(h_0, e_0) = h_0 e_0^{-n}.$$

Hence

$$f(h, e) = A_n = h_0 e_0^{-n} + e_0^{-n} \Delta h - nh_0 e_0^{-(n+1)} \Delta e. \qquad (32)$$

Introduce a new parameter $h_n \equiv A_n e_0{}^n$, i.e. insert $A_n = h_n e_0^{-n}$ in (32). When reduced to the simplest form, equation (32) becomes

$$h_n = h - \left(\frac{h_0 \Delta e}{e_0}\right)n, \qquad \ldots \ldots \quad (33)$$

which is of the form $y = c + mx$, where $y = h_n$, $c = h$, $m = -h_0 \Delta e / e_0$, $x = n$.

The 36 observations included 14 values of h_n corresponding to $n = 3/3$, 9 values of h_n corresponding to $n = 4/3$, and 13 values of h_n corresponding to $n = 5/3$. When each of the 14 observations was given equal weight, the arithmetic mean value of h_n derived from them was $6 \cdot 5473 \times 10^{-27}$; the 9 values gave $h_n = 6 \cdot 5364 \times 10^{-27}$, and the 13 values gave $h_n = 6 \cdot 5395 \times 10^{-27}$. The problem to be solved was then as follows.

Given three equations

$$6 \cdot 5473 \times 10^{-27} = h - (h_0 \Delta e / e_0) 3/3,$$
$$6 \cdot 5364 \times 10^{-27} = h - (h_0 \Delta e / e_0) 4/3,$$
$$6 \cdot 5395 \times 10^{-27} = h - (h_0 \Delta e / e_0) 5/3,$$

to find the most accurate values of h and $h_0 \Delta e / e_0$ and hence of e by the method of least squares. The first equation was given the weight 14, the second 9, and the third 13, since the equations were based on 14, 9 and 13 values respectively.

Now when it is required to find the constants in the equation $y = mx + c$, given values x_1, y_1 of weight w_1, x_2, y_2 of weight w_2, x_3, y_3 of weight w_3, . . . , the method of least squares (p. 267) gives

$$c = \frac{\Sigma wy \Sigma wx^2 - \Sigma wx \Sigma wxy}{\Sigma w \Sigma wx^2 - (\Sigma wx)^2} \quad \cdots \cdots \quad (34)$$

and

$$m = \frac{\Sigma w \Sigma wxy - \Sigma wx \Sigma wy}{\Sigma w \Sigma wx^2 - (\Sigma wx)^2}, \quad \cdots \cdots \quad (35)$$

with a probable error in c of

$$0{\cdot}6745 \left(\frac{\Sigma w \, \delta^2}{n - 2} \right)^{\frac{1}{2}} \left\{ \frac{\Sigma wx^2}{\Sigma w \Sigma wx^2 - (\Sigma wx)^2} \right\}^{\frac{1}{2}},$$

and a probable error in m of

$$0{\cdot}6745 \left(\frac{\Sigma w \, \delta^2}{n - 2} \right)^{\frac{1}{2}} \left\{ \frac{\Sigma w}{\Sigma w \Sigma wx^2 - (\Sigma wx)^2} \right\}^{\frac{1}{2}}.$$

Here $n = 3$ and δ is the deviation of each of the three values of h_n given above from that calculated with the values of c and m calculated from equations (34) and (35).

Using Bond's data and these equations, Birge obtained $h_0 \Delta e/e_0 = (0{\cdot}0119 \pm 0{\cdot}0071) \times 10^{-27}$, and using $h_0 = 6{\cdot}547 \times 10^{-27}$ and $e_0 = 4{\cdot}770 \times 10^{-10}$ e.s.u., he obtained

$$h = (6{\cdot}5575 \pm 0{\cdot}0096) \times 10^{-27}, \; e = (4{\cdot}7787 \pm 0{\cdot}0052) \times 10^{-10} \text{ e.s.u.}$$

The value of e here obtained was independent of that obtained by Millikan's oil-drop method, which does not involve h. By taking the oil-drop result into account as well, by adopting what he believed to be the best arbitrary system of weighting, by using the most accurate results available in 1932, and by applying a method of calculation resembling the one just described, Birge obtained as his values

$$h = (6{\cdot}5442 \pm 0{\cdot}0091) \times 10^{-27}, \; e = (4{\cdot}7677 \pm 0{\cdot}0040) \times 10^{-10} \text{ e.s.u.}$$

References

Tuttle and Satterley, *The Theory of Measurement* (Longmans, 1925).
Birge, *Physical Review*, Vol. 40, pp. 228–261, 319–320 (1932).
Brunt, *Combination of Observations* (Cambridge University Press).
Whittaker and Robinson, *The Calculus of Observations* (Blackie & Son, Ltd., 1929).

EXAMPLES

CHAPTER I

1. Determine the time of oscillation of a drop of liquid under surface-tension forces.

2. Obtain Poiseuille's equation for the volume of viscous liquid flowing per second through a cylindrical tube of circular cross-section.

3. Find by dimensional methods how the viscous force of resistance to the fall of a sphere under gravity depends on the radius of the sphere, its terminal velocity, and the coefficient of viscosity of the fluid through which it is moving.

4. Show that the quantity of heat H, lost per unit length per second per degree temperature excess from a long cylinder of diameter d submitted to forced convection in a fluid of thermal conductivity K, thermal capacity per unit volume c, kinematic viscosity v, moving with relative velocity v, is given by $H/K = F(cvd/K) \cdot f(cv/K)$.

5. Determine the rate of radiation of energy from an accelerated electron.

6. Show that if the linear dimensions of the entire apparatus used in determining G by a torsion balance (see Chapter III, p. 35) are changed, the sensitiveness of the apparatus remains unaltered.

CHAPTER II

1. Assuming the earth to be a perfectly homogeneous sphere, spinning with angular velocity Ω about its geographic axis, prove that the angle between a straight line drawn from a point P on the earth's surface to the centre and a line drawn from P in the apparent direction of the force of gravity is approximately equal to $\Omega^2 R \sin 2L/2(g_0 + \Omega^2 R \cos^2 L)$ radians, where L is the latitude of P, R is the radius of the earth, and g_0 is the force on unit mass at P due to attraction only.

2. Assuming that the earth consists of a sphere of radius R and mean density ρ_1, enclosed in a thin concentric spherical shell of matter of thickness h and mean density ρ_2, prove that g_1/g_2, the ratio of the gravitational acceleration at a point on the outer surface to that at a point on the surface of the inner sphere, is $\{1 - 2h/R + 3h\rho_2/R\rho_1\}$ approximately. (Airy's mine experiment.)

3. Referring to p. 17, prove that Du Buat's correction term γ is equal to zero if Bessel's condition of symmetry of external form is fulfilled.

4. Referring to p. 18, prove that if the knife-edges are equal cylinders the radius disappears from the expression for T.

5. Referring to p. 18, prove that if the knife-edges are not equal cylinders, then $g(T_1{}^2 + T_2{}^2)/8\pi^2 = l_1 + l_2$, where T_1 and T_2 are the measured times of oscillation about the two knife-edges. (Pierce's correction.)

6. Referring to p. 18, prove that if the support yields a distance e to a horizontal force of one dyne, $gT^2/4\pi^2 = l_1 + l_2 + eMg$.

7. Referring to p. 18, prove that if two pendulums, of symmetrical external shape, are of equal weight but have different lengths, and have transferable knife-edges, then

$$g(T_1{}^2 - T_2{}^2)/4\pi^2 = l_1 - l_2. \quad \text{(Defforges's correction.)}$$

8. Prove equations (39), (40) on p. 28, i.e.

$$R \sin 2\theta = 2U_{xy} \quad \text{and} \quad R \cos \theta = U_{xx}{}^2 - U_{yy}{}^2.$$

9. Verify equation (3), p. 13, by direct substitution, i.e. show that

$$0 = Ae^{-bt} \cos\{(c^2 - b^2)^{\frac{1}{2}}t + \varphi\}$$

is a solution of the equation $\ddot{\theta} + 2b\dot{\theta} + c^2\theta = 0$.

CHAPTER III

1. Defining the normal flux of force through an element dS of a surface drawn in a gravitational field as the product of the normal component $F \cos \theta$ of the force on unit mass and the area dS, prove Gauss's theorem as applied to gravitation, that the total outward normal flux of force over any closed surface is $-4\pi G$ times the mass enclosed.

2. Show that a thin spherical shell of attracting matter of thickness x, mean radius r, and uniform density ρ has the same external field as if all the mass were concentrated in a single particle at its centre. Hence prove that a sphere composed of concentric shells, not necessarily all of the same density, acts in the same way.

3. Apply Gauss's theorem to find the gravitational field (force on unit mass) and potential at points (a) inside the central cavity, (b) inside the material, and (c) outside of a thick spherical shell of matter, of radii r and $r + a$, the density of the matter being ρ.

4. Let the mean density of a non-uniform sphere be ρ_1, and the density of its uniform crust be ρ_2. Find the force on unit mass placed at a point h cm. from its surface, inside the crust, the external radius being R cm. $(h \ll R)$.

5. Referring to Boys' experiment for measuring G, calculate the value of the angle φ (p. 34) corresponding to the maximum displacing moment, given the values of M, m, l, r and c as on p. 35.

6. Referring to Boys' experiment, calculate the moment of the restoring couple due to the attractions between spheres at different levels, for a given angle $\varphi = 64° 38'$, and prove that it is negligible compared with that due to attractions between spheres at the same level, using the values of M, m, l, r and c on p. 35.

7. Consider two torsion balances cf Boys' type, in one of which all the linear dimensions, including those of the large and small spheres, are n times as great as those in the other. Let the material of the spheres be the same in each case, but in the second let the suspension fibre be changed so that the period is the same as that in the first. Prove that the angle of deflection is the same in the

two cases. Hence show that with a small balance it is possible to use relatively bigger " large spheres " than are practicable with large balances.

8. (a) What are the dimensions of the quantity A_1 in Heyl's experiments (p. 36)? (b) What is the effect on the period of oscillation of increasing the linear dimensions of every part of the apparatus to n times their original values?

9. What must be the velocity of a body if its mass when moving is 10 per cent greater than its mass when at rest?

10. Find, to 0·005 per cent, the percentage change in mass of a body whose velocity is one-twentieth of the velocity of light, as compared with its mass at rest.

CHAPTER IV

1. A uniform beam is clamped at one end and supported on the same horizontal level. Find the bending moment and the shearing stress at any point and also the maximum depression.

2. A uniform beam is clamped horizontally at one end and has a given concentrated load W and a couple C at the other end. Find the bending moment.

3. A uniform weightless beam clamped horizontally at one end has a concentrated load W at a point A at a distance a from the fixed end. Find the depression at a and at the end of the beam.

4. A light rod is supported symmetrically on two knife-edges a distance $l/2$ apart, where l is the length of the rod. Two weights, each of value W, are suspended from the ends of the rod, and a weight w is attached to its centre. If the centre and the two ends all lie in the same straight line, find the ratio W/w.

5. Find the energy stored in a beam which is clamped at one end and free at the other if the load is w per unit length.

6. Find the energy stored in a light beam as in (4) but with a concentrated load W on the end.

7. Find the energy stored in a stretched wire.

8. Find the energy stored in a stretched flat spiral spring.

9. Find the time of angular oscillation of a loaded spring.

10. Show that the depression of (1) a rod with a weight attached to one end, (2) a flat spiral spring, due to the shearing force, is negligible compared with that due to the bending moment and torsion respectively.

CHAPTER V

1. Show that for perfect gases the ratio of the adiabatic to the isothermal elasticity is equal to γ, the ratio of the specific heat at constant pressure to the specific heat at constant volume.

2. Deduce equation (17), p. 82.

3. Deduce equation (21), p. 83.

CHAPTER VI

1. Suppose that at time $t = 0$ a seismic wave of the form $\xi = \xi_0 \sin \omega t$ arrives at the vertical pendulum seismograph of pp. 92–5. Assuming that damping is negligible, prove that

$$\theta = \frac{\xi_0 \{\sin \omega t + A \sin nt\}}{l(\alpha^2 - 1)},$$

where $A = -\alpha$, $\alpha = n/\omega$, and n has the meaning in the text.

2. Draw a graph connecting the angle of lag of the vertical pendulum seismograph of p. 92 behind the seismic wave and α, where $\alpha = n/\omega$.

3. Find the angle of lag in the following special cases:

(a) ω great, α very small.
(b) $n = \omega$, $\alpha = 1$.
(c) ω very small, α very great.

4. Prove that when the damping coefficient k is great, the sensitiveness of the seismograph is greatest when the natural period of the instrument is great and that of the seismic oscillations is small.

5. With reference to the method of finding the depth of a seismic focus, described on p. 97, prove that if a graph is plotted with new variables $Y = v^2 t^2 - x^2$, $X = 2v^2 t$, it will be a straight line. Show how to obtain t_0 and d from such a graph.

CHAPTER VII

1. A spherical soap bubble of radius r deflates itself by expelling the air within it through an orifice of cross-section A sq. cm. Prove that the time taken for the radius to fall to zero is $\dfrac{2\sqrt{2\pi}}{7A} \sqrt{\dfrac{\rho r^4}{T}}$, where ρ is the initial density of the air within, and T is the surface tension of the soap solution.

2. A bubble of gas resting on the surface of a liquid has the form of a segment of a sphere. Its precise form is governed by the law that the potential energy in the surface, due to surface tension, is a minimum, consistent with the condition that the volume of the segment is constant. Prove that the bubble takes a hemispherical form.

3. A small spherical bubble of radius r is accidentally formed at a certain depth below the surface of a liquid. Show that if the bubble contains nothing but the saturated vapour of the liquid it is unstable, that is, it will not return to its initial size, if for any reason it undergoes a slight change of radius. Then find the minimum pressure of the gas which must be present in order that the bubble may be stable. Relate this to " bumping " and " steady boiling ".

4. A large drop of mercury rests on a horizontal plate. Light from a horizontal bright filament in a distant lamp falls on the curved side of the drop. The reflected beam enters a horizontal telescope. The vertical height of the latter is adjusted until an image of the filament coincides with the horizontal cross-wire of the telescope. The source is displaced vertically through a distance z and the experiment is repeated. Prove that $z = 2\sqrt{\dfrac{T}{\rho}}\left(\sin\dfrac{A'}{2} - \sin\dfrac{A}{2}\right)$, where T is the surface tension and ρ the density of mercury, and A, A' are the angles made with the vertical by the normal to the surface of the drop at the point of incidence of the light, in the first and second cases. (The incident and reflected beams and the normal are in the same vertical plane.)

5. A cylindrical film of indefinite length, mean radius r_1, and (small) thickness d_1 contracts under the influence of surface tension, starting from rest. Prove that the time it takes to contract to a cylinder of mean radius r_2 is

$$t = \sqrt{\frac{\rho\, d_1 r_1 (r_1 - r_2)}{gT}},$$

where T is the surface tension and ρ is the density.

6. A liquid rises in a tube of any shape under the action of surface tension and reaches equilibrium. Prove that the weight of liquid contained in a cylinder bounded by the free surface of the liquid, by the general level of the liquid outside the tube, and by vertical generators drawn from the curve of contact of liquid and solid down to the general level, is equal to the line integral of the vertical projections of the surface tension acting all round the curve of contact.

7. Using the theorem in Example 6, prove that if two adjacent parallel plates inclined at an angle A to the vertical dip into a liquid, the height through which the liquid rises in the narrow space between the plates is independent of the angle of inclination A.

8. Allowing for the spherical cap, calculate the depression of the mercury inside a circular tube of radius r below the general level outside. Calculate the approximate percentage error in the value of the surface tension obtained by using the elementary formula and taking the depression as that measured to the top (umbilic) of the meniscus, when the tube has a diameter of 1 cm.

9. Obtain the equation of equilibrium of a needle floating on a liquid, regarding the needle as a long cylinder, and assuming an angle of contact equal to zero.

10. Assume that the excess pressure on the inside of any gas balloon is $p = T_1/R_1 + T_2/R_2$, where R_1, R_2 are the principal radii of curvature and T_1, T_2 are the tensions in the surface membrane normal to the principal sections. Prove that if the balloon is a figure of revolution $2T_2 = pR_2$ and $2T_1 = pR_2(2 - R_2/R_1)$.

CHAPTER IX

1. Determine the root mean square velocity of a hydrogen molecule at N.T.P.; the density of hydrogen at 0° C. is 0·09 gramme/litre.

2. Show that the gas constant R represents two-thirds of the kinetic energy of the molecules of a gramme-molecule of the gas at 1° abs.

3. Prove that γ, the ratio of the specific heats of a gas at constant pressure and constant volume respectively, is given by $\gamma = 1 + 2/x$, where x is the number of degrees of freedom of a gas molecule.

4. Prove that the mean velocity $\bar{c}$ and the root mean square velocity C are connected by the relation $\bar{c}/C = (8/3\pi)^{\frac{1}{2}}$.

5. Show that $\rho\bar{c} = 4p(M/2\pi RT)^{\frac{1}{2}}$, where M is the molecular weight of the gas.

6. Show that, owing to the finite molecular diameter σ, the mean free path is reduced from that appertaining to point molecules in the ratio $\lambda_\sigma/\lambda = 1 - 2\sigma/3\lambda$.

7. Deduce Dalton's law of partial pressures, i.e. that the total pressure exerted by a mixture of gases is equal to the sum of the pressures which they would each exert individually if they alone occupied the given volume, on the basis of the kinetic theory of gases.

8. Show that the mean velocity of molecules emitted from a small aperture in the side of an enclosure at temperature T is $C_1 = (4RT/M)^{\frac{1}{2}}$, where M is the molecular weight of the molecules.

9. Prove that the constant b of van der Waals' equation is equal to four times the volume of the molecules.

CHAPTER X

1. Using the symbols on p. 223, prove that for a dilute solution in which a fraction α of the molecules are dissociated, each into ν ions,

$$1 - \beta = (\nu - 1)\alpha^\nu n^{\nu-1}/\nu K.$$

2. Referring to pp. 226–7, prove that $1/x$ is that distance in which the potential in the neighbourhood of an electrode dipping into a solution containing ions diminishes to $1/\varepsilon$ of its value at the surface (ε being the base of Napierian logarithms).

3. Prove that for an aqueous solution of a single monovalent binary salt at $0°$ C., $1 - \beta = 0.263(2\gamma)^{\frac{1}{2}}$, where γ is the concentration of the salt in gramme-molecules per litre and D for water is 88.23 e.s.u.

4. Discuss the analogy between the corrections to the perfect gas equation introduced by van der Waals, and those to van't Hoff's equation introduced by Debye and Hückel.

5. Prove that in an aqueous solution of an electrolyte of any type at $0°$ C. $x = 0.229\,\Gamma^{\frac{1}{2}}$, where $\Gamma = \Sigma\gamma_i z_i^2$, z_i is the valency of an ion of type i, and γ_i is the gramme-molecular concentration per litre of those ions.

CHAPTER XI

1. Using fig. 1, p. 235, prove that the differential equation representing the diffusion of a salt in solution along a cylinder is $K\dfrac{\partial^2 n}{\partial x^2} = \dfrac{\partial n}{\partial t}$, it being assumed that there is no lateral escape of the salt.

2. Using fig. 3, p. 237, prove equation (10), p. 237.

3. A very tall narrow cylindrical vessel, of length L, is half filled with a solution of concentration n_0, and at time $t = 0$ the upper half is filled with pure solvent. Show that the concentration at any height x above the bottom, at any subsequent time t, is

$$n = \frac{4n_0}{\pi}\left\{\varepsilon^{-Ka^2t}\cos\alpha x + \tfrac{1}{3}\varepsilon^{-9Ka^2t}\cos 3\alpha x + \ldots\right\},$$

where $\alpha = \pi/2L$, and K, the diffusivity, is independent of the concentration.

CHAPTER XII

1. The end of a capillary tube, whose bore is a circular cylinder of radius r cm., is dipped in a liquid, the axis of the cylinder making an angle θ with the vertical. The viscosity of the liquid is η. The tube is open at both ends and the bore is moistened beforehand with the liquid. The liquid rises in the tube. Prove that the velocity with which the liquid ascends the tube is $\dfrac{\rho r^2 \cos\theta(l/x-1)}{8\eta}$ at any instant, where ρ is the density of the liquid, x is the instantaneous length of the column of liquid, and l is the final length when equilibrium is reached.

2. Two flat circular discs of radius a are mounted coaxially, parallel to one another at a distance d apart, and the lower one is rotated with constant angular velocity ω. Neglecting edge corrections, find the torque communicated to the upper disc if η is the coefficient of viscosity of the medium surrounding the discs.

CHAPTER XIII

1. In a certain experiment the following values of the mechanical equivalent of heat were obtained: $4\cdot169 \times 10^7$, $4\cdot180 \times 10^7$, $4\cdot184 \times 10^7$, $4\cdot181 \times 10^7$, $4\cdot180 \times 10^7$, and $4\cdot175 \times 10^7$ ergs per calorie. Calculate the arithmetic mean and its probable error.

2. Sherratt and Awbery obtained the following values of the velocity of sound in the air in a certain tube: $527\cdot7$, $527\cdot1$, $527\cdot9$, $527\cdot3$, $527\cdot9$, $527\cdot6$ and $527\cdot6$ metres per second. Calculate the arithmetic mean and the probable error.

3. C. V. Boys made nine observations on the mean density ρ of the earth. Four of them were made under favourable conditions, giving $\rho = 5\cdot5291$, $5\cdot5268$, $5\cdot5306$ and $5\cdot5269$ grammes per c.c. respectively. The other five results, made under less favourable conditions, were $\rho = 5\cdot5213$, $5\cdot5167$, $5\cdot5159$, $5\cdot5189$ and $5\cdot5172$ grammes per c.c. respectively. Calculate the arithmetic mean and its probable error, using (a) the first four results and (b) all nine results. (Boys gave $\rho = 5\cdot527$ as the best value to be derived from his experiments and did not calculate a probable error. See his comments in *Dictionary of Applied Physics*, Vol. III, p. 282.)

4. Six different methods give the following values of Planck's constant: $(6\cdot547 \pm 0\cdot011) \times 10^{-27}$, $(6\cdot560 \pm 0\cdot015) \times 10^{-27}$, $(6\cdot550 \pm 0\cdot009) \times 10^{-27}$, $(6\cdot543 \pm 0\cdot010) \times 10^{-27}$, $(6\cdot548 \pm 0\cdot015) \times 10^{-27}$ and $(6\cdot539 \pm 0\cdot010) \times 10^{-27}$ erg secs. Calculate the weighted mean of these results and its probable error.

5. A right circular cylinder has a length l cm., which is measurable with a probable error $\pm\alpha_1$, and a radius r cm., which is measurable with a probable error of $\pm\alpha_2$. What is the area of its curved surface and what is the probable error of that value?

6. On the flat face of a hemisphere of radius $r \pm \alpha_1$ there stands a right circular cone, whose base has the same radius $r \pm \alpha_1$, and whose height is $h \pm \alpha_2$. Find the volume of the whole body and its probable error.

7. Ferguson and Miller measured the specific heat of benzene at various temperatures. In one set of experiments their results were: $S = 0\cdot3993$ at $22\cdot61°$ C.; $S = 0\cdot4025$ at $25\cdot62°$ C.; $S = 0\cdot4092$ at $30\cdot69°$ C.; $S = 0\cdot4220$ at $39\cdot51°$ C.; $S = 0\cdot4264$ at $43\cdot93°$ C.; $S = 0\cdot4321$ at $48\cdot56°$ C. Assuming that $S = a + b(t - 20)$, where t is the temperature, calculate a and b by the method of least squares.

ANSWERS AND HINTS FOR SOLUTION

Chap. I.

1. Take surface tension, density, and radius of drop as variables: $t \propto \rho^{1/2} r^{3/2} S^{-1/2}$.

2. Take coefficient of viscosity, radius of tube, and pressure gradient down tube as variables: $V = \pi p r^4 / 8l\eta$.

3. $F = 6\pi\eta va$.

4. Take 0, $\varkappa$, d, c, ν, and v as variables.

5. $R = \frac{2}{3} q^2 a^2 / c^3$.

Chap. II.

1. Calculate the force due to motion of P round a circle of latitude. Find the sine of the angle required, neglect small terms, and use the binomial theorem.

2. Express g_1 as the sum of the attractions of the inner sphere and of the shell, using the law of gravitation. Use the binomial theorem to obtain approximations.

Chap. III.

1. Consider the flux through dS due to a single particle. Introduce the solid angle subtended by dS.

2. Apply Gauss's theorem.

3. (a) Zero.   (b) $4\pi G\rho\{R^3 - r^3\}/3R^2$.   (c) $4\pi G\rho\{(r + a)^3 - r^3\}/3R^2$.

4. $16\pi\rho_2 Gh(1 + h^2/4R^2)/3$ app.

5. $64° \, 38'$.

6. Moment of couple is $2GMmlr \sin\varphi/\{h^2 + l^2 + r^2 + 2lr \cos\varphi\}^{3/2}$, where h is the difference in level.

7. Obtain an expression for θ from the various equations on pp. 34, 35. Write nl for l, &c.

8. (a) $+2$ of mass, -1 of length, 0 of time. (b) No effect.

9. $c/3 \cdot 316$.

10. $0 \cdot 125$ per cent.

Chap. IV.

1. End conditions are $y = Dy = 0$ for $x = 0$, $y = D^2 y = 0$ for $x = l$.
$$G = w(\tfrac{1}{2}x^2 - \tfrac{5}{8}lx + \tfrac{1}{8}l^2), \quad F = w(\tfrac{5}{8}l - x).$$

Maximum depression when $Dy = 0$, given by $x(\tfrac{1}{6}x^2 - \tfrac{5}{16}lx + \tfrac{1}{8}l^2) = 0$.

2. $qAk^2D^2y = G = (C + Wl) - Wx$ at any point x. Also when $x = 0$, $y = Dy = 0$; if $\theta_1 = $ slope at $x = l$, $qAk^2 \tan\theta_1 = (C + Wl)l - \frac{1}{2}Wl^2$, and θ_1 may be written approximately for $\tan\theta_1$.

$$G = \frac{qAk^2}{l^3}\{y_l(6l - 12x) - l\theta_1(2l - 6x)\}.$$

3. $qAk^2D^2y = W(a - x)$.

If $y_1 = $ depression at A and $y_2 = $ depression at end of beam,

$$qAk^2y_1 = \frac{1}{3}Wa^3; \quad qAk^2y_2 = Wa^2(l/2 - a/6).$$

4. Let the reaction at each of the knife-edges be R. Consider separately (1) the portion of the rod between the mid-point and a knife-edge, (2) the portion between a knife-edge and the nearest end of the rod.

For (1), equation (12) becomes

$$qAk^2 D^2y = R(l/4 - x) - W(l/2 - x),$$

where x is measured from the centre of the rod.

For (2), equation (12) becomes

$$qAk^2 D^2y = Wz,$$

where z is measured from the end of the rod.

For the two sections, the boundary conditions at the knife-edge must give the same slope Dy.

Answer, $W/w = 5/22$.

5. Bending moment at distance x from free end is $G = \frac{1}{2}wx^2$. Hence from (33)

$$V = \int_0^l \frac{w^2x^4}{8qAk^2}\,dx = \frac{w^2l^5}{40qAk^2}.$$

6. $V = \frac{1}{6}\dfrac{W^2l^3}{qAk^2},\ y_1 = \frac{1}{3}\dfrac{Wl^3}{qAk^2},$ and hence $V = \frac{1}{2}Wy_1$.

7. $\frac{1}{2}Wx$.

8. $\frac{1}{2}Wx = \dfrac{W^2la^2}{\pi aR^4} = \frac{1}{4}\pi alR^4\varphi^2$.

9. If the tangent to the lower end of the spiral is twisted through an angle φ, the bend per unit length is φ/l. To produce this bend, a couple $G = \varphi/l \cdot qAk^2$ must be applied. Hence if I_B and I_s are the moments of inertia of bar and spring respectively,

$$(I_b + I_s)\frac{d^2\varphi}{dt^2} = -\frac{\varphi}{l}\,qAk^2,$$

which is of the form

$$\frac{d^2\varphi}{dt^2} = -m^2\varphi, \quad \text{where} \quad m^2 = \frac{qAk^2}{(I_b + I_s)l}.$$

Hence

$$t = 2\pi\sqrt{\frac{I_b + I_s}{qAk^2/l}} = 2\pi\sqrt{\frac{I_b + \frac{1}{3}wa^2}{q\pi R^4/4l}}.$$

10. (a) Rod. From Ex. 3, depression due to bending $= y_1 = \frac{1}{3}\dfrac{Wl^3}{qAk^2}$. Depression due to shearing stress $= y_2 = \dfrac{W}{A} \cdot \dfrac{l}{n}$. Hence $\dfrac{y_2}{y_1} = \dfrac{3q}{n}\left(\dfrac{k}{l}\right)^2$; for a square section, side b, $k^2 = b^2/12$.

Hence $\dfrac{y_2}{y_1} = \dfrac{q}{4n}\left(\dfrac{b}{l}\right)^2$, and since $b \ll l$, $y_2 \ll y_1$.

(b) Spring. Depression x_1 due to torsion $= 2Wa^2l/\pi nR^4$; depression x_2 due to shear $= Wl/\pi nR^2$.

Hence $x_2/x_1 = \frac{1}{2}(R/a)^2$, and since $R \ll a$, $x_2 \ll x_1$.

CHAP. V.

1. Use the equations $pv = k$, $pv^\gamma = k$ to deduce the two compressibilities.

CHAP. VI.

3. (a) $\delta = \pi$; (b) $\delta = \pi/2$; (c) $\delta = 0$.

CHAP. VII.

1. Introduce a symbol for the velocity of efflux. Assume that the loss of potential energy during an elementary contraction is equal to the gain of kinetic energy of efflux in the same time. Eliminate the velocity of efflux between two equations.

2. The flat face of the segment does not enter into the expression for the surface energy. Find the conditions for a minimum surface tension and constant volume by elementary calculus methods.

3. Write down the equation of equilibrium of the bubble as far as pressures are concerned, and consider the effect of a slight change of radius.

4. Begin with the equation of the meridional profile curve of a large drop.

5. The total mass of the annular cylinder remains constant. The loss of potential energy of the film is equal to its gain of kinetic energy. Introduce a symbol for the radial velocity.

6. Write down the weight of an elementary cylinder of height dz and upper surface dS. Use the differential equation of the free surface (equation (4), p. 102) to change the form of the expression, and integrate. Introduce an expression for the difference $dS' - dS$, where dS' is an element of a surface S', obtained from S by marking off points along normals to S, at a constant distance dn from S. Use this expression to change the form of the expression for the weight of the cylinder.

7. Write down expressions for the two quantities mentioned in Ex. 6 and equate them. The angle of contact is not equal to zero. Use the height measured in the centre of the narrow space.

8. Use Archimedes' theorem to find the area of the curved surface of the cap and hence its volume.

9. Assume contact all round the lower part of the cylinder. Apply the equation of the profile curve of a right section of the system (see p. 103). Include a term for the upthrust on the immersed parts.

10. Draw a central section through the axis of revolution, and consider what are the principal radii of curvature. Find one of them from the figure and use equation (4), p. 102, to find the other. Note that in a rubber or other membrane the tension is not the same in all directions.

CHAP. IX.

1. 1700 metres/sec.

4. Use Maxwell's law of distribution of velocities.

5. If α represents the most probable velocity of the gas molecules, Maxwell's distribution law may be written

$$N_{dc} = \frac{4N}{\alpha^3 \pi^{\frac{1}{2}}} c^2 e^{-mc^2/2kT} dc,$$

where N_{dc} is the fraction of the N molecules present whose velocity lies between c and $c + dc$, and k is Boltzmann's constant. The mean square velocity of the molecules issuing from a small aperture in a uniform temperature enclosure will be

$$C_1{}^2 = \frac{\int_0^\infty \dfrac{4N}{\alpha^3 \pi^{\frac{1}{2}}} c^2 e^{-mc^2/2kT} cc^2\, dc}{\int_0^\infty \dfrac{4N}{\alpha^3 \pi^{\frac{1}{2}}} c^2 e^{-mc^2/2kT} c\, dc} = 2\alpha,$$

since $C_1{}^2 = \dfrac{\Sigma N_{dc} cc^2}{\Sigma N_{dc} c}$, where $N_{dc} c$ is the number of molecules emerging with velocity c. Inside the enclosure $C^2 = 3\alpha/2$: hence $C_1{}^2 = 4/3C^2 = 4kT/m$.

6. The average distance of approach of two molecules is

$$\bar{x} = \int_0^{\pi/2} \frac{2\pi v \sigma^3 \sin^2\theta \cos\theta}{\pi\sigma^2 v}\, d\theta = \tfrac{2}{3}\sigma.$$

8. The product of c^2 and the number of molecules in the emitted beam, that is, cN_{dc}, must be integrated from zero to infinity and divided by the integral of the number of particles issuing with velocity c; hence

$$C_1{}^2 = \frac{\int_0^\infty \dfrac{4N}{\alpha^3 \pi^{\frac{1}{2}}} c^2 \times c \times c^2 e^{-c^2/\alpha^2}\, dc}{\int_0^\infty \dfrac{4N}{\alpha^3 \pi^{\frac{1}{2}}} c \times c^2 e^{-c^2/\alpha^2}\, dc}.$$

9. The average distance of approach of two spherical molecules is $2\sigma/3$, by Ex. 6, where σ is the diameter of the molecules. Hence the mean free path is shortened, compared with its value for disc-like molecules, by the amount $\lambda_s = \lambda - 2\sigma/3$. Hence, using this expression and equation (2), p. 178, we have

$$\frac{\lambda_s}{\lambda} = 1 - \frac{2\sigma/3}{\lambda} = 1 - \frac{2}{3}\frac{\pi\sigma^3 n}{V} = \frac{V - 4(\tfrac{4}{3}\pi r^3 n)}{V}.$$

Chap. X.

1. Apply the law of mass action to prove that $\alpha^v n^{v-1} = K(1 - \alpha)$; then prove that $P = K\theta\{n(1 - \alpha) + v\alpha n\}$, from van't Hoff's law, and evaluate $1 - \beta = (P_a - P)/P_a$.

Chap. XI.

3. As in problems on conduction of heat along a bar, consider the solute entering and leaving a slice of thickness dx. Hence deduce $\dfrac{\partial n}{\partial t} = K \dfrac{\partial^2 n}{\partial x^2}$. The solution $n = A\varepsilon^{-k\beta^2 t} \cos\beta x$ is appropriate here. Apply the boundary and initial conditions and use Fourier's theorem. Note that at the bottom of the tube $\dfrac{\partial n}{\partial x} = 0$, for all values of t.

Chap. XII.

1. Write down Poiseuille's equation as applied to the column at any instant, and also an expression for the pressure difference on the two sides of the hemispherical meniscus. The lower end of the tube only just enters the liquid.

2. Find the elementary torque acting on an annulus of radii r and $r + dr$. The total torque $\Gamma = \pi\eta\omega a^4/2d$.

CHAP. XIII.

1. $(4 \cdot 178 \pm 0 \cdot 001) \times 10^7$ ergs per calorie.

2. $527 \cdot 59 \pm 0 \cdot 07$ metres per second.

3. (a) $5 \cdot 5283 \pm 0 \cdot 0005$ grammes per c.c.
   (b) $5 \cdot 5226 \pm 0 \cdot 0012$ grammes per c.c.

4. $(6 \cdot 5466 \pm 0 \cdot 0017) \times 10^{-27}$ erg/secs.

5. Area $= 2\pi r l$ sq. cm.
   Probable error $\alpha = 2\pi \{ r^2 \alpha_1{}^2 + l^2 \alpha_2{}^2 \}^{\frac{1}{2}}$.

6. Volume $= \dfrac{\pi}{3} \{ 2r^3 + hr^2 \}$.

   Probable error $\alpha = \left\{ \left(2\pi r^2 + \dfrac{2h\pi r}{3} \right)^2 \alpha_1{}^2 + \left(\dfrac{\pi r^2}{3} \right)^2 \alpha_2{}^2 \right\}^{\frac{1}{2}}$.

7. $S = 0 \cdot 3956 + 0 \cdot 001287(t - 20)$.

INDEX